Instructor's Guide with Solutions

for

Moore and McCabe's

Introduction to the Practice of Statistics

Third Edition

Darryl K. Nester
Bluffton College

David S. Moore
Purdue University

George P. McCabe
Purdue University

Linda Doyle McCabe

D1224611

W. H. Freeman and Company
New York

Cover image: Andy Warhol, *200 Campbell's Soup Cans,* 1962. Oil on canvas, 72 X 100 inches. © 1998 Andy Warhol Foundation for the Visual Arts/ARS, New York. Photo courtesy Leo Castelli Photo Archives. ™Campbell Soup Company.

Copyright © 1999 by W. H. Freeman and Company

No part of this book may be reproduced by any mechanical, photographic, or electronic process, or in the form of a phonographic recording, nor may it be stored in a retrieval system, transmitted, or otherwise copied for public or private use, without written permission from the publisher.

Printed in the United States of America

ISBN: 0-7167-2774-9

Third printing, 1999

CONTENTS

Appendix

INTRODUCTION

This Instructor's Guide tries to make it easier to teach from the third edition of *Introduction to the Practice of Statistics* (IPS). The most helpful material is without doubt the full solutions of all exercises, which make up the second part of the Guide. The first part of the Guide—largely prepared by David Moore, edited and expanded by Darryl Nester, and drawing heavily on material from the previous edition's Guide by George and Linda McCabe—contains some specific teaching helps, such as additional examples, sample examinations, and suggestions for using the *Against All Odds* and *Decisions Through Data* videos in class. It also contains brief discussions of the approach we have taken in IPS for presenting statistics to beginning students. Reasonable people can (and do) differ about the nature of basic instruction in statistics. Our comments in this Guide are one side of a many-sided conversation. Your position in this conversation will no doubt differ at some points. We hope we have at least made clear the reasons for our choices.

We welcome comments, suggestions for improvement of IPS, and reports of errors that escaped detection and can be fixed in new printings. You can reach us as follows:

David S. Moore
Department of Statistics
Purdue University
West Lafayette, IN 47907-1399
Telephone: (765) 494-6050
Fax: (765) 494-0558
email: dsm@stat.purdue.edu

George P. McCabe
Department of Statistics
Purdue University
West Lafayette, IN 47907-1399
(765) 494-46047
(765) 494-0558
mccabe@stat.purdue.edu

Notes, comments, and corrections about this Instructor's Guide—especially the solutions—should be sent to

Darryl K. Nester
Bluffton College
Department of Mathematics
Bluffton, OH 45817-1196
Telephone: (419) 358-3483
Fax: (419) 358-3232
email: nesterd@bluffton.edu

1 TO THE INSTRUCTOR

1.1 Philosophy and Goals

The text is intended to be used in a first course in statistics for students with limited mathematical background. It covers the basic material presented in many courses at this level—data analysis, a little probability and standard statistical methods. The emphasis is on understanding how to use statistics to address real problems. In this regard it differs from most introductions.

Many students view statistics (indeed, all of the mathematical sciences) as a collection of formulas that give correct results if the computations are performed accurately. The competence of the student is measured by the complexity of the formula that can be computed correctly. Unfortunately this view is often reinforced by the way statistics is traditionally taught.

In contemporary practice, computations in statistics and other technical fields are always automated. Students, like users, should ideally employ statistical software, graphing calculators, or spreadsheets for computations and graphics. Even if the available technology is limited, students must prepare for reading and using statistical arguments with understanding. Our focus as teachers should be to helping students use statistical tools and reasoning effectively by providing conceptual understanding and practical strategies. We are also free to move closer to the practice of statistics as a tool for learning about the real world.

Consider, for example, a pre-election poll taken for a major news organization. The results are reported as percentages with a margin of error. Typically stratification is used and perhaps even cluster sampling. The formulas for the standard error are complex. The most important issues for understanding and using the results, however, do not require knowing the details: How was the question phrased? How was the sample designed? What about undercoverage and nonresponse? What does the margin of error tell us in straightforward language? If students are able to analyze and interpret data produced by a simple random sample, then the transfer of the basic ideas to the more complex situation is easy. The meaning of a confidence interval, for example, does not depend upon the formula used to calculate the standard error.

The first edition of *Introduction to the Practice of Statistics* was a bit nonstandard. Now that the first two editions have been widely adopted, our approach can be considered one standard choice for an introductory course. We describe in the Preface an emerging consensus on the nature of a first course among statisticians concerned with teaching, and we try to express that consensus in our writing. As a reminder, here are important ways in which IPS differs from more traditional texts:

- There is more attention to data analysis. Chapters 1 and 2 give quite full coverage. It is now becoming common to emphasize data in a first course, but many texts still begin with a quite brief treatment of "descriptive statistics." Note that we introduce distributions, specifically the normal distributions, in Chapter 1 as models for the overall pattern of data long before probability appears. This is legitimate in itself, and it helps break up the indigestible lump of formal probability that is a traditional stumbling block in learning statistics. Note also that the descriptive aspects of several-variable data (scatterplots, correlation, least-squares lines) are presented as part of data analysis rather than late in the book in conjunction with inference in these settings. We think that this order has important advantages. It emphasizes the centrality of data analysis in statistics and gives students a chance to build fluency in the strategies of data analysis in both one- and several-variable settings. It allows examples and exercises on relationships among variables that don't meet the narrower requirements of inference.

- There is more attention to designing data production. It is surprising to a practicing statistician how little attention these ideas, among the most influential aspects of statistics, receive in most first courses. Chapter 3 discusses sampling and experimental design, with attention to some of the practical issues involved. The importance of deliberate use of randomness and informal discussion of the distribution of results in repeated sampling motivate the introduction of probability and the very important idea of a sampling distribution.

- The introduction to probability in Chapter 4 begins with experience with randomness and is designed to allow instructors to cover only the essentials or to present the full traditional material by omitting or including the optional Section 4.5. For many groups of students, more statistics is a worthy exchange for less probability. Some of the most important probability facts (law of large numbers, central limit theorem) appear in the discussion of sampling distributions in Chapter 5. Some traditional details about binomial distributions are marked as optional. The criterion for optional material in Chapters 4 and 5 is simple: it is not required for the statistical inference presented later in the text.

- There is more emphasis on the reasoning of inference. Chapter 6 discusses this reasoning in some depth, with an optional section 6.4 comparing the "P-value" and "two types of error" approaches to testing. We emphasize P-values. This reflects common practice and helps students understand the output of statistical software.

- There is more attention to statistics in practice. Realism may be too much to claim in a beginning text. Nonetheless, we often give longer-than-usual discussions of examples in order to connect textbook procedures with real-world practice.

Upon completion of a course based on IPS, students should be able to think critically about data, to select and use graphical and numerical summaries, to apply standard statistical inference procedures, and to draw conclusions from such analyses. They are ready for more specialized statistics courses (such as applied regression or quality control), for "research methods" courses in many fields of study, and for projects, reports, or employment that require basic data analysis.

1.2 Calculations and Computers

The practice of statistics requires a good deal of graphing and numerical calculation. Doing some graphing and calculating "by hand" may build understanding of methods. On the other hand, graphics and calculations are always automated in statistical practice. Moreover, struggling with computational aspects of a procedure often interferes with a full understanding of the concepts. Students are easily frustrated by their inability to complete problems correctly. Automating the arithmetic greatly improves their ability to complete problems. We therefore favor automating calculations and graphics as much as your resources and setting allow.

All students should have a calculator that does "two-variable statistics," that is, that calculates not only $\bar{x}$ and s but the correlation r and the least-squares regression line from keyed-in data. Even if you use computer software, students should have a calculator for use at home and on exams. Two-variable statistics calculators sell for less than \$20. We don't discuss anachronistic "computing formulas" (e.g., for standard deviation and correlation) that presuppose a four-function calculator.

IPS is designed to be used in courses where students have access to computing facilities, and also where they do not. Many of the examples used in the text involve computations that can readily be performed with a two-variable statistics calculator rather than a computer. Each chapter contains exercises with small amounts of data or with the results of some computations given that are suitable for students without a computer. Although the use of a computer for a course based on IPS is not required, most people who *do* statistics today use a computer. Any serious attempt to introduce the practice of statistics must recognize this fact. You will find examples of output from a variety of technological tools (statistical software, spreadsheets, graphing calculators) throughout the text. The output appears because any statistics student should become accustomed to looking at output and using the fruits of the study of statistics to recognize terms and results in output from any source.

As computing continues to become cheaper and more readily available, and as statistics software becomes more "user-friendly," use of computers in courses at this level will increase. At Bluffton, for example, most students in beginning math courses have graphing calculators. At Purdue, more than two-thirds of the students in first statistics courses have computers in their apartments or dorm rooms. Almost all have some prior acquaintance with personal computers. For students with this background, modern graphical interface statistical software speeds work and allows more elaborate work without the added burden that learning software once presented. We encourage use of software, and have included some exercises that are not realistic without it.

As a practical encouragement to software use, the CD-ROM packaged with the text includes most of the data (all of the larger sets of data) used in exercises in IPS. The data appear as plain text (ASCII) files and also in the special formats of several common software systems.

The files are named by their location in the book:

eg1.05.dat = Example 1.5
ex1.38.dat = Exercise 1.38
ta1.08.dat = Table 1.8

1.3 Course Design

Think of the content of IPS this way: The nonoptional parts of Chapters 1–8 form a core. Chapters 9 (two-way tables), 10 (inference for simple linear regression), 12 (one-way analysis of variance), and 14 (nonparametric tests) offer a selection of further topics that are independent of each other. Depending on the length of your course and the quantitative background of your students, you will probably elect one or more of these. Note that Chapter 14 appears on the CD-ROM rather than in the printed text. Chapters 11 (multiple regression), 13 (two-way analysis of variance), and 15 (logistic regression, on the CD-ROM) are brief introductions to more advanced topics based primarily on case studies. Each of these chapters requires at least one of the elective chapters as a prerequisite, and all go better with software.

IPS is an elementary but serious introduction to modern statistics for general college audiences. This means that the material is presented in a way that it can be learned by students who are not particularly skillful in mathematics. IPS does require more attentive reading (words, not equations) then some other texts. The amount of time required for learning—and hence, the amount of material that can be covered—depends upon the skill level and (more important) the maturity of the students in a particular course.

We have personally used IPS for general undergraduates in nontechnical disciplines (agriculture, health sciences, consumer studies, etc.); for graduate students in nonquantitative disciplines (education, social sciences, retailing, etc.) who will be analyzing data for their research; and as a first course for majors in actuarial science, mathematics, and statistics. These are quite varied groups. The general undergraduates are taking a required course they wouldn't elect. Motivation is the big problem in teaching them. More data and less formal probability help. The graduate students often have a weak quantitative background but are mature and hard-working. Many of them will take another course in statistics but some will not. They need some exposure to analysis of count data, regression, and analysis of variance. Accomplishing this for students with moderate mathematics skills requires skipping or treating lightly many of the optional sections in addition to a great deal of work on the part of the students. The practical relevance of the examples and exercises is an important factor for sustaining the motivation and drive that these students bring with them to the first lecture. Our course for potential undergraduate majors is software-intensive and data-intensive. We end with multiple regression, including some material not in IPS.

The sample outlines for courses using IPS are aids for instructors, not strict rules. You should adapt the pace and extent of your course to your students.

Outline 1. This is a semester course for students with low or moderate skills and motivation. We suggest this outline for general, less quantitative undergraduates. For students with moderate mathematics skills, you can add a little more depth for some topics and assign or discuss some of the more challenging Exercises. We are always tempted to go faster than this outline suggests, and when we do we find that the students don't come with us. In particular, each exam, viewed as an opportunity to solidify learning, uses a week. We suggest: spend one class on active review. Consider distributing a sample exam in class and asking the students to work on the first problem for about 5 minutes, long enough to determine whether they know how to approach it. Then discuss that problem together. Continue through the sample exam in this manner. Starting work under conditions similar to an exam concentrates the mind. The exam itself occupies a second class period, and returning and discussing it fills most of a third. This isn't lost time: exams are learning tools. We recommend omitting all starred subsections for this audience, but use your judgment.

Week	Material to be Covered
1	Chapter 1, Section 1, Section 2 – measures of center
2	Chapter 1, Sections 2 and 3
3	Chapter 2, Sections 1, 2, and 3
4	Chapter 2, Sections 4, 6, and 7
5	Review Chapters 1 and 2; Exam I on Chapters 1 and 2
6	Chapter 3, Sections 1, 2, and 3
7	Chapter 3, Section 4; Chapter 4, Sections 1, 2, and 3
8	Chapter 4, Section 4; Chapter 5, Section 1
9	Chapter 5, Section 2
10	Review Chapters 3, 4, and 5; Exam II on Chapters 3, 4 and 5
11	Chapter 6, Section 1, start Section 2
12	Chapter 6, Sections 2 and 3
13	Chapter 7, Sections 1 and 2
14	Chapter 8, Sections 1 and 2
15	Review and extended examples
Comprehensive Final Exam	

Outline 2. A semester course for students with either higher skills or stronger motivation. We follow this outline for nonquantitative graduate students. Omit optional material except where noted.

Week	Material to be Covered
1	Chapter 1, Sections 1, 2, and 3
2	Chapter 2, Sections 1, 2, and 3
3	Chapter 2, Sections 4, 6, and 7
4	Chapter 3, Sections 1, 2, 3, and 4
5	Review Chapters 1 to 3; Exam I on Chapters 1 to 3
6	Chapter 4, Sections 1, 2, and 3
7	Chapter 4, Section 4; Chapter 5, Section 1
8	Chapter 5, Section 2;
9	Review Chapters 4 and 5; Exam II on Chapters 4 and 5
10	Chapter 6, Sections 1 and 2
11	Chapter 6, Sections 2 and 3, power from Section 4
12	Chapter 7, Sections 1, 2, and 3
13	Chapters 8 and 9
14	Chapter 12
15	Review and extended examples
	Comprehensive Final Exam

Outline 3. A semester course for students with adequate quantitative skills who may need more probability than the previous outlines offer. As outlined, ending with multiple regression, the course is quite ambitious. Use software to accelerate the later chapters.

Week	Material to be Covered
1	Chapter 1, Sections 1, 2, and 3
2	Chapter 2, Sections 1, 2, and 3
3	Chapter 2, Sections 4, 6, and 7
4	Chapter 3, Sections 1, 2, 3 and 4
5	Exam I on Chapters 1 to 3; Chapter 4, Sections 1 and 2
6	Chapter 4, Sections 3 and 4
7	Chapter 4, Section 5;
8	Chapter 5, Sections 1 (including optional parts) and 2
9	Chapter 6, Sections 1 and 2
10	Chapter 6, Sections 2 and 3; start Chapter 7
11	Chapter 7, Sections 1, 2, and 3
12	Exam on Chapters 4 to 7; start Chapter 8
13	Chapters 8 and 9
14	Chapter 10
15	Chapter 11
	Comprehensive Final Exam

Outline 4. A one-quarter course for students with low to moderate skills. It covers the essentials, ending with the t procedures (and the introduction to inference in practice) in Chapter 7 of IPS. This provides a good foundation for any of a number of more specialized courses in statistics or related areas. This outline is quite tentative; the number of class meetings per week varies in institutions using the quarter system. You may be able to assign more than is shown, e.g., Sections 2.6 and optional material in Section 5.1. The main point of this outline is the goal of completing Chapter 7 in even the briefest introduction. IPS contains sufficient material for a sequence of two quarter courses, particularly taking into account the two chapters on the CD-ROM. You have considerable flexibility in choosing from Chapters 8–14 for the second quarter.

Week	Material to be Covered
1	Chapter 1, Sections 1 and 2
2	Chapter 1, Section 3; Chapter 2, Section 1
3	Chapter 2, Sections 2, 3, 4, and 7
4	Chapter 3, Sections 1, 2, and 3; Review Chapters 1 to 3
5	Exam on Chapters 1 to 3; Chapter 4, Sections 1 and 2
6	Chapter 4, Sections 3 and 4
7	Chapter 5, Sections 1 and 2
8	Chapter 6, Sections 1 and 2
9	Chapter 6, Section 3; Chapter 7, Section 1
10	Chapter 7, Sections 2 and 3
	Comprehensive Final Exam

1.4 General Comments

When students complete a course based on IPS they should be able to analyze real data and draw conclusions. Since the emphasis is on *doing* statistics rather than talking about statistics, much of the class time should be spent discussing how statistical analysis tells us something about data. The methodologies presented are all based upon sound statistical theory. Details of how the theory leads to particular formulas are neither interesting to the students nor are they essential to the central purpose of learning to do statistics. A minimum amount of time should be spent on examining formulas and procedures in the abstract. Theoretical ideas need to be understood in the context of how they *apply* to the analysis of data.

Consider, for example, the problem of outliers. They are a fact of life for anyone applying statistics to real problems. It is not sufficient to take a strictly mathematical view and assume that they do not exist. A procedure based on normal theory may give very misleading conclusions if applied to data contaminated by outliers. In the practice of statistics it is important to identify outliers and, with an understanding of the area of application, to do something about them. On the other hand, it is not important at this level to know that a t distribution can be represented at the ratio of a standard normal to the square root of a chi-square.

To teach students how to use statistical methods with understanding, you will spend most of your class time doing statistics. This means discussing data, not just numbers devoid of any real meaning. It means saying something about the context in which the data were collected and the field of application. Instructors in statistics courses typically are comfortable with the rather elementary mathematical and statistical ideas needed to discuss the methods presented in the text. On the other hand, few of us are experts in the various substantive fields from which the examples and exercises are drawn. Most of these, however, require only a basic understanding, most of which is presented in stating the example or exercise.

Using data from real problems provides many opportunities for the students to become actively involved in the class. Incomplete knowledge of all of the fields covered by the examples and exercises can be turned into a very effective teaching tool. Students have diverse backgrounds and often know a great deal more than we think. It is a very pleasant experience to leave a class session having learned something from the students. Once, when discussing the corn yield data presented in Example 2.5, George was unable to remember whether or not the fields were irrigated, but he did remember that they were in Nebraska. He mentioned this, and one woman in the class immediately raised her hand and explained that if it was corn in Nebraska, then it certainly was irrigated. This sort of participation occurs naturally in a teaching environment where the students are encouraged to think about data rather than numbers.

If we could offer just one piece of advice to teachers using IPS, it would be this: **A number or a graph, or a formula such as "Reject H_0," is not an adequate answer to a statistical problem**. Insist that students state a brief conclusion in the context of the specific problem setting. We are dealing with data, not just with numbers.

There is a tendency today to try to design statistics courses specifically for students in one particular major or general field. This is particularly true for students in business and the social and behavioral sciences. Even in general courses some students express the opinion that they would prefer examples and homework based on problems coming exclusively from their own field of interest. If we are attempting to educate rather than to simply train students, this view is short-sighted. It overlooks, for example, the fact that most students will change careers several times during their working lives. Ideas learned well in one context are easily translated to others. Roger Maris's 61 home runs do have something in common with the agricultural production in a drought year. One of the interesting things about statistics as a field is that the same fundamental ideas occur in many diverse settings. Different settings facilitate learning of the big ideas. Furthermore, many fields are not as homogeneous as they might appear at a first glance. Often, interesting problems require the assimilation of material from diverse areas. This is particularly true of business. In summary, do not apologize to your students because all of the examples are not from their field. Explain to them that breadth is part of education.

There are enough examples in the text for some to be used in class lectures. Sometimes it is useful to build a lecture around one or a sequence of exercises. If computers are used, it is a good idea to run some of the examples or Exercises on the system you are using. You can distribute copies of output, enlarge the output on a transparency, or ask students to do specific computer work in advance and bring the results to class. Many classrooms now allow you to do the work in real time with projection for the class to follow. If you teach in a computer lab, we recommend doing examples along with the class so that students follow on their machines and can see your projected screen if they get lost.

1.5 Teaching Suggestions

Statistics has a well-earned reputation as the dullest of subjects. Tell someone that you teach statistics, and a typical reaction is something like, "I took a course in statistics once. ... I just barely made it through." We teachers have the responsibility of overcoming that preconception by demonstrating to students that our subject is both intellectually stimulating and useful. We believe that almost any statistics course can be improved by including more data and more emphasis on reasoning, at the expense of fewer recipes and less theory. "Data" means not just numbers, but problems set in a context that require a conclusion or discussion rather than just a calculation or graph. In *Introduction to the Practice of Statistics* we have tried to emphasize data and reasoning, limited of course by our own ability and by the need to present an exposition accessible to beginning students. We hope the text will at least not stand in the way of teachers who want their students to come away with more than a list of recipes. Here are some suggestions from our experience.

Involve the class Mixing blackboard work with direct address (get out from behind the lectern) helps keep students awake. Even better is discussion with the class. Use some exercises as bases for discussion, assigning them "for discussion" in the next class rather than requiring written answers. Ask a student to present an analysis and then give a nontechnical conclusion, as if reporting to a boss. Then ask the other students to respond with questions or comments.

Leading discussions is interesting but difficult. You must resist the temptation to leap in with the "correct" view. Try rather to guide the class by questions and to get other students to offer alternatives to weak answers. Be patient when asking questions on the spot. An educational psychologist of our acquaintance notes that teachers rarely wait long enough for students to assimilate a question and produce a response. He suggests 30 seconds, which seems an eternity while passing in silence but does produce more response in the end. Above all, don't put down a student who is incorrect or confused. Students notice even the silent disappointment that contrasts so clearly with your response to an intelligent answer. Try to give a positive response to every student who is brave enough to speak up—they are helping you. When you know the class better, you can direct easier questions at the weaker students, thus preventing monopoly by the bright and aggressive. Remember that you are building confidence, not simply conveying information. Discussion isn't easy for teachers oriented toward problem-solution or theorem-proof presentation. But the attempt is essential if your students are afraid of statistics and perceive it as remote from their experience.

Problem assignments The practice of statistics is learned by doing statistics rather than by reading about it. To master the material in IPS, students need to work exercises—many of them. Note that brief solutions for the odd-numbered Exercises appear in the back of the text. These allow students to check their work, but they are often not complete as responses to the problems because they lack graphics or detailed conclusions.

Ask during the session previous to the session in which homework is due if students are having difficulty with any problems. Most students will not have started the homework yet—you are trying to encourage them to start early. Always ask about special difficulties when the assignment is turned in and spend time clarifying them. If necessary, comment on any additional difficulties when you return the assignments. Don't be overly concerned about "giving away" homework answers. Homework is to help learning; the exams will detect those who didn't do their own work.

Remember that your students don't think like mathematicians Good teaching requires an awareness of who your students are. Statistics courses are not mathematics classes, so don't emphasize mathematical fine points or mathematical explanations and derivations. You think mathematically, but your students don't. Instead, teach by examples and add comments on statistics in practice when appropriate. Try to sometimes begin with a motivating example rather than always presenting a technique, then illustrating it by an example. Don't just repeat the text. Outline the material (students like an outline style), explain how each point fits into the overall course, then interpret the text. Point out the tough parts, use different examples, say things a different way, try to explain the intuition behind the formal material. Mathematical understanding is not the only kind of conceptual understanding. Don't always do the same thing: vary your style over the class period and from day to day.

1.6 Using Video

One of the most effective ways to convince your students that statistics is useful is to show them real people (not professors) employing statistics in a variety of settings. Video allows you to do this in the classroom. Two related video series that contain many short documentaries of statistics in use "on location" are:

- *Against All Odds: Inside Statistics.* This telecourse, consisting of 26 half-hour programs, was prepared by COMAP for the Annenberg/Corporation for Public Broadcasting Project. It is available in the United States at a subsidized price. Call 1-800-LEARNER for information or to order a copy.

- *Statistics: Decisions Through Data.* This set of 21 shorter modules (5 hours total) is intended for use as a classroom supplement in secondary schools. It was prepared by COMAP for the National Science Foundation and draws on the location segments of *Against All Odds.* It is available from COMAP. Call 1-800-77-COMAP for information.

If you are outside the United States, you can obtain information about both video series from

> COMAP Inc.
> Suite 210
> 57 Bedford Street
> Lexington, MA 02173 USA
> Fax 1-617-863-1202

Because David Moore was the content developer for these video series, they fit the style and sequence of IPS well. In several cases, data from the videos appear in the text. We do not recommend showing complete programs from *Against All Odds* in the classroom. The shorter modules from *Decisions Through Data* are more suitable for classroom use, but we recommend only a few of them. Video is a poor medium for exposition, and it leaves viewers passive. It is therefore not a good substitute for a live teacher.

Nonetheless, video has several strengths that make it an ideal supplement to your own teaching. Television can bring real users of statistics and their settings into the classroom. And psychologists find that television communicates emotionally rather than rationally, so it is a vehicle for changing attitudes. One of our goals in teaching basic statistics is to change students' attitudes about the subject. Because video helps do this, consider showing video segments regularly even if you don't think they help students learn the specific topic of that class period.

Here are a few segments we particularly recommend.

- The 14-minute video "What Is Statistics?" is a good way to start a course. This collage of examples from *Against All Odds* forms part of the first unit of AAO and is the first module of DTD. It is available separately (and inexpensively) from

  > The American Statistical Association
  > 1429 Duke Street
  > Alexandria, VA 22314 USA
  > (703) 684-1221

- *Saving the manatees* from Program 8 of AAO, Module 11 of DTD. There is a strong linear relation between the number of power boats registered in Florida and the number of manatees killed by boats. (These data are used in several exercises in IPS.)

- *Sampling at Frito-Lay* from Program 13 of AAO or Module 17 of DDD illustrates the many uses of sampling in the context of making and selling potato chips. All-time student favorite.

- *The Physicians' Health Study* from Program 12 of AAO (Module 15 in DDD) is a major clinical trial (aspirin and heart attacks) that introduces design of experiments. (These data are used in several exercises in IPS.)

- *Sampling distributions* are perhaps the single most important idea for student understanding of inference. Module 19 of DTD presents the general idea, the basic facts about the sampling distribution of the sample mean $\bar{x}$, and the application of these ideas to an $\bar{x}$ control chart. The animated graphics are hard to match with a blackboard! The setting is a highly automated AT&T electronics factory.

- *Battery lifetimes* in Module 20 of DTD lead to an animated graphic that illustrates the behavior of confidence intervals in repeated sampling.

- *Taste testing of colas* is the setting for an exposition of the reasoning of significance tests in Module 21 of DTD, again using graphics for exposition.

Here is a list of the documentary segments in AAO, with timings for use if your VCR measures "real time" and star ratings. Start your VCR timer when the first signal on the tape appears. Remember that AAO programs are packaged two to a tape; the timings for the even-numbered programs may need some adjustment because the gap between programs seems to vary a bit. This handy guide was prepared by Professor Edward R. Mansfield of the University of Alabama. We are grateful to him for permission to reproduce it here.

PROGRAM 1: What Is Statistics?

    4:48 Domino's Pizza ***
    13:15 The "What is statistics?" collage of later examples

PROGRAM 2: Picturing Distributions (no timings/ratings available for Program 2)

        When does lightning strike?
        TV programming and demographics
        Diagnostic-related groups

PROGRAM 3: Describing Distributions

    5:55 Comparable worth in Colorado Springs *
    16:07 Calories in hot dogs **
    21:00 Musical analysis of urine data **

PROGRAM 4: Normal Distributions

    33:50 Age distributions and Social Security *
    46:07 Boston Beanstalk social club for tall people *
    50:38 Why don't baseball players hit .400 any more? ***

PROGRAM 5: Normal Calculations

    7:07 Auto emissions at GM Proving Ground *
    14:10 Cholesterol values **
    19:50 Sizes of military uniforms **

PROGRAM 6: Time Series

    34:50 The body's internal clock *
    43:48 Psychology: reaction time study *

PROGRAM 7: Models for Growth

    3:00 Children's growth rates and hormone treatment ***
    14:00 Gypsy moth infestations **

PROGRAM 8: Describing Relationships

    32:25 Manatees vs. motor boats in Florida ***
    37:55 Cavities vs. fluoride levels
    39:31 1970 draft lottery ***
    44:04 Obesity: metabolic rate vs. lean body mass *

PROGRAM 9: Correlation

    5:42 Identical twins raised apart ***
    16:22 Baseball players' salaries **
    20:53 The Coleman Report (education in the 1960s) *

PROGRAM 10: Multidimensional Data Analysis

    32:28 Chesapeake Bay pollution **
    47:42 Bellcore graphics **

PROGRAM 11: The Question of Causation

    5:42 Simpson's paradox ****
    12:47 Smoking and cancer (historical survey) ***

PROGRAM 12: Experimental Design

    32:46 Observational study of lobster behavior *
    36:14 Physicians' Health Study: aspirin and heart attacks ****
    43:39 Is Ribavirin too good to be true? ***
    47:22 Police response to domestic violence *

PROGRAM 13: Blocking and Sampling

    4:45 Strawberry field research *
    13:28 Undercounting in the Census ***
    20:48 Sampling potato chips at Frito Lay ****

PROGRAM 14: Samples and Surveys

    41:21 National Opinion Research Center ****

PROGRAM 15: What Is Probability?

>10:50 Persi Diaconis on randomness *
>17:49 Traffic control in New York (simulation model) **

PROGRAM 16: Random Variables

>33:36 Cheating on AP Calculus *
>34:33 Space Shuttle *Challenger* disaster ****
>43:02 Points in a professional basketball game
>49:10 Earthquakes in California *

PROGRAM 17: Binomial Distributions

>3:46 The "hot hand": free throws in basketball ***
>9:45 A finance class experiment **
>17:22 Sickle cell anemia *
>24:25 Quincunx: falling balls **

PROGRAM 18: The Sample Mean and Control Charts

>33:45 Roulette
>35:04 Interviews with gamblers **
>40:44 The casino always wins ****
>47:03 Control charts at Frito-Lay ***
>53:41 W. Edwards Deming ****

PROGRAM 19: Confidence Intervals

>11:35 Duracell batteries **
>18.25 Rhesus monkeys in medical studies *
>21:21 Feeding behavior of marmosets

PROGRAM 20: Significance Tests

>34:18 Is this poem by Shakespeare? **
>49:06 Discrimination within the FBI ***

PROGRAM 21: Inference for One Mean

>5:55 National Institute of Standards and Technology **
>13:30 Taste testing of cola ***
>21:08 Autism *

PROGRAM 22: Comparing Two Means

>33:32 Welfare programs in Baltimore **
>45:05 Product development at Union Carbide ***
>51:00 SAT exams: can coaching help?

PROGRAM 23: Inference for Proportions

    3:03 Measuring unemployment (Bureau of Labor Statistics) *
    11:58 Safety of drinking water ***
    20:15 The Salem witch trials

PROGRAM 24: Inference for Two-Way Tables

    34:11 Ancient humans (markings on teeth) **
    43:30 Does breast cancer treatment vary by age? **
    52:02 Mendel's peas **

PROGRAM 25: Inference for Relationships

    3:32 How fast is the universe expanding (Edwin Hubble)? ****

PROGRAM 26: Case Study

    35:49 How AZT for treatment of AIDS was tested ***

2 COMMENTS ON CHAPTERS

2.1 Chapter 1: Looking at Data — Distributions

Students taking a first course in statistics often do not know what to expect. Some may view statistics as a field where the major task is to tabulate large collections of numbers accurately. Others have heard that statistics is more like mathematics with a lot of complicated formulas that are difficult to use. Few are expecting a course where they need to use their common sense and to *think*.

The presentation of the material in Chapter 1 sets the tone for the entire course. Statistics is a subject where intelligent judgments are needed and common sense plays a large role. To the extent that you can get the students to think deeply about the material at this stage, you will have succeeded in setting the proper tone. Most of the examples presented in the text can serve as the basis for extensive class discussions. Depending upon the interests of the students, some of these may be more suitable than others. You can also try to find or collect data that the particular students you are teaching can relate to.

In one class based on this text, students were asked to take their pulse on the first day of class. No particular instructions concerning how to take one's pulse were given. The data that resulted were used in discussions that illustrated several major themes of the course. A stemplot was immediately constructed. There was one very large outlier—180 beats per minute. We discussed whether or not this value was reasonable. Several of the physical education students commented that someone who was very out of shape might elevate their pulse to such a high level by running up to the third floor where the course was held. Someone from psychology mentioned that a person who was very anxious about the course might have an elevated pulse. One conclusion drawn was that if you want to measure anything on people, you must pay attention to the circumstances present when the measurement is taken.

Further examination of the data revealed an exceptionally large number of readings that ended with the digit zero. Students in aerobics classes typically take their pulse for 6 seconds and multiple by 10. This led to a discussion of the possibility that different methods were used to obtain the reported pulse rates. Since it was impractical to ask all 50 or so students what method each used, a random sample was taken using the class list and the table of random numbers given in the back of the text (Table B). Students had no trouble following the method. Successive pairs of digits were used and numbers outside the range 1 to 50 were discarded. It was not surprising to find a number corresponding to a student who was not present in the class on that day. A short discussion about missing data and the problems associated with statistics in the *real* world followed.

The methods reported by the sampled students were very revealing. Most were what you would expect. Measure for 60 seconds, measure for 30 seconds and multiply by 2, measure for 15 seconds and multiply by 4, and of course, the method of those who had taken an aerobics course. One said that he did not have a watch so the value given was a guess. Another (a very polite foreign student whose command of spoken English was not very good) explained that she had no idea about what was asked and simply reported the value given by another student.

The lesson was quite clear. It is not easy to gather good data. What is measured and how it is measured are the two most important questions to ask when undertaking any statistical analysis. Understanding the issues related to these questions does not require mathematical sophistication or the ability to calculate $\sqrt{1/n_1 + 1/n_2}$ by hand. If the students can be sufficiently motivated at the beginning of the course and understand that many interesting things can be learned by looking at data, they will be willing to put in the effort required to master the skills needed for the computations required later.

Look for sets of data that will be interesting to your students. They are not very difficult to find. If the students are concentrated in a few majors, ask faculty from those departments for reprints of articles using elementary statistical methods. Ask questions about how things are measured and whom or what is measured. Do the items or people measured represent any larger group or do they simply represent themselves? Usually we think of statistics as being used used only for inference to some larger known or imagined population. However, many interesting sets of data do not fall into this category and much about data analysis can be learned by studying them. Government statistics often come from a census or samples so large that the sampling variability is negligible. A good job of describing such data is often not a trivial exercise.

The key concepts in this chapter concern ways of looking at and describing one set of data. We start with graphical displays and then move to numerical summaries. The point of the numerical summary is that it quantifies and expresses compactly something that can be seen roughly in a graphical display. The effectiveness of a numerical summary is based on how well it calls to mind what appears in the graphical display. Thus viewed, the mean is not a very good numerical summary for a set of data with two distinct clusters of observations.

From numerical summaries we proceed to models for data, illustrated by the important case of the normal distributions. The progression from graphical display to numerical measures to a compact mathematical model is one of the strategies that unifies data analysis and makes it more than a collection of clever methods.

1.1 Displaying Distributions with Graphs

The introductory material on measurement is short but important. What is measured and how it is measured are two fundamental issues that lie at the foundation of any statistical analysis. Many of the judgments made at this level are subjective and require common sense. Make the point that statistics is about data, not just numbers.

Variation is another key concept. Why are all of the observations in a set of data not the same? Good class discussions can be based on sources of variation in particular sets of data.

The first real statistical analysis presented is the stemplot. Stress the idea that we start with a graphical display before proceeding to numerical summaries. We have presented stemplots with the values increasing as you proceed down the stems. Some computer packages put the larger numbers at the top. Similarly, in the text truncation is recommended (this is clearly the easiest method to use if constructing the plot by hand), whereas some programs will round. Keep in mind that the purpose of the plot is to get a quick look at the data and to help in deciding what sorts of numerical summaries are appropriate. Be flexible. Splitting leaves and other sorts of judgments should be based on common sense rather than on adherence to a set of inflexible rules.

Similar comments regarding flexibility apply to histograms. The histogram is presented as a method for displaying a set of data when a stemplot is unsuitable. It also serves an important role pedagogically. In the last section of this chapter, the density curve is introduced as a model that describes the shape of a histogram when the sample size increases and the widths of the intervals decrease.

The major theme of this section is that we should always carefully look at data. In graphical displays we look for an overall pattern and deviations from that pattern. Simon Newcomb was a famous scientist who was measuring well-defined physical quantities. If he had outliers in his data, we should not be surprised to find them in other sets of data that we may encounter. This section introduces the basic strategy for looking at data: seek first an overall pattern, then deviations from the pattern. This strategy will be used in other settings in Chapters 2 and 3.

1.2 Describing Distributions with Numbers

The mean should be familiar to almost all students. Therefore, the introduction of the summation notation is facilitated by noting that it is a compact way to express something that they already know. Although the idea behind the median is quite intuitive, some students get confused by the manipulations required to find it. Emphasize that it is a numerical measure for something that can be seen in a stemplot or histogram.

Quartiles and the five-number summary build on the idea of the median. Again emphasize that they are numerical summaries for something that can be seen graphically. With the boxplot we complete a circle of sorts. Starting with a graphical summary, we calculate numerical summaries and then present these graphically. Note that there are many variations on boxplots. If you use statistical software, the rules for constructing them may differ slightly from those presented in the text. This should not pose any serious problems. In fact, it can be used to illustrate the point that caution is needed in using statistical packages. We need to know how things are computed if we are to interpret the output meaningfully.

No single numerical summary is appropriate for all sets of data. There is a tendency to think that robust or resistant measures always work (although they may be inefficient). The SAT score data used in Exercise 1.64 are an example of real data where the boxplot fails to capture a very important aspect of the distribution—its bimodality.

The standard deviation is a fundamental quantity, the meaning of which will be made clear in Section 1.3 on normal distributions. Here, the variance is a necessary intermediate step required for the calculation of the standard deviation. For students who have a great deal of trouble with computations, the calculations can be organized in a table with columns corresponding to x, x^2, $x - \bar{x}$ and $(x - \bar{x})^2$. We recommend that students have a calculator that computes $\bar{x}$ and s from keyed-in data. This inexpensive tool greatly reduces the arithmetical burden for many standard statistical procedures.

Linear functions are used in several places later in the text. Thus, the material on changing the unit of measurement has two purposes. One idea is that when data are transformed in this way, nothing fundamental is changed. The summary statistics in the new scale are easily computed from the original ones. We are simply choosing a different way to express the same thing. The second idea is that we can use an equation of the form $x^* = a + bx$ (or later $y = a + bx$) to express a relationship between two variables.

1.3 The Normal Distributions

Note that normal distributions are introduced here as a common model for the overall pattern of many sets of data, and not in the context of probability theory. Although this ordering of material is unusual, it has several advantages. The normal distributions appear naturally in the description of large amounts of data, so that the later assumption for inference that *the population has a normal distribution* becomes clearer. Moreover, mastering normal calculations at this point makes it easier to teach the material on probability (Chapters 5 and 6). If the students already know how to compute normal probabilities and have a fair understanding of the relative frequency interpretation from this section, the transition to general ideas about probability is facilitated. Of course, later chapters present additional facts about normal distributions in the context of probability.

The key idea is that we can use a mathematical model as an approximation to real phenomena. The 68–95–99.7 rule is a useful device for interpreting μ and σ for normal distributions.

From the viewpoint of statistics, in contrast to that of probability, we always think of our models as approximations rather than the truth. This point can be illustrated by considering Example 1.26. The $N(505, 110)$ distribution is very useful for describing SAT scores of high school seniors. It can give reasonably accurate answers to interesting questions as illustrated in this example. However, it does not work very well in the extreme tails. For example, since the highest score possible is 800, the proportion of students scoring 835 or better is not appropriately calculated by using $Z \geq (835 - 505)/110 = 3$ and normal calculations. In a population of 100,000 students, the calculation would give $100,000(0.00135) = 135$ students scoring above 835!

Normal quantile plots are used frequently in the text. Students should learn to interpret them. If computer software is not available for constructing these plots, we do not recommend that they be drawn by hand. In this case, stemplots should be used to assess normality on a routine basis for the exercises.

Note that software packages that create quantile plots may differ in what variable is put on each axis. Plots in the book place the variable being studied on the vertical axis, and the z score on the horizontal axis. One benefit of this arrangement is that we can interpret the plot in a natural way: if (e.g.) the upper right part of the plot bends down (below the line), we can interpret it by saying, "The high values of the variable are lower than they 'should' be [to be from a normal distribution]." (This is natural, since the *high* part of the plot is *below* the line.) Likewise, if the lower left part of the plot bends up, we can say, "The low values of the variable are too high [to be from a normal distribution]."

2.2 Chapter 2: Looking at Data — Relationships

This chapter concludes the part of the text dealing with methods for looking at data. In the first chapter, techniques for studying a single variable were explored. Here the focus is on general methods for describing relationships between pairs of variables.

Scatterplots are used to examine pairs where both variables are quantitative. Details of least-squares regression are presented. Correlation is introduced and its connection with regression is examined. Relations between categorical variables are described using proportions or percentages calculated from two-way tables. Issues related to the question of causation are illustrated by consideration of smoking and lung cancer.

The descriptive methods in this chapter, like those Chapter 1, correspond to the formal inference procedures presented later in the text. By carefully describing data first, we avoid using inference procedures where they clearly do not apply. Fitting a least-squares line is a general procedure, while using such a line to give a 95% prediction interval requires additional assumptions that are not always valid. In addition, students become accustomed to examining data *before* proceeding to formal inference, an important principle of good statistical practice. The data for a regression (Chapter 10) are displayed in a scatterplot. Side-by-side boxplots are useful with two-sample *t* tests (Chapter 7) and analysis of variance (Chapter 12). The percentages obtained from two-way tables are the basis for the formal inferences on count data (Chapter 9).

2.1 Scatterplots

From the previous chapter the students will be familiar with the idea that graphical displays of data are useful. The extension to a scatterplot should reinforce this idea. The distinction between explanatory and response variables is a relatively simple distinction that is essential to the least squares method.

Constructing scatterplots is an easy task, particularly with a computer. Interpreting them, on the other hand, is an art that takes practice. For classroom discussion, you can use the examples given in the text or those presented in the exercises. Stress the idea that common sense and some understanding of the data are necessary to do a good job of description. Computers can make the plots, but people are needed to describe them. Again, the general rule is to look for overall patterns and deviations from them. Dichotomies such as positive and negative association are useful in many cases but can lead to distorted descriptions when imposed in situations where they do not apply.

Scatterplot smoothing is a useful data analytic tool for looking at some kinds of scatterplots. Try to avoid the type of thinking that says: if I have situation *a*, then use method *b*. A method is useful if it helps you to learn something about the data. Sometimes you do not know if it is useful until you try it.

Side-by-side boxplots can give a very informative data summary when one variable (usually the response variable) is quantitative and the other is categorical or concentrated on a small number of possible values. Since the students have already encountered boxplots, the idea of putting several of them alongside each other should follow quite easily.

2.2 Correlation

A key point is that a correlation (or the square of a correlation) is a numerical summary of a relationship between two variables that are linearly related. Thus, as an aid to interpreting a scatterplot, it a potentially useful descriptor. With outliers, influential observations or nonlinear relationships, however, it may give a very distorted impression. Correlations are somewhat complicated for hand computation, and most of the time they should be found with a calculator or software. However, there may be some benefit to having students compute correlations for some small data sets by hand, to get a "feel" for how correlations work.

2.3 Least-Squares Regression

The principle of least squares is introduced and a method of computation (using r, $\bar{x}$, s_x, $\bar{y}$ and s_y) is presented. Try not to burden the students with excessive computation; most least-squares lines should be found using a computer or calculator. Note that the output may contain many pieces of information related to inference that are not relevant at this time. If computing facilities are not available, assign exercises where most of the computations are given and the amount of arithmetic required is minimal.

2.4 Cautions about Correlation and Regression

A crucial part of using regression and correlation procedures is knowing what can go wrong and when they may not be appropriate tools. Plotting the residuals versus x is very important. Again, construction of the plot is easy and can be done effectively by a computer, but interpreting the results is an art.

Outliers and influential observations can provide interesting class discussion. When a cause can be found or a lurking variable discovered, the value of carefully looking at data is reinforced. Formal rules for dealing with these situations are not advised. The point is that outliers and influential observations are present in many real data sets. A good analysis finds them and assesses their effects on the results.

2.5 An Application: Exponential Growth and World Oil Production

The optional section on exponential growth introduces no new statistical concepts. The only difference from Section 2.4 is that the function being fitted is more complex. Many students at this level have rather unpleasant thoughts when they hear the word logarithm. They are surprised to learn that logs can be viewed simply as that which is done to data to transform exponential growth into linear growth.

Some software and calculators have "exponential regression" computations built into them; that is, they (invisibly, to the user) take the logarithms of the y values, fit the linear model, then exponentiate the resulting equation and report an exponential function. If available, this can ease this analysis for students, though perhaps at the cost of decreased understanding. (In particular, sometimes these packages may report a correlation r; students may not understand that this is the correlation for the *transformed* data.) This may also allow you to explore with your students ways to model relationships with different kinds of functions (quadratics, sine functions, etc.), depending on what features your software offers.

2.6 Relations in Categorical Data

The computation required in this section in minimal. Percents and proportions are the numerical summaries. On the other hand, some very important ideas are presented. Judgment is required to select what percents to calculate. The idea of conditional distributions appears here and can be emphasized if you intend to cover the optional material on conditional probability in Chapter 4. Simpson's paradox is not easily understood when first encountered. Careful class discussion of the examples in the text is needed if students are to grasp this idea.

An accessible (made up) example is: Suppose you watch the women's and men's basketball teams practicing. You observe 100 shots by each team; the men make 70% of their shots, and the women make 50%. Can you conclude that men are better shooters? Students (at least those familiar with sports) will quickly recognize that we can compare these numbers only if men and women were taking similar types of shots. If the men were practicing free throws and the women were attempting three-pointers, that would change our interpretation of these numbers.

The essential idea is that when presented with data, one must ask: What other information (hidden, or otherwise not given) would be useful in interpreting this data? In other words, we are searching for lurking variables—which leads naturally to Section 2.7.

2.7 The Question of Causation

The final section of this chapter contains no formulas, but there are a lot of important ideas. It brings out the fact that drawing conclusions about relationships may require judgment and expertise beyond the realm of formal statistical inference.

2.3 Chapter 3:   Producing Data

This is a relatively short chapter with a lot of ideas and little numerical work. The message is that production of good data requires careful planning. Random digits (Table B) are used to assign units to treatments and to select simple random samples. There are several good examples that can serve as the basis for classroom discussion.

3.1 First Steps

This introductory section gives an overview of why careful planning of data collection is needed and makes the point that anecdotal evidence is not a good basis for drawing conclusions. Sampling and experimentation are described in general terms.

3.2 Design of Experiments

Terminology used in experimental design is introduced and is illustrated with examples. The advantages of comparative experiments are shown pointedly with the gastric freezing experiment. Students seem to particularly enjoy this example and they often express outrage at the blatant misuse of the data described.

Once the need for comparison and randomization is established, methods for randomization of experimental units to treatments is presented. Note that there are many correct ways to do these randomizations. Many exercises using Table B are given. If you use statistical software, some particular randomization routines may be available. In very general terms, most randomizations can be accomplished by a random sort of the data. In any package that has a random number generator and a sort, this can be done by assigning a random uniform to each case and then sorting the resulting file. For example, to assign 10 people to each of two treatments, set up a file with cases corresponding to the integers 1 to 20. The assign a random number to each case and sort the file on the basis of the random numbers. The first 10 cases receive treatment one and the others receive treatment two. Note that this is not a particularly efficient algorithm but it is very clear and it helps the students understand the principle of randomization.

3.3 Sampling Design

The simple random sample (SRS) is described. Note that in later chapters the assumption that data or errors are normally distributed is expressed by saying that they are an SRS from a normal population.

Other sampling designs are mentioned, including stratified samples, multistage designs, and systematic random samples. The problems of nonresponse and bias are also discussed.

3.4 Toward Statistical Inference

This section introduces some key ideas that will be further explained and used in later chapters. The idea of a parameter in a population contrasted with a statistic in a sample is fundamental. Through an opinion poll example, this distinction is made clear. The sampling distribution of the sample proportion is shown by simulation for samples of size 100 and 2500, thus illustrating the central limit theorem and the fact that the variability decreases as the sample size increases.

Because students often find probability hard and fail to see it's relevance, we have tried to motivate probability by first discussing randomization in data collection and its consequences. In teaching this section, try to get the students to think about and discuss the general ideas. This will facilitate their learning of the details to follow in later chapters.

2.4 Chapter 4:   Probability: The Study of Randomness

In Chapter 3 it is explained that randomization is needed for the proper design of experiments and sampling plans. Therefore, the study of probability as a model for randomness naturally fits here.

An overview of the entire course is given in the following paradigm. In the first three chapters we studied how to look at and describe data. Thus, in a sense, we concentrated on the *sample*. Chapter 3 discussed how data are produced and introduced the idea of the *population* for which inference in desired. Now, we study the population in detail, with emphasis on the mechanisms by which samples are generated. In later chapters, we reverse the orientation and study the methods by which samples lead to inferences about populations.

This chapter and the one that follows will be difficult for many of the students. We have tried to emphasize a conceptual approach to the topics presented. Nonetheless, there are several rules and manipulations that must be mastered.

You should carefully consider how much depth and breadth you want to include for this material. By omitting the optional sections and treating some subjects (such as sample spaces) lightly, you can teach the minimum probability required for a proper understanding of statistical inference. On the other hand, the text provides sufficient material for more comprehensive coverage.

4.1 Randomness

Certainly everyone has some concept of what is meant by the word "random"—but many may have the wrong idea, especially in not understanding the underlying order of "random" events. (Many people might list "chaotic" or "unpredictable" as synonyms for "random.") This section gives some background to understanding randomness and probability in terms of "long-run frequency" by repeated actual or simulated experimentation.

4.2 Probability Models

Sample spaces, assignment of probabilities and basic probability rules are introduced in this section. Try to emphasize that all of these ideas follow from common sense and are not an arbitrary mathematical system devoid of a intuitive foundation. Many of the students will have had unpleasant experiences with some of this material previously.

Many of the topics can be introduced through an example with the formalization coming later. Give a set of probabilities that have a sum greater than one and ask why this does not make sense. Then explain that their conclusion that the sum must be one is a basic rule of probability theory. Similarly, most of the students can apply the addition rule and the complement rule to real problems without ever having encountered these rules formally. Let them figure out the rule first and then present it formally.

4.3 Random Variables

Random variables are the raw material for statistical inference. We therefore introduce them early in the presentation of probability. If an experiment or sample survey is repeated, different results will be obtained. The probability theory for random variables tells us that there is a certain type of regularity or predictability in these results.

4.4 Means and Variances of Random Variables

The mean, variance and standard deviation are familiar quantities from Chapter 1. Emphasize that they are a little different here because we are dealing with a population. If the students have a lot of difficulty with this transition, you can ask them to think about some very large samples. For example, in Example 4.20, think of an experiment with 10,000 trials in which the results are exactly as expected: 625 zeros, 2500 ones, 3750 twos, 2500 threes and 625 fours. The calculations can then be performed on this hypothetical large sample (in which the difference between n and $n - 1$ is negligible) and the connection between probability and relative frequency can be reinforced.

In a similar way the rules for means and variances build on the parallel rules for sample statistics. This material can be treated briefly and reinforced with homework exercises.

The law of large numbers is the key concept in this section. It expresses a fundamental idea that is part of the foundation for much of statistical inference. Most of the students will have some intuitive idea about this law. Through class discussion these ideas can be explored and clarified.

4.5 General Probability Rules

This optional section presents some of the traditional material on probability. The addition rules, multiplication rules and conditional probability are all discussed. The section is optional because these ideas are not essential to an understanding of the statistical ideas that follow in later chapters. Ample exercises are provided for the instructor who wants to cover this material.

Although the basic ideas contained in these probability laws are very intuitive, many students have a great deal of difficulty with the symbolic manipulations involved. By a detailed presentation of examples or exercises you can emphasize that these calculations are based on common sense and are not simply a collection of abstract rules.

2.5 Chapter 5:   From Probability to Inference

There are two key ideas in this chapter. First, a statistic is a random variable, the value of which varies from experiment to experiment or sample to sample. Second, as a random variable, it has a sampling distribution with a mean and a standard deviation that can be calculated from the distribution of the basic random variables that are combined to calculate the statistic.

The binomial distribution is treated in detail. The normal approximation to the binomial is given as an important special case that sets the stage for the central limit theorem presented in the second section. The chapter concludes with an optional section on control charts where probability ideas are shown to be both useful and important.

5.1 Sampling Distributions for Counts and Proportions

The amount of time you choose to spend on this section is quite flexible. The inference for proportions presented in Chapter 8 is all based on the large sample normal approximation to the binomial. Therefore, the minimum coverage needed consists of the fact that the distribution of $\hat{p}$ is approximately normal with mean p and standard deviation $\sqrt{p(1-p)/n}$ when n is sufficiently large.

On the other hand, there is sufficient material for a full treatment of the binomial distribution. Table C gives individual probabilities for a variety of values of n and p and the formula for calculating binomial probabilities is explained in detail. Many computer routines are also available for calculating individual or cumulative binomial probabilities.

Try not to let the computational details interfere with the important pedagogical role played by this section. The students should understand that $\hat{p}$ is a random variable with a sampling distribution that is approximately normal for large n. In a given experiment or sample, only *one* realization or value of this statistic is obtained. Our inference will be based on this single observation and probability calculations will be based on an assumed (testing) or estimated (confidence intervals) sampling distribution for this statistic.

5.2 The Sampling Distribution of a Sample Mean

This is a rather short but important section where the mean and standard deviation for the sample mean are explained and the central limit theorem is presented. In terms of statistical applications, there are two key ideas. First, the central limit theorem is widely applicable and is the basis for normal based inference. Second, the standard deviation of the mean decreases as $\sqrt{n}$. This section completes the discussion of normal distributions begun in Chapter 1 by showing the normal distributions as sampling distributions.

5.3 Control Charts

This optional section illustrates how some probability calculations are used in practice. It is not intended as rigorous treatment of control charts. It can be used very effectively to help the students understand both probability and statistical inference. An out-of-control signal is unlikely to occur if the process is in control. Therefore, we *suspect* that the process has been disturbed if such a signal is observed.

2.6 Chapter 6: Introduction to Inference

This is a chapter with a lot of fundamental ideas. Confidence intervals and tests are presented with some cautions concerning the use and abuse of tests. Throughout, the setting is inference about the mean μ of a normal population with known standard deviation. As a consequence, the z procedures presented are not applicable to most real sets of data, but rather serve to ease the transition to the more useful procedures presented in Chapter 7.

Experience has shown that many students will not master all this material upon seeing it for the first time. Fortunately, they will see all the key ideas again in Chapter 7. By the time they have completed both chapters and worked many exercises, they should be able to grasp the fundamentals. Remember that mastery of the reasoning of inference is far more important than the number of procedures learned.

6.1 Estimating with Confidence

Confidence intervals are straightforward but easily misinterpreted. Try to emphasize the meaning rather than the details of computation. For most students this is accomplished more effectively by a discussion of Figure 6.2 or similar results than by an algebraic deviation of a formula for the coverage probability.

At this stage the students should be comfortable with the sample mean, population parameters versus sample statistics, the fact that $\bar{x}$ is approximately normal with mean μ and standard deviation $\sigma/\sqrt{n}$, and the table of normal probabilities (Table A). Stress the fact that we are simply putting these ideas together in this section to produce a useful statistical procedure. Similar comments hold for Section 6.2.

The subsection on choosing the sample size reinforces the idea that the width of the interval depends upon n. This material is particularly important for students who will design studies in the future.

6.2 Tests of Significance

Although this section is not much longer than the previous one, it contains a few things that students generally find more difficult. The choice of one-sided versus two-sided tests and P-values versus fixed significance level testing are in this category. Try not to let these complications interfere with the presentation of the basic ideas.

Students seem to have the most difficulty when they become sufficiently frustrated that they put their common sense aside and start seeking formulas or rules that cover every possible case. Graphs illustrating the calculation of P-values are very useful here. Note that statistical software universally gives P-values. Therefore, an understanding of this approach to testing is essential for students who will either read or perform statistical studies.

6.3 Use and Abuse of Tests

This section give some important ideas about significance testing that can serve as the basis for classroom discussion. Students are often reluctant to make judgments about the *importance* of an effect in contrast to its statistical significance. Emphasize that this judgment is an important part of using statistics with real data. Computers are easily programmed to perform calculations and produce P-values. Informed judgments (by humans) are needed to translate and interpret these results.

6.4 Power and Inference as a Decision

The optional material on power is similar to the material on selecting the sample size for confidence intervals. It reinforces what has already been said about the dependence of the behavior of the procedure on the sample size and is very important for students who will be planning studies. The use of software—for example, G•Power, available on the Internet for many platforms—can make this more approachable.

The last subsection on inference as a decision is also optional. It uses the traditional dichotomy between Type I and Type II errors and serves as a brief introduction to more general applications of decision theory.

2.7 Chapter 7:   Inference for Distributions

The principles underlying confidence intervals and significance tests were presented in Chapter 6. We now apply these principles to inference problems for one and two samples. Throughout the chapter, we work under the realistic assumption that the population standard deviation is unknown.

The first section deals with inference for one sample. The problem of paired comparisons is treated as a special case. Optional sections on power and a nonparametric alternative to the normal based procedure are also given.

Two sample procedures are presented in the second section. The chapter concludes with an optional section on inference for the standard deviation.

From earlier chapters, the students should be familiar with looking at data from one or two samples carefully and with computing sample means and standard deviations. The additional arithmetic required for the construction of confidence intervals and significance tests is not particularly difficult. Many of the exercises provide means and standard deviations so that the students can concentrate on the new ideas presented here.

The transition from the normal to the t table requires some careful explanation. Because we are dealing with a family of distributions indexed by the degrees of freedom, only selected values can be given in a table. Since most of the exercises are based on real data, no attempt has been made to assure that an entry for the exact degrees of freedom for a particular problem are given in the table. Therefore, approximate values of t^* are to be used for confidence intervals. Similarly, bounds on the P-value can be obtained rather than exact P-values, using Table E. (Nonetheless, since software may be used to give more "exact" answers, the solutions in the latter part of this guide contain these more exact answers, as well as those that come easily from Table E.)

A conservative approach for confidence intervals is to use a value for the degrees of freedom that is less than or equal to the required value. This results in intervals that are at least as wide as the exact interval, thereby ensuring that the coverage probability is at least as large as that specified. (In effect, by taking smaller degrees of freedom than we are "entitled" to, we are pretending that we have less information [a smaller sample] than was actually available to us.) The same approach for tests ensures that the probability of a false rejection of H_0 is less than or equal to the value given. Table E provides sufficient detail so that for all practical purposes, inaccuracies resulting from these difficulties are very small. Students checking their solutions for odd-numbered exercises in the back of the text should be aware of these considerations.

Of course, if a probability function for the t distribution is available in computer software, exact values are easily obtained. Note that it is common practice for many computer packages (and in reporting the results of a statistical analysis) to give P-values in the form $P < $ some number. Using Table E, when an extreme value of the t statistic is found, the P-value will be reported as $P < 0.0005$ for a one sided-test and $P < 0.001$ for a two-sided test.

7.1 Inference for the Mean of a Population

The term *standard error* is introduced for the estimated standard deviation of a statistic. Thus, t statistics are normalized by dividing by a standard error, and confidence intervals are constructed by taking the value of a statistic plus or minus a constant times the standard error.

The usual one-sample confidence intervals and significance tests (which assume normal distributions) are presented in this section. By first taking differences between pairs of observations, paired comparisons problems are treated in the same way. The idea of robustness is introduced and practical guidelines for using the t procedures are given.

7.2 Comparing Two Means

Procedures based on normal assumptions for comparing two means are presented in this chapter. To place the problems in a proper perspective, the situation where the standard deviations are known is discussed first.

When replacing the known standard deviations by sample estimates, difficulties regarding the appropriate degrees of freedom for the t distribution arise. Most computer software packages use an approximation similar to that given just before Example 7.18. This formula is given for information only. From an educational point of view, very little is accomplished by having students do a large amount of computation with this formula. In most practical situations use of the minimum of $n_1 - 1$ and $n_2 - 1$ as the degrees of freedom for the t gives essentially the same results. Rather than having students spend a lot of time with computation, it is better to have them concentrate on the appropriate use of the procedures and the interpretation of the results.

The pooled two-sample t procedures are presented in the optional last part of this section. Occasionally, students will question the usefulness of these procedures. Why assume that the standard deviations are equal when we have already learned procedures that are valid under less restrictive assumptions? From a theoretical point of view there are answers. We have exact rather than approximate distributions, confidence intervals will be shorter in some stochastic sense and significance tests have more power. On the other hand, from a practical point of view, there will be very little difference in the results (unless, of course, there are large differences in the standard deviations so that the pooled procedures are invalid). The primary reason for including this material is that it facilitates the introduction of similar ideas in Chapter 12, where analysis of variance is introduced. If you do not plan to cover analysis of variance and time is tight, you could easily omit this material.

7.3 Optional Topics in Comparing Distributions

The usual F test for comparing two variances is presented in this section. It is pointed out that this procedure is not robust with respect to the assumption of normality and a general discussion of robustness follows. This section can easily be omitted. The very poor performance of F in the two-sample variance setting should not be overlooked merely to teach a procedure for this case.

Note that this is the first place in the text that F distributions are used. They appear later in the chapters on regression and analysis of variance (Chapters 10–13). If you do not cover this section, you will need to spend a little more time explaining the tables when they are needed later in the text.

The power of the t test is treated in a subsection. This material is very similar to that presented in the fourth section of Chapter 6 and makes use of the noncentral t distributions. As was mentioned before, this material reinforces the fundamental idea that the performance characteristics of statistical procedures depend upon the sample size. It is important for students who will be planning statistical studies to be familiar with these ideas.

The final optional subsection discusses what can be done in some situations when the data are not normal. Transformations are mentioned and an explanation of the sign test for paired comparisons is given. The intention here is to point to the two major strategies available, not to discuss them in detail.

2.8 Chapter 8:   Inference for Proportions

The two sections of this chapter present the standard z procedures for one-sample and two-sample binomial problems. By now the students should be comfortable with the general framework for confidence intervals and significance tests. For those who have not yet completely mastered these concepts, this material affords an additional opportunity to learn these important ideas.

8.1 Inference for a Single Proportion

Confidence intervals and significance tests for a single proportion are presented. A new complication that arises with these problems concerns the standard deviation of $\hat{p}$. For confidence intervals we use the standard error $\sqrt{\hat{p}(1 - \hat{p})/n}$, whereas for tests we use

$\sqrt{p_0(1 - p_0)/n}$. Although this may seem confusing to the students at first, the basic idea is quite reasonable.

We use all of the information available in a problem for our calculations. For the confidence interval, p is assumed to be unknown and the standard error must therefore be estimated using the value of $\hat{p}$ obtained from the data. On the other hand, when testing H_0: $p = p_0$, our calculations are based on the assumption that H_0 is true, and therefore we use the value p_0 in the calculations. Note that these choices destroy the exact correspondence between confidence intervals and tests (reject if the hypothesized parameter value is outside of the confidence interval).

The section concludes with a description of the procedure for choosing a sample size to guarantee a given bound on the width of a confidence interval. From a practical point of view, the table given in Example 8.7 is very informative. The widths of intervals vary relatively little for values of $\hat{p}$ between 0.3 and 0.7.

8.2 Comparing Two Proportions

Confidence intervals and significance tests for comparing two proportions are presented in this section. From Chapter 7, students should be familiar with the basics of two-sample problems. As in Section 8.1, we use different standard errors for confidence intervals and tests. The idea of pooling information from two samples to estimate a standard error was first presented in the optional part of the second section of Chapter 7. This principle will be used again in Chapter 11 when we treat analysis of variance.

2.9 Chapter 9: Inference for Two-Way Tables

If desired, this material can be omitted without loss of continuity. The notation here is more complex than in earlier chapters. (There is no easy way to describe the general form of a two-dimensional array of data without two subscripts.)

9.1 Inference for Two-Way Tables

You have some choice regarding depth of coverage for this section. As mentioned, this section can be eliminated entirely if desired. The computations for the X^2 statistic are rather straightforward although a fair amount of arithmetic is required and care must be taken to ensure accurate results. Computers can be a big help here.

9.2 Computations and Models for Two-Way Tables

The vague idea of testing for a relationship between two categorical variables is also fairly straightforward. Therefore, it is possible to teach this section spending a minimum amount of time on the two models described.

On the other hand, discussion of the models in detail gives the students a good background for learning about model-based inference for more complex situations. The statistical model gives a clear statement of the assumptions needed for a given procedure and specifies the parameters about which inference is desired. A major part of statistical inference concerns the translation of a vague notion, such as dependence between two categorical variables, into a testable hypothesis stated in terms of the parameters of a statistical model. To draw meaningful conclusions, the results of the analysis, stated in terms of the model, must then be translated back into the context of the real problem.

2.10 Chapter 10:   Inference for Regression

Having completed Chapter 2, the students should be familiar with the data analytic issues that arise with simple linear regression. We now focus on applying statistical inference principles to this problem. The material from Chapter 7 is particularly important in this regard. On the other hand, nothing in Chapters 8 and 9 is needed for an understanding of this chapter.

10.1 Simple Linear Regression

Note that there are many interesting problems for which the relationship between two variables can be summarized graphically and numerically with a least-squares line. Not all of these can be analyzed using the methods presented in this chapter. Inference for linear regression is based on a statistical model that expresses the assumptions underlying the inference procedures.

10.2 More Detail About Simple Linear Regression

Confidence intervals and significance tests should be familiar concepts for the students at this point. Although the computational details are more difficult in this section, the underlying principles are not new. Use of statistical software is very effective here. It allows the students to concentrate on learning the concepts without being unduly concerned with a long sequence of computations leading to a numerically correct answer. Stress that the number is not the *answer*; the interpretation of the number in the context of a real problem is the proper end result of a statistical analysis.

Prediction intervals are a new idea. By contrasting them with confidence intervals, the students can avoid common misinterpretations of confidence intervals.

Most computer packages provide an analysis of variance table as part of the output for a regression. For simple linear regression the table is not particularly useful. Often it generates more confusion than useful information for students at this point. On the other hand, the ANOVA table is very important for multiple regression and it is essential for performing analysis of variance. If you plan to cover these topics, discussion of the ANOVA table for linear regression provides an excellent introduction to this topic. Explain that it is a different way to present some of the information already discussed and that it will be important for topics to be covered later.

The section concludes with optional material on inference for correlation. It is pointed out that the test for a zero correlation is equivalent to the test for a zero slope in the regression. The square of the correlation is expressed in a form that generalizes easily to the multiple regression setting.

2.11 Chapter 11: Multiple Regression

The model for multiple regression and a brief overview of the inference procedures are presented. This chapter can be omitted without loss of continuity. For students who will take another statistics course in which this material will be covered in great detail, a discussion of the case study can be very valuable. Many important ideas are presented in the context of the problem of predicting grade point average from high school grades and SAT scores.

2.12 Chapter 12: One-Way Analysis of Variance

The idea of using a statistical test to compare population means is familiar from Chapter 7. New issues arise because we may have more than two means to compare. The DATA = FIT + RESIDUAL idea is used in presenting the statistical model underlying the analysis. The model is treated first, thereby emphasizing the principle that inference is based upon assumptions and definitions of parameters given by a model.

The analysis of variance table is constructed using some familiar ideas. Pooling of variances was treated in Chapter 8 and again the idea of DATA = FIT + RESIDUAL is used. The ANOVA tables from the regression chapters (Chapter 10 and 11) anticipated many of the ideas presented here.

Some new ideas arise with contrasts and multiple comparisons. Without some discussion of at least one of these topics, one is left with a statistical procedure giving very little in terms of useful interpretable results. Most statistical software packages will perform these computations.

The issue of what multiple comparison procedure to use is rather difficult. We have chosen to present only one procedure—the Bonferroni. However, it is presented in such a way that any other procedure could easily be substituted.

The optional section on power reminds us again that the performance of a statistical procedure depends upon the sample sizes and the true values of the parameters. It is interesting to note that these kinds of calculations are rather easy to perform with any statistical software that has a function for the noncentral F distribution. Tables of power and even graphs of power functions are relatively easy to generate. The use of G•Power (mentioned earlier) also eases these computations.

2.13 Chapter 13:   Two-Way Analysis of Variance

Two-way analysis of variance is treated conceptually. A major goal is for the students to understand the meaning of interaction. No computational formulas are given; computation is left for the computer. The emphasis is on understanding the assumptions and interpreting the output.

This chapter is really an introduction to more complex analysis of variance designs. In this context, the initial discussion of advantages of two-way anova is particularly important. Again the description of the model plays a key role.

Interaction is the important new idea. It is illustrated with a variety of examples chosen to demonstrate the different types of interpretations that arise in practice. Stress that the statement that there is interaction between two factors is essentially meaningless in itself. Interpretation requires a careful examination of the means in the context of a given problem.

2.14 Chapter 14:   Nonparametric Tests

This chapter (on the CD) presents techniques for use with non-normal data. It can be used as supplementary material for interested and capable students, building on the sign test introduced in Chapter 7. (In fact, many of the ideas in this chapter are no more difficult than those of earlier chapters; they are arguably much easier than the regression and analysis-of-variance material, even though the Kruskal-Wallis test is, in fact, an alternative to ANOVA!)

There are only 30 exercises in Chapter 14, but note that one can use these methods on exercises on comparing means (Chapter 7) and analysis of variance (Chapter 12)—although in many cases, there may be no reason to question underlying normality.

2.15 Chapter 15:   Logistic Regression

This chapter might provide useful supplementary material for students who have covered regression, but be aware that even fairly sophisticated statistical software packages may not have the capability to do *multiple* logistic regression. With the right software, and sufficiently prepared students, this short chapter (only 16 exercises) can be covered in a week or two.

3 SAMPLE EXAMINATIONS

In writing exams, here are several points to keep in mind:

- Use current events and local references.

- Decide how much computation to require, and let the students know in advance. Having students compute standard deviations or correlations on exams may not be the best way to measure their comprehension.

- As an alternative to computation, consider placing computer or calculator output on the test and asking students to interpret it.

- Decide what mix of multiple-choice, problem solving and discussion questions to use. If class size makes it necessary, use some multiple-choice questions, but by and large, the subject matter of this course is best tested with questions that require writing ("Give reasons to support your answer"). No multiple-choice questions are given in these samples.

The exams given here can be used as examination items or as class examples. As mentioned earlier, a sample exam distributed in class is useful as review before a scheduled exam.

Most of these questions have been taken from the Instructor's Guide to the Second Edition, as well as the Instructor's Guides for *The Basic Practice of Statistics* and *Statistics: Concepts and Controversies*, both by David Moore. More material for this course can be found in those two guides and also at Darryl Nester's web site (http://www.bluffton.edu/~nesterd).

3.1 Sample examination I

These questions cover Chapters 1 and 2.

1. A study examined how long aircraft air conditioning units operated after being repaired. Here are the operating times (in hours) for one unit:

$$
\begin{array}{rrrrrrrrr}
97 & 51 & 11 & 4 & 141 & 18 & 142 & 68 & 77 \\
80 & 1 & 16 & 106 & 206 & 82 & 54 & 31 & 216 \\
46 & 111 & 39 & 63 & 18 & 191 & 18 & 163 & 24
\end{array}
$$

(a) Make a histogram, using classes that are 40 hours wide, beginning with

$$0 \le \text{time} < 40$$

$$40 \le \text{time} < 80$$

(b) Describe the overall shape of the distribution: is it roughly symmetric, skewed to the right, or skewed to the left? Are there any outliers?

(c) Is the five-number summary or the mean and standard deviation a better brief summary for this distribution? Explain your choice. Calculate the one of these summaries that you choose.

2. Biologists and ecologists record the distributions of measurements made on animal species to help study the distribution and evolution of the animals. The African finch *Pyrenestes ostrinus* is interesting because the distribution of its bill size has two peaks even though other body measurements follow normal distributions. For example, a study in Cameroon found that the wing length of male finches varies according to a normal distribution with mean 61.2 mm and standard deviation 1.8 mm.

(a) What proportion of male finches have wings longer than 65 mm?

(b) What is the wing length that only 2% of male finches exceed?

3. The drug AZT was the first effective treatment for AIDS. An important medical experiment demonstrated that regular doses of AZT delay the onset of symptoms in people in whom the AIDS virus is present. The researchers who carried out this experiment wanted to know

- Does taking either 500 mg of AZT or 1500 mg of AZT per day delay the development of AIDS?

- Is there any difference between the effects of these two doses?

The subjects were 1200 volunteers already infected with the AIDS virus but with no symptoms of AIDS when the study started.

(a) Outline the design of the experiment.

(b) Describe briefly how you would use a table of random digits to do the randomization required by your design. Then use Table B beginning at line 110 to choose *the first five* subjects for one of your groups.

4. A long-term study of changing environmental conditions in Chesapeake Bay found the following annual average salinity readings in one location in the bay:

Year	1971	1972	1973	1974	1975	1976	1977
Salinity (%)	13.2	9.3	14.9	13.9	14.8	13.3	15.0

Year	1978	1979	1980	1981	1982	1983	1984
Salinity (%)	15.3	15.1	13.1	17.0	19.3	15.6	15.3

(a) Make a plot of salinity against time. Was salinity generally increasing or decreasing over these years? Is there an overall straight-line trend over time?

(b) What is the correlation between salinity and year? What percent of the observed variation in salinity is accounted for by straight line change over time?

(c) Find the least-squares regression line for predicting salinity from year. Explain in simple language what the slope of this line tells you about Chesapeake Bay.

(d) If the trend in these past data had continued, what would be the average salinity at this point in the bay in 1988?

3.2 Sample examination I solutions

1. (a) At right.

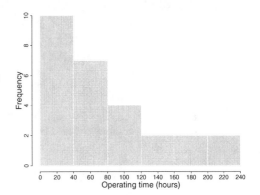

(b) The distribution of operating times is strongly skewed to the right. There are no outliers.

(c) The five-number summary is preferable for this strongly skewed distribution. First arrange the observations in increasing order:

| 1 | 4 | 11 | 16 | 18 | 18 | 18 | 24 | 31 | 39 | 46 | 51 | 54 | 63 |
| 68 | 77 | 80 | 82 | 97 | 106 | 111 | 141 | 142 | 163 | 191 | 206 | 216 |

The five-number summary of these $n = 27$ observations is

$$1 \quad 18 \quad 63 \quad 111 \quad 216$$

2. (a) Wing length x has the $N(61.2, 1.8)$ distribution. So we want the area under a normal curve such that

$$x > 65$$

$$\frac{x - 61.2}{1.8} > \frac{65 - 61.2}{1.8}$$

$$z > 2.11$$

Table A gives this area as $1 - 0.9826 = 0.0174$. About 17.4% of male finches have wing lengths exceeding 64.9 mm.

(b) We want the x with area 0.02 to its right, or area 0.98 to its left. In the body of Table A, find $z = 2.06$ as the entry with left tail area closest to 0.98. So

$$x = 61.2 + (1.8)(2.06) = 64.9 \text{ mm}$$

3. (a) The goals of the experiment require *three* treatment groups, one of which receives a placebo. (Because AZT was the first AIDS drug, it was considered ethical to give a placebo to test its effectiveness. Later drugs were tested against AZT.) Here is the design:

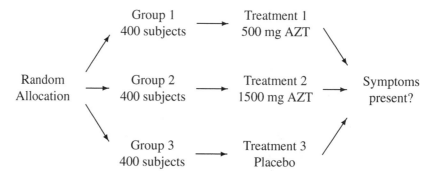

(b) First assign labels. We use labels 0001 to 1200. Then read 4-digit groups from line 110, continuing to the following lines. The first 5 subjects chosen are

    0676 0041 0404 1197 0640

4. (a) There is an increasing linear trend over time.

(b) The correlation (use a calculator) is $r = 0.6386$. Because $r^2 = 0.4079$, linear change over time explains about 41% of the observed variation in salinity over this period.

(c) The least-squares line (use a calculator) is

$$\hat{y} = -659.4385 + 0.340879x$$

That is, salinity is increasing by 0.34% per year on the average.

(d) The prediction for $x = 1988$ is

$$\hat{y} = -659.4385 + (0.3409)(1988) = 18.23\%$$

3.3 Sample examination II

These questions cover Chapters 3 through 5.

1. About 22% of the residents of California were born outside the United States. You choose an SRS of 1,000 California residents for a sample survey on immigration issues. You want to find the probability that 250 or more of the people in your sample were born outside the United States.

(a) You would like to use the normal approximation for the sampling distribution of a sample proportion to answer this question. Explain carefully why you can use the approximation in this setting.

(b) What is the probability that 250 or more of the people in your sample were born outside the United States?

2. The weights of newborn children in the United States vary according to the normal distribution with mean 7.5 pounds and standard deviation 1.25 pounds. The government classifies a newborn as having low birth weight if the weight is less than 5.5 pounds.

(a) What is the probability that a baby chosen at random weighs less than 5.5 pounds at birth?

(b) You choose 3 babies at random. What is the probability that their average birthweight is less than 5.5 pounds?

3. Answer each of the following short questions.

(a) Give the upper 0.025 critical value for the standard normal distribution.

(b) An animal scientist is studying factors that affect the level of milk production in dairy cows. He wonders:

> Is the mean production different for cows who are given forage spread on the ground than for cows whose forage is in bunks?

State the null and alternative hypotheses that you would use in a statistical test of this question. (We can't test these hypotheses yet.)

(c) An opinion poll asks 1500 randomly chosen United States residents their opinion about relations with Russia. The announced margin of error for 95% confidence is ± 3 points. But some people were not on the list from which respondents were chosen, some could not be contacted, and some refused to answer. Does the announced margin of error include errors from these causes?

(d) A student organization plans to ask of 100 randomly selected students whether they favor a change in the grading system. You argue for a sample of 900 students instead of 100. You know that the standard deviation of the proportion $\hat{p}$ of the sample who say "Yes" will be __ times as large with the larger sample. Should this blank be filled with nine, one-ninth, three, or one-third? Explain your answer.

(e) You read in a journal a report of a study that found a statistically significant result at the 5% significance level. What can you say about the significance of this result at the 1% level: Is it certainly significant at the 1% level, certainly not significant at the 1% level, or maybe significant and maybe not significant?

4. A friend who hears that you are taking a statistics course asks for help with a chemistry lab report. She has made four independent measurements of the specific gravity of a compound. The results are

    3.82, 3.93, 3.67, 3.78

    The lab manual says that repeated measurements will vary according to a normal distribution with standard deviation $\sigma = 0.15$. (This standard deviation shows how precise the measurement process is.) The mean μ of the distribution of measurements is the true specific gravity.

    (a) The lab manual asks for a 95% confidence interval for the true specific gravity. Your friend doesn't know how to do this. Do it for her.

    (b) Now explain to your friend in simple language what "95% confidence" means.

    (c) What critical value from the normal table would you use if you wanted 80% confidence instead of 95% confidence? Would the 80% confidence interval be wider or narrower than your 95% confidence from (a)? [Do *not* actually compute the 80% confidence interval.]

    (d) The lab manual also asks whether the data show convincingly that the true specific gravity is less than 3.9. State the null and alternative hypotheses used to answer this question. Then calculate the test statistic, and find its P-value.

    (e) Explain to your friend in one or two sentences what the specific P-value you found in (c) means.

5. Here are several statistical statements. In each case, explain to someone who knows no statistics what the boldface term means. Use just a sentence or two, and avoid technical jargon.

    (a) A spinning penny has **probability 0.6** of coming up tails.

    (b) With **90% confidence** we can say that the national unemployment rate for June was between 5.3% and 5.5%.

    (c) The **expected winnings** on a $1 lottery ticket are $0.53.

6. If you pay me $1, I will let you play the following gambling game. You drop your pencil point into the middle of a table of random digits and then look at the digit on which it lands.

    If it is a 7, you win $5.
    If it is a 1, you win $2.
    Otherwise you win nothing.

    Find the expected value of the amount you win in one play of this game. Explain in simple language what the expected value tells you about your winnings if you play the game many times. Is it to your advantage to pay $1 to play?

3.4 Sample examination II solutions

1. (a) First, (rule of thumb 1) the population of California is much larger than 10 times the sample size $n = 1000$. So we can use the usual formula for the standard deviation of $\hat{p}$.

    Second, (rule of thumb 2) for $n = 1000$ and $p = 0.22$ we have $np = 220$ and $n(1 - p) = 780$. Both are much larger than 10, so the normal approximation will be quite accurate.

    (b) The question concerns the *count* of 1000 California residents born outside the United States. Translate into a question about the *proportion*:

    $$\text{count} \geq 250 \quad \text{is} \quad \hat{p} = \frac{\text{count}}{1000} \geq \frac{250}{1000} = 0.25$$

    The mean of $\hat{p}$ is $p = 0.22$. The standard deviation is

    $$\sqrt{\frac{p(1 - p)}{n}} = \sqrt{\frac{(0.22)(0.78)}{1000}} = 0.0131$$

    Now use the normal approximation to find the probability:

    $$\begin{aligned} P(\hat{p} \geq 0.25) &= P\left(\frac{\hat{p} - 0.22}{0.0131} \geq \frac{0.25 - 0.22}{0.0131}\right) \\ &= P(Z \geq 2.29) \\ &= 1 - 0.9890 = 0.0110 \end{aligned}$$

2. (a) The weight x of a single child has the $N(7.5, 1.25)$ distribution. So

    $$P(x < 5.5) = P\left(\frac{x - 7.5}{1.25} < \frac{5.5 - 7.5}{1.25}\right) = P(Z < -1.60) = 0.0548$$

    (b) The mean birth weight $\bar{x}$ of a sample of 3 children still has mean 7.5 pounds, but its standard deviation is

    $$\frac{\sigma}{\sqrt{3}} = \frac{1.25}{\sqrt{3}} = 0.7217 \text{ pound}$$

    The probability we want is therefore

    $$P(\bar{x} < 5.5) = P\left(\frac{\bar{x} - 7.5}{0.7217} < \frac{5.5 - 7.5}{0.7217}\right) = P(Z < -2.77) = 0.0028$$

3. (a) Use Table C to see that the upper 0.025 critical value is $z^* = 1.960$. *Or*, use the 68–95–99.7 rule to approximate it by 2.

(b) The key words are "is different," indicating that the alternative hypothesis is two-sided:

$$H_0 : \mu_G = \mu_B \qquad \text{vs.} \qquad H_a : \mu_G \neq \mu_B$$

Here μ_G and μ_B are the mean milk production for all cows of this breed with forage spread on the ground and in bunks, respectively.

(c) No. The margin of error in a confidence interval covers only the random sampling error due to chance variation in random sampling.

(d) The standard deviation goes down as the sample size n goes up, at the rate $\sqrt{n}$. (The standard deviation of a sample proportion $\hat{p}$ is $\sqrt{p(1-p)/n}$.) So a sample 9 times larger has a standard deviation *one-third* as large.

(e) A result significant at the 5% level is in the extreme 5% of the sampling distribution; so it *may or may not* also be in the extreme 1%.

4. (a) First, $\bar{x} = 3.80$. The 95% confidence interval is

$$\bar{x} \pm z^* \frac{\sigma}{\sqrt{n}} = 3.80 \pm 1.960\frac{0.15}{\sqrt{4}} = 3.80 \pm 0.147$$

(b) "95% confidence" means that we got this interval by using a method that in 95% of all samples will produce an interval that covers the true specific gravity.

(c) $z^* = 1.282$, the upper 0.10 critical value. The 80% confidence interval is narrower than the 95% confidence interval because the critical value required is smaller.

(d) The hypotheses are

$$H_0 : \mu = 3.9 \qquad \text{vs.} \qquad H_a : \mu < 3.9$$

The test statistic is

$$z = \frac{\bar{x} - \mu_0}{\sigma/\sqrt{n}} = \frac{3.8 - 3.9}{0.15/\sqrt{4}} = -1.33$$

and its P-value (one-sided on the low side) is

$$P(Z \leq -1.33) = 0.0918$$

(e) There is probability 0.0918 that the mean of 4 readings would be as small as 3.8 if the true specific gravity were 3.9. That is, we observed a value in the smallest 9.2% of all results we could get if 3.9 were correct. This is only weak evidence that the specific gravity is less than 3.9, because a value this small would come up more than 9% of the time just by chance.

5. (a) In the long run, the coin comes up tails about 60% of the time.

(b) The interval was derived from a method that gives an interval that includes the true unemployment rate 90% of the time.

(c) If we buy many lottery tickets, the average winnings will be close to $0.53.

6. The expected winnings are $(0.1)(\$5) + (0.1)(\$2) = \$0.70$. This represents average winnings for many plays of the game; it is not a good idea to spend $1 on this game.

3.5 Sample final examination

This is comprehensive, covering material from (roughly) chapters 1–12.

1. An historian examining British colonial records for the Gold Coast in Africa suspects that the death rate was higher among African miners than among European miners. In the year 1936, there were 223 deaths among 33,809 African miners and 7 deaths among 1541 European miners in the Gold Coast. (Data courtesy of Raymond Dumett, Department of History, Purdue University.)

   Consider this year as a sample from the prewar era in Africa. Is there good evidence that the proportion of African miners who died during a year was higher than the proportion of European miners who died? [State hypotheses, calculate a test statistic, give a P-value as exact as the tables in the text allow, and state your conclusion in words.]

2. An agricultural researcher reasons as follows: A heavy application of potassium fertilizer to grasslands in the spring seems to cause lush early growth but depletes the potassium before the growing season ends. So spreading the same amount of potassium over the growing season might increase yields. The researcher therefore compares two treatments: 100 pounds per acre of potassium in the spring (Treatment 1) and 50, 25, and 25 pounds per acre applied in the spring, early summer, and late summer (Treatment 2). The experiment is continued over several years because growing conditions may vary from year to year.

   The table below gives the yields, in pounds of dry matter per acre. It is known from long experience that yields vary roughly normally. (Data from R. R. Robinson, C. L. Rhykerd, and C. F. Gross, "Potassium uptake by orchardgrass as affected by time, frequency and rate of potassium fertilization," *Agronomy Journal*, 54(1962) 351–353.)

Treatment	Year 1	Year 2	Year 3	Year 4	Year 5
1	3902	4281	5135	5350	5746
2	3970	4271	5440	5490	6028

   (a) Do the data give good evidence that Treatment 2 leads to higher average yields? [State hypotheses, carry out a test, give a P-value as exact as the tables in the text allow, and state your conclusions in words.]

   (b) Give a 98% confidence interval for the mean increase in yield due to spreading potassium applications over the growing season.

3. Prior to an intensive TV advertising campaign, the producers of Nike athletic shoes find that 29 of a random sample of 200 upper-income adults are aware of their new leisure shoe line. A second random sample of 300 such adults is taken after the campaign. Now 96 of the persons sampled can identify the new line.

Give a 99% confidence interval for the increase in the proportion of upper income adults showing brand awareness.

4. Here are data on the years of schooling completed, x, and annual income, y (in thousands of dollars), for a sample of 18 40-year-old men.

Years	10	16	12	6	12	12	16	16	18
Income	28	38	16	13	25	30	35	27	28

Years	12	10	12	16	14	11	12	19	16
Income	28	26	21	34	30	21	27	29	24

A scatterplot (don't do it) shows a generally linear relation, but with considerable scatter about the line of best fit. A computer least-squares regression program gives the output shown. (The "Coef" column gives the intercept a and slope b; the "Std Err" column gives the standard errors of these statistics. The "Residual Standard Error" is the observed standard deviation s about the regression line.)

```
              Coef      Std Err     t Value
Intercept   10.84249   5.103363    2.124577
x2           1.186813  0.372311    3.187693

Residual Standard Error = 5.02275     R-Square = 0.3884116
N = 18         F Value = 10.16139 on 1, 16 df
```

(a) What percent of the observed variation in income is explained by the straight-line relation between income and education?

(b) Is there strong evidence that there is a straight-line relation between education and income? (State hypotheses, carry out a test, use a table to find values between which the P-value falls, and state your conclusion.)

(c) Consider 40-year-old men who have 16 years of education. (These are men with four years of college but no further education.) Give a 95% confidence interval for their average income.

5. Answer each of the following questions. (No explanation is needed — just a short answer.)

(a) You are reading an article in your field that reports several statistical analyses. The article says that the P-value for a significance test is 0.045. Is this result significant at the 5% significance level?

(b) Is the result with P-value 0.045 significant at the 1% significance level?

(c) For another significance test, the article says only that the result was significant at the 1% level. Are such results always, sometimes, or never significant at the 5% level?

(d) Reaction times of a subject to a stimulus are often strongly skewed to the right because of a few slow reaction times. You wish to test

$$H_0 : \mu_1 = \mu_2$$

where μ_1 is the mean reaction time for Stimulus 1, μ_2 for Stimulus 2. You have two independent samples, 8 observations for Stimulus 1 and 10 for Stimulus 2. Which, if any, of the tests you have studied can be used to test this?

(e) The article contains a 95% confidence interval. Would the margin of error in a 99% confidence interval computed from the same data be less, the same, or greater?

6. A friend in a political science course asks for your help. She just read that the correlation between the percent of eligible citizens in a city who register to vote and the percent of registered voters in the city who really do vote is 0.88. She read further that the correlation is significant ($P < 0.01$).

(a) Explain to your friend in plain language what $r = 0.88$ means.

(b) Then explain what it means to say that this correlation is statistically significant ($P < 0.01$). Use plain language—no technical terms.

(c) Now explain to you friend what the fact that $r^2 = 0.77$ says about predicting voter turnout from registration data.

7. Here are data on the percent of sugar in some popular breakfast cereals.

Product	% Sugar
All Bran	19
Alpha Bits	38
Cap'n Crunch	40
Cheerios	3
Corn Flakes	5
Golden Grahams	30
Grape Nuts Flakes	13
Post Toasties	5
Product 19	10
Raisin Bran (General Foods)	48
Raisin Bran (Kellogg)	29
Rice Krispies	8
Special K	5
Sugar Smacks	56
Wheaties	8

(a) Make a stemplot of these data. Describe the overall shape of the distribution. Are there any clear outliers?

(b) Based on your findings in part (a), choose a numerical summary for this distribution. Calculate your summary.

3.6 Sample final examination solutions

1. This is a two-sample setting with

> Population 1 = African miners
> Population 2 = European miners

We want to test

$$H_0 : p_1 = p_2 \qquad \text{vs.} \qquad H_a : p_1 > p_2$$

The two sample proportions are

$$\hat{p}_1 = \frac{223}{33,809} = 0.006596 \quad \text{and} \quad \hat{p}_2 = \frac{7}{1541} = 0.004543$$

The pooled sample proportion is therefore

$$\begin{aligned} \hat{p} &= \frac{\text{count of deaths in both samples combined}}{\text{count of miners in both samples combined}} \\ &= \frac{223 + 7}{33,809 + 1541} \\ &= \frac{230}{35,350} = 0.006506 \end{aligned}$$

and the test statistic is

$$\begin{aligned} z &= \frac{\hat{p}_1 - \hat{p}_2}{\sqrt{\hat{p}(1 - \hat{p}) \left(\frac{1}{n_1} + \frac{1}{n_2} \right)}} \\ &= \frac{0.006596 - 0.004543}{\sqrt{(0.006506)(0.993494) \left(\frac{1}{33,809} + \frac{1}{1541} \right)}} \\ &= \frac{0.002053}{0.0020943} = 0.980 \end{aligned}$$

Table A gives the *P*-value as $1 - 0.8365 = 0.1635$. There is, surprisingly, no significant evidence that the African death rate is higher.

2. This is a *matched pairs* setting because the observations are paired by years.

   (a) The hypotheses, expressed in terms of the mean differences, Treatment 2 − Treatment 1, are

   $$H_0 : \mu = 0 \qquad \text{vs.} \qquad H_a : \mu > 0$$

   The differences are

   $$68 \quad -10 \quad 305 \quad 140 \quad 282$$

   with

   $$\bar{x} = 157 \quad \text{and} \quad s = 135.672$$

   Apply the one-sample t test to these differences. The test statistic is

   $$t = \frac{\bar{x} - 0}{s/\sqrt{n}} = \frac{157}{135.672/\sqrt{5}} = 2.588$$

   The P-value based on the t distribution with $n - 1 = 4$ degrees of freedom falls between 0.025 and 0.05 (using Table C). This is moderately strong evidence that Treatment 2 produces a higher mean yield.

   (b) For 98% confidence and 4 degrees of freedom, use $t^* = 3.747$. The confidence interval is

   $$
   \begin{aligned}
   \bar{x} \pm t^* \frac{s}{\sqrt{n}} \ &= \ 157 \pm 3.747 \frac{135.672}{\sqrt{5}} \\
   &= \ 157 \pm 227.3 \\
   &= \ (-70.3, \ 384.3)
   \end{aligned}
   $$

3. There are two independent samples. We want a confidence interval for a difference between two population proportions. The sample proportions are

   $$\hat{p}_1 = \frac{29}{200} = 0.145 \quad \text{and} \quad \hat{p}_2 = \frac{96}{300} = 0.320$$

   We can use procedures based on the normal approximation because the population is large and

   $$n\hat{p}_1 = 29 \quad n(1 - \hat{p}_1) = 191 \quad n\hat{p}_2 = 96 \quad n(1 - \hat{p}_2) = 204$$

   are all more than 5.

   The standard error for $\hat{p}_2 - \hat{p}_1$ is

   $$
   \begin{aligned}
   \text{SE} \ &= \ \sqrt{\frac{\hat{p}_1(1 - \hat{p}_1)}{n_1} + \frac{\hat{p}_2(1 - \hat{p}_2)}{n_2}} \\
   &= \ \sqrt{\frac{(0.145)(0.855)}{200} + \frac{(0.320)(0.680)}{300}} \\
   &= \ \sqrt{0.0013452} = 0.03668
   \end{aligned}
   $$

The 99% confidence interval for $p_2 - p_1$ is

$$
\begin{aligned}
(\hat{p}_2 - \hat{p}_1) \pm z^* \text{SE} &= (0.320 - 0.145) \pm (2.576)(0.03668) \\
&= 0.175 \pm 0.0945 \\
&= (0.0805, \ 0.2695)
\end{aligned}
$$

We are 99% confident that between 8% and 27% of upper-income adults are aware of the new shoe line.

4. (a) The output says R-Square = 0.3884116, so the linear relationship explains 38.8% of the observed variation in income.

    (b) The null hypothesis of "no relation" says that the slope of the true regression line is 0. The hypotheses are

$$
H_0 : \beta = 0 \qquad \text{vs.} \qquad H_a : \beta \neq 0
$$

   The computer output shows that the t statistic for the test is $t = 3.187693$. The degrees of freedom are $n - 2 = 16$. From Table C we see that t falls between the 0.0025 and 0.005 upper critical values of $t(16)$. Doubling these values because H_a is two-sided, $0.005 < P < 0.01$. There is strong evidence that a linear relationship exists.

    (c) The predicted mean income for $x = 16$ is

$$
\hat{y} = 10.84249 + (1.186813)(16) = 29.831
$$

   or \$29,831. The rest of this is a bit tedious by hand, so consider your options. (Not all students may be capable of handling this on a test.) Here goes. Using a calculator for $\bar{x}$ and s_x gives that $\bar{x} = 13.33$ and

$$
\sum (x - \bar{x})^2 = (n - 1)s_x^2 = (17)(3.27198)^2 = 182
$$

   The proper standard error for estimating the mean income is

$$
\begin{aligned}
\text{SE}_{\hat{\mu}} &= s \sqrt{\frac{1}{n} + \frac{(x^* - \bar{x})^2}{\sum (x - \bar{x})^2}} \\
&= 5.02275 \sqrt{\frac{1}{18} + \frac{(16 - 13.33)^2}{182}} \\
&= 5.02275 \sqrt{0.0946275} = 1.5451
\end{aligned}
$$

   The 90% confidence interval is therefore

$$
\begin{aligned}
\hat{y} \pm t^* \text{SE}_{\hat{\mu}} &= 29.831 \pm (2.120)(1.5451) \\
&= 29.831 \pm 3.276 \\
&= (26.555, \ 33.107)
\end{aligned}
$$

   or \$26,555 to \$33,107.

5. (a) Yes. The *P*-value is less than 0.05.

   (b) No. The *P*-value is greater than 0.01.

   (c) A result significant at the 1% level lies in the extreme 1% of a sampling distribution. This is certainly in the extreme 5%, so the result is always significant at the 5% level.

   (d) The samples are small and the distributions are strongly skewed. It would be unwise to use the *t* test in this setting. A nonparametric test (if these have been studied) might be appropriate.

   (e) The margin of error would be greater. Higher confidence is paid for with a greater margin of error.

6. (a) There is a strong tendency for both quantities—percent registered, and the percent who turn out—to both be high, or both be low. That is, when one is high, the other is usually also high, and when one is low, the other is usually low.

   (b) If there was no relationship between the two quantities, a correlation this high would be observed less than 1% of the time.

   (c) There will be variation in voter turnout from one city to the next. If we know the percent registered, we can account for (explain) about 77% of that variation.

7. (a) The distribution is right-skewed, with no particular outliers.

   ```
   0 | 355588
   1 | 039
   2 | 9
   3 | 08
   4 | 08
   5 | 6
   ```

   (b) Because of the skewness, use the five-number summary: 3 5 13 38 56.

4 Solutions to Exercises

4.1 About these solutions

The solutions that follow were prepared by Darryl K. Nester. I occasionally pillaged or plagiarized solutions from the second edition (prepared by George McCabe), but I take full responsibility for any errors that may remain. Should you discover any errors or have any comments about these solutions (or the odd answers, in the back of the text), please report them to me:

> Darryl Nester
> Bluffton College
> Bluffton, Ohio 45817
> email: nesterd@bluffton.edu
> WWW: http://www.bluffton.edu/~nesterd

4.2 Using the table of random digits

Grading SRSs chosen from the table of random digits is complicated by the fact that students can find some creative ways to (mis)use the table. Some approaches are not mistakes, but may lead to different students having different "right" answers. Correct answers will vary based on:

- The line in the table on which they begin (you may want to specify one if the text does not).

- Whether they start with, e.g., 00 or 01.

- Whether or not they assign multiple labels to each unit.

- Whether they assign labels across the rows or down the columns (nearly all lists in the text are alphabetized down the columns).

Some approaches can potentially lead to wrong answers. Mistakes to watch out for include:

- They may forget that all labels must be the same length, e.g., assigning labels like $0, 1, 2, \ldots, 9, 10, \ldots$ rather than $00, 01, 02, \ldots$.

- In assigning multiple labels, they may not give the same number of labels to all units. E.g., if there are 30 units, they may try to use up all the two-digit numbers, thus assigning 4 labels to the first ten units and only 3 to the remaining twenty.

4.3 Using statistical software

The use of computer software or a calculator is a must for all but the most cursory treatment of the material in this text. Be aware of the following considerations:

- *Standard deviations:* Students may easily get confused by software which gives both the so-called "sample standard deviation" (the one used in the text) and the "population standard deviation" (dividing by n rather than $n - 1$). Symbolically, the former is usually given as "s" and the latter as "σ" (sigma), but the distinction is not always clear. For example, many computer spreadsheets have a command such as "STDEV(...)" to compute a standard deviation, but you may need to check the manual to find out which kind it is.

    As a quick check: for the numbers 1, 2, 3, $s = 1$ while $\sigma \doteq 0.8165$. In general, if two values are given, the larger one is s and the smaller is σ. If only one value is given, and it is the "wrong" one, use the relationship $s = \sigma \sqrt{\frac{n}{n-1}}$.

- *Quartiles and five-number summaries:* Methods of computing quartiles vary between different packages. Some use the approach given in the text (that is, Q_1 is the median of all the numbers below the location of the overall median, etc.), while others use a more complicated approach. For the numbers 1, 2, 3, 4, for example, we would have $Q_1 = 1.5$ and $Q_3 = 2.5$, but Minitab reports these as 1.25 and 2.75, respectively.

    Since I used Minitab for most of the analysis in these solutions, this was sometimes a problem. However, I remedied the situation by writing a Minitab macro to compute quartiles the IPS way. (In effect, I was "dumbing down" Minitab, since its method is more sophisticated.) This and other macros are available at my website.

- *Boxplots:* Some programs which draw boxplots use the convention that the "whiskers" extend to the lower and upper deciles (the 10th and 90th percentiles) rather than to the minimum and maximum. (DeltaGraph, which I used for most of the graphs in these solutions, is one such program. It took some trickery on my part to convince it to make them as I wanted them.)

    While the decile method is merely *different* from that given in the text, some methods are (in my opinion) just plain *wrong*. Some graphing calculators from Sharp draw "box charts," which have a center line at the mean (not the median), and a box extending from $\bar{x} - \sigma$ to $\bar{x} + \sigma$! I know of no statistics text that uses that method.

4.4 Acknowledgments

I should mention the software I used in putting these solutions together:

- For typesetting: TEX — specifically, Textures, from Blue Sky Software.

- For the graphs: DeltaGraph (SPSS), Adobe Illustrator, and PSMathGraphs II (MaryAnn Software).

- For statistical analysis: Minitab, G•Power, JMP IN, and GLMStat—the latter two mostly for the Chapters 14 and 15. George McCabe supplied output from SAS for Chapter 15. G•Power is available as freeware on the Internet, while GLMStat is shareware. Additionally, I used the TI-82, TI-85, TI-86, and TI-92 calculators from Texas Instruments.

Chapter 1 Solutions

Section 1: Displaying Distributions with Graphs

1.1 (a) Categorical. **(b)** Quantitative. **(c)** Categorical. **(d)** Categorical. **(e)** Quantitative. **(f)** Quantitative.

1.2 Gender: categorical. Age: quantitative. Household income: quantitative. Voting Democratic/Republican: categorical.

1.3 The individuals are vehicles (or "cars"). Variables: vehicle type (categorical), where made (categorical), city MPG (quantitative), and highway MPG (quantitative).

1.4 Possible answers (unit; instrument):
- number of pages (pages; eyes)
- number of chapters (chapters; eyes)
- number of words (words; eyes [likely bloodshot after all that counting])
- weight or mass (pounds/ounces or kilograms; scale or balance)
- height and/or width and/or thickness (inches or centimeters; ruler or measuring tape)
- volume (cubic inches or cubic centimeters; ruler or measuring tape [and a calculator])

Any one of the first three could be used to estimate the time required to read the book; the last two would help determine how well the book would fit into a book bag.

1.5 A tape measure (the measuring instrument) can be used to measure (in units of inches or centimeters) various lengths such as the longest single hair, length of hair on sides or back or front. Details on how to measure should be given. The case of a bald (or balding) person would make an interesting class discussion.

1.6 Possible answers (reasons should be given): unemployment rate, average (mean or median) income, quality/availability of public transportation, number of entertainment and cultural events, housing costs, crime statistics, population, population density, number of automobiles, various measures of air quality, commuting times (or other measures of traffic), parking availability, taxes, quality of schools.

1.7 For (a), the number of deaths would tend to rise with the increasing population, even if cancer treatments become more effective over time: Since there are more people, there are more potential cases of cancer. Even if treatment is more effective, the increasing cure rate may not be sufficient to overcome the rising number of cases.

For (b), if treatments for other diseases are also improving, people who might have died from other causes would instead live long enough to succumb to cancer.

Even if treatments were becoming *less* effective, many forms of cancer are detected earlier as better tests are developed. In measuring five-year survival rates for (c), if we can detect cancer (say) one year earlier than was previously possible, then effectively, each patient lives one year longer after the cancer is detected, thus raising the five-year survival rate.

1.8 (a) 1988: $\frac{949}{24,800,000} \doteq 0.00003827 = 38.27$ deaths per million riders. 1992: $\frac{903}{54,632,000} \doteq 0.00001653 = 16.53$ deaths per million riders. Death rates are less than half what they were; bicycle riding is safer. **(b)** It seems unlikely that the number of riders more than doubled in a six-year period.

1.9 Using the proportion or percentage of repairs, Brand A is more reliable: $\frac{2942}{13,376} \doteq 0.22 = 22\%$ for Brand A, and $\frac{192}{480} = 0.4 = 40\%$ for Brand B.

1.10 (a) Student preferences may vary; be sure they give a reason. Method 1 is faster, but less accurate—it will only give values that are multiples of 10. **(b)** In either method 1 or 2, fractions of a beat will be lost—for example, we cannot observe 7.3 beats in 6 seconds, only 7. The formula $60 \times 50 \div t$, where t is the time needed for 50 beats, would give a more accurate rate since the inaccuracy is limited to the error in measuring t (which can be measured to the nearest second, or perhaps even more accurately).

1.11 Possible answers are total profits, number of employees, total value of stock, and total assets.

1.12 (a) Yes: The sum of the ethnic group counts is 12,261,000. **(b)** A bar graph or pie chart (not recommended) may be used. In order to see the contrast of the heights of the bars, the chart needs to be fairly tall.

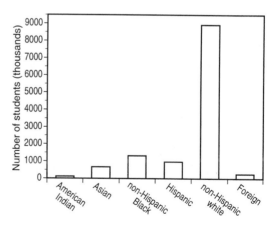

1.13 (a) Shown at right. The bars are given in the same order as the data in the table—the most obvious way—but that is not necessary (since the variable is nominal, not ordinal). **(b)** A pie chart would not be appropriate, since the different entries in the table do not represent parts of a single whole.

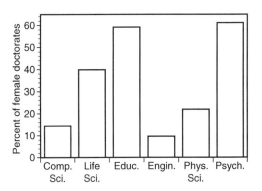

1.14 (a) Below. For example, "Motor Vehicles" is 46% since $\frac{41,893}{90,523} = 0.4627\ldots$. The "Other causes" category is needed so that the total is 100%. **(b)** Below. The bars may be in any order. **(c)** A pie chart *could* also be used, since the categories represent parts of a whole (all accidental deaths).

Cause	Percent
Motor vehicles	46
Falls	15
Drowning	4
Fires	4
Poisoning	8
Other causes	23

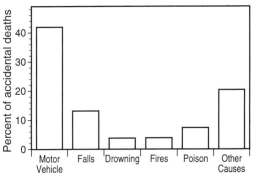

1.15 Figure 1.10(a) is strongly skewed to the right with a peak at 0; Figure 1.10(b) is somewhat symmetric with a central peak at 4. The peak is at the lowest value in 1.10(a), and at a central value in 1.10(b).

1.16 The distribution is skewed to the right with a single peak. There are no gaps or outliers.

1.17 There are two peaks. Most of the ACT states are located in the upper portion of the distribution, since in such states, only the stronger students take the SAT.

1.18 The distribution is roughly symmetric. There are peaks at .230–.240 and .270–.290. The middle of the distribution is about .270. Ignoring the outlier, the range is about $.345 - .185 = .160$ (or $.350 - .180 = .170$).

1.19 Sketches will vary. The distribution of coin years would be left-skewed because newer coins are more common than older coins.

1.20 (a) Among the women, 200 appears to an outlier. Among the men, the two high scores would probably not be considered outliers. **(b)** The women's median is 138.5; the range is 99 (101 to 200). The men's median is 114.5; the range is 117 (70 to 187). Generally, women have higher scores.

Men		Women
50	7	
8	8	
21	9	
984	10	139
5543	11	5
6	12	669
2	13	77
60	14	08
1	15	244
9	16	55
	17	8
70	18	
	19	
	20	0

1.21 The back-to-back stemplot shown has split stems. There does not seem to be a substantial difference between the two groups; this is supported by the fact that the medians are 111.5 (calcium) and 112 (placebo)—almost identical. Before treatments, the two groups are very similar.

Calcium		Placebo
	9	8
2	10	2
77	10	9
2210	11	0224
	11	79
3	12	3
9	12	
	13	0
6	13	

1.22 If the first two digits are used as stems, both distributions appear very spread out and one might conclude that there are outliers. This stemplot uses the hundreds digit for (split) stems and the tens digit for leaves. (The usual practice with stemplots is to truncate—ignore the ones digit—rather than to round.) This display suggests that the experimental chicks had greater weight gain; the medians were 358 grams for the control chicks and 406.5 grams for the high-lysine group.

Control		Experimental
87	2	
44221	3	123
98866555	3	6799
310	4	00001222334
65	4	67

1.23 A histogram (using the classes 10–14, 15–19, 20–24, etc.) is essentially the same as the stemplot shown (with split stems). Preferences may vary; for example, some students find stemplots easier to make, or prefer them because one can find actual data values by looking at stemplots. The distribution is slightly left-skewed.

1	44
1	5899
2	2
2	55667789
3	13344
3	555589
4	0011234
4	5667789
5	1224

1.24 The stemplot gives more information than a histogram (since all the original numbers can be read off the stemplot), but both give the same impression. The distribution is roughly symmetric with one value that is somewhat low. The center of the distribution is between 5.4 and 5.5 (the median is 5.46).

```
48 | 8
49 |
50 | 7
51 | 0
52 | 6799
53 | 04469
54 | 2467
55 | 03578
56 | 12358
57 | 59
58 | 5
```

1.25 **(a)** Preferences will vary. The first plot has the advantage of being compact, while the split stems suggest that there may be a second peak. **(b)** In either plot, the distribution is roughly symmetric, with center around 12.6 or 12.7 percent. Alaska and Florida appear to be outliers; Alaska is low presumably because of its less attractive climate, while Florida is high because many retirees move there.

```
 4 | 9
 5 |
 6 |
 7 |
 8 | 8
 9 |
10 | 0029
11 | 011344469
12 | 003445556666
13 | 0133445677999
14 | 23455
15 | 2379
16 |
17 |
18 | 6
```

```
 4 | 9
 5 |
 5 |
 6 |
 6 |
 7 |
 7 |
 8 |
 8 | 8
 9 |
 9 |
10 | 002
10 | 9
11 | 0113444
11 | 69
12 | 00344
12 | 5556666
13 | 013344
13 | 5677999
14 | 234
14 | 55
15 | 23
15 | 79
16 |
16 |
17 |
17 |
18 |
18 | 6
```

1.26 **(a)** A stemplot is shown; a histogram would have a similar appearance. Percents are truncated, and stems were split to keep the branches from getting too long. **(b)** −26.6% is substantially lower than all other returns. With the outlier omitted, the distribution is fairly symmetric with center around 2% to 3%, spread from −14.7% to 19.2%. **(c)** The time plot (below) reveals no apparent pattern.

−2	6
−2	
−1	
−1	44000
−0	98765
−0	4443333222222222100
0	00000111122222223333333444444
0	556666777778899
1	0001133
1	789

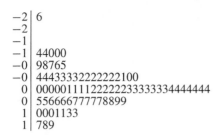

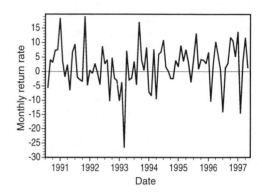

1.27 A stemplot is shown; a histogram would also be appropriate. There are no outliers, although the distribution is clearly right-skewed. The split stems emphasize the skewness by showing the gaps.

0	44
0	55555667778888888888889999999
1	000000000001112222333444
1	56777899
2	1144
2	
3	2
3	8
4	0
4	
5	12
5	9

1.28 **(a)** There are four variables: GPA, IQ, and self-concept are quantitative, while gender is categorical. (OBS is not a variable, since it is not really a "characteristic" of a student.) **(b)** Below. **(c)** The distribution is skewed to the left, with center (median) around 7.8. GPAs are spread from 0.5 to 10.8, with only 15 below 6. **(d)** There is more variability among the boys; in fact, there seems to be a subset of boys with GPAs from 0.5 to 4.9. Ignoring that group, the two distributions have similar shapes.

0	5
1	8
2	4
3	4689
4	0679
5	1259
6	0112249
7	22333556666666788899
8	0000222223347899
9	002223344556668
10	01678

Female		Male
	0	5
	1	8
	2	4
4	3	689
7	4	069
952	5	1
4210	6	129
98866533	7	223566666789
997320	8	0002222348
65300	9	2223445668
710	10	68

1.29 Stemplot at right, with split stems. The distribution is fairly symmetric—perhaps slightly left-skewed—with center around 110 (clearly above 100). IQs range from the low 70s to the high 130s, with a "gap" in the low 80s.

```
 7 | 24
 7 | 79
 8 |
 8 | 69
 9 | 0133
 9 | 6778
10 | 0022333344
10 | 555666777789
11 | 0000111122223334444
11 | 55688999
12 | 003344
12 | 677888
13 | 02
13 | 6
```

1.30 Stemplot at right, with split stems. The distribution is skewed to the left, with center around 59.5. Most self-concept scores are between 35 and 73, with a few below that, and one high score of 80 (but not really high enough to be an outlier).

```
2 | 01
2 | 8
3 | 0
3 | 5679
4 | 02344
4 | 6799
5 | 1111223344444
5 | 556668899
6 | 00001233344444
6 | 55666677777899
7 | 0000111223
7 |
8 | 0
```

1.31 **(a)** Table at right. **(b)** Histogram below. Children (under 10) represent the single largest group in the population; about one out of five Americans was under 10 in 1950. There is a slight dip in the 10–19 age bracket, then the percentages trail off gradually after that. **(c)** Histogram below. The projections show a much greater proportion in the higher age brackets—there is now a gradual rise in the proportion up to ages 40–49, followed by the expected decline in the proportion of "senior citizens."

Age Group	1950	2075
0–9	19.4%	11.2%
10–19	14.4	11.5
20–29	15.9	11.8
30–39	15.1	12.3
40–49	12.8	12.2
50–59	10.3	12.1
60–69	7.3	11.1
70–79	3.6	8.8
80–89	1.1	6.1
90–99	0.1	2.5
100–109	0.0	0.5

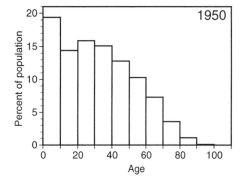
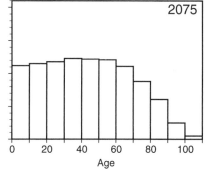

1.32 Use relative frequency histograms, since there are considerably more men than women. The two histograms are both skewed to the right (as income distributions often are). Women's salaries are generally lower than men's.

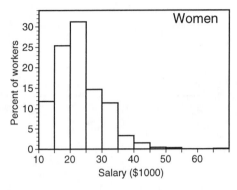 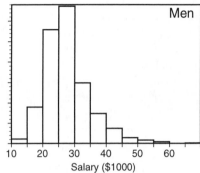

1.33 A class that is $20,000 wide should have bars one-fourth as tall as the bars for the $5,000-wide classes.

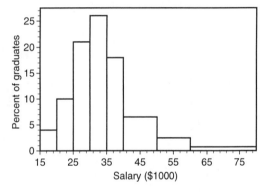

1.34 (a) Right. **(b)** The plot shows a decreasing trend—fewer disturbances overall in the later years—and more importantly, there is an apparent cyclic behavior. Looking at the table, the spring and summer months (April through September) generally have the most disturbances—probably for the simple reason that more people are outside during those periods.

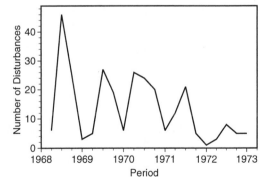

1.35 (a) Right. The death rate decreases fairly steadily over time. **(b)** The drop from the mid-1970s to the mid-1980s appears to be part of the overall trend; there is no particular suggestion in the plot that the decrease is any greater during that time, and thus no evidence that the lower speed limits saved lives (especially since the decrease continues after the mid-1980s). **(c)** A histogram *could* be made, but it would probably not be very useful: The most important thing to study about these numbers is the change over time, not the number of times that, e.g., the death rate was between 4.5 and 5.0.

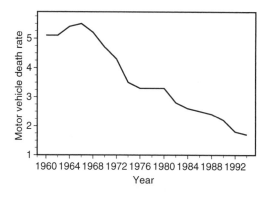

1.36

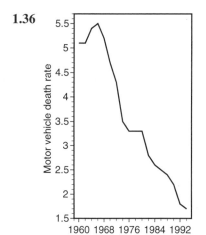

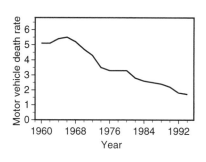

1.37 In his first five years, Ruth had few home runs (pitchers don't play in as many games as outfielders). After that, until the last years of his career, his home-run output fluctuated but was consistently high (25 or more).

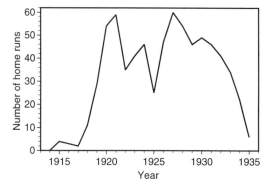

1.38 Men's times gradually decreased over time, with little change since the late 1970s. The times of women decreased quite rapidly from 1972 until the mid-1980s; since that time, they have been fairly consistent.

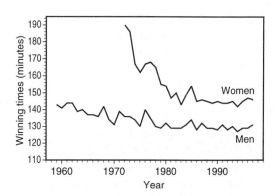

1.39 **(a)** Weights are generally lower for toddlers with summer and late fall birthdays (June–November), and highest for toddlers with December–March birthdays. **(b)** Toddlers with summer birthdays appear to be slightly taller than those with winter birthdays (though there is more deviation from this pattern than there was for the weight pattern). **(c)** Both plots have extremes in the summer and winter, but they are opposite: When one is high, the other is low. As a crude summary, the two plots together suggest that summer two-year-olds are tall and skinny, while winter two-year-olds are short and heavy.

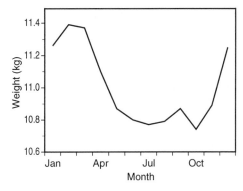 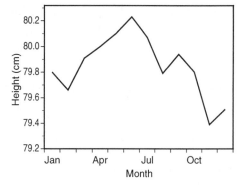

1.40 (a) Diarrhea is the worst from April through August, especially April, May, and June. In other months the percentage is generally low (about 2.5% or less). (b) There is some hint of a second, smaller peak in October/November, and maybe even a third small peak in January (recall that this graph would theoretically wrap around from December to January). However, these smaller peaks may be mere random

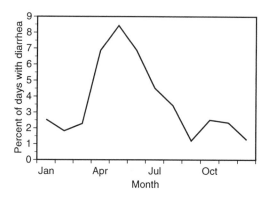

fluctuation. (c) The prevalence of diarrhea in April, May, and June may account for the low weights for children with birthdays from June through November.

Section 2: Describing Distributions with Numbers

1.41 (a) Stemplot shown with stems split five ways. The mean is 516.3 revolutions; the median is 516.5 revolutions. These are similar because the distribution is fairly symmetric. (b) $s = 44.2$. Because of the symmetry, $\bar{x}$ and s are appropriate.

```
4 | 55
4 |
4 |
5 | 001
5 | 3
5 | 555
5 |
5 | 8
```

1.42 (a) Stemplot at right; it is relatively symmetric. (b) $M = 50.7$.
(c) $Q_3 = 58.1$; there were landslides in 1964, 1972, and 1984.

```
4 | 33
4 | 999
5 | 003
5 | 578
6 | 01
```

1.43 (a) See solution to Exercise 1.20. (b) & (c) The right skewness makes $\bar{x} > M$ in both cases. The IQR for the women is 28, so the outlier test gives an upper limit of $154 + 42 = 196$—making the score of 200 an outlier.

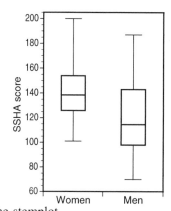

	$\bar{x}$	M	Five-number summaries				
Women	141.06	138.5	101	126	138.5	154	200
Men	121.25	114.5	70	98	114.5	143	187

(d) All the displays and descriptions reveal that women generally score higher than men. The men's scores ($IQR = 45$) are more spread out than the women's (even if we don't ignore the outlier); this is fairly clear from the boxplot but not so obvious from the stemplot.

1.44 With the outlier: $\bar{x} = 141.06$ and $M = 138.50$. Without the outlier: $\bar{x} = 137.59$ and $M = 137$. Both drop, but the removal of the outlier has a greater effect on the mean than the median.

1.45 **(a)** Control: $\bar{x} = 366.3$ grams and $s = 50.8$ grams. Experimental: $\bar{x} = 402.95$ grams and $s = 42.73$ grams. **(b)** Both distributions appear to be relatively symmetric, with no outliers—which makes $\bar{x}$ and s appropriate descriptions.

1.46 For measurements in ounces, divide $\bar{x}$ and s by 28.35. Thus for the control group $\bar{x}_{new} = 12.92$ oz and $s_{new} = 1.79$ oz, and for the experimental group $\bar{x}_{new} = 14.21$ oz and $s_{new} = 1.507$ oz.

1.47 The distribution of wealth will be skewed to the right, so the median is less than the mean: $M = \$800,000$ and $\bar{x} = \$2.2$ million.

1.48 One would expect stock prices to be skewed to the right (many inexpensive stocks, with a few stocks having higher prices), so the median should be less than the mean.

1.49 $\bar{x} = \$62,500$ and $M = \$25,000$. Seven of the eight employees—all but the owner—earned less than the mean.

1.50 If three brothers earn \$0, \$0, and \$20,000, the reported median is \$20,000. If the two brothers with no income take jobs at \$14,000 each, the median decreases to \$14,000. The same thing can happen to the mean: In this example, the mean drops from \$20,000 to \$16,000.

1.51 The mean rises to \$87,500, while the median is unchanged.

1.52 **(a)** $\bar{x} = 5.4479$ and $s = 0.2209$. **(b)** The first measurement corresponds to $5.50 \times 62.43 = 343.365$ pounds per cubic foot. To find $\bar{x}_{new}$ and s_{new}, we similarly multiply by 62.43: $\bar{x}_{new} \doteq 340.11$ and $s_{new} \doteq 13.79$.

1.53 **(a)** The stemplot with split stems shows a peak in the high 80s, and suggests a slight skew to the right. (Without split stems, the skewness is not very apparent.) **(b)** $\bar{x} = 89.67$, $s^2 = 61.3089$, and $s = 7.83$. **(c)** $M = 88.5$, $Q_1 = 84.5$, $Q_3 = 93$, and $IQR = 8.5$. There are no outliers: no scores are less than $Q_1 - 1.5 \times IQR = 71.75$ or greater than $Q_3 + 1.5 \times IQR = 105.75$. **(d)** Answers may vary; the slight skewness suggests that the quartiles should be used.

```
 7 | 9
 8 | 13
 8 | 6789
 9 | 01
 9 | 5
10 | 2
10 | 5
```

1.54 Details at right.

$$\bar{x} = \frac{11,200}{7} = 1600,$$

$$s^2 = \frac{214,872}{6} = 35,812, \text{ and}$$

$$s = \sqrt{35,812} \doteq 189.24.$$

x_i	$x_i - \bar{x}$	$(x_i - \bar{x})^2$
1792	192	36864
1666	66	4356
1362	−238	56644
1614	14	196
1460	−140	19600
1867	267	71289
1439	−161	25921
11200	0	214872

1.55 (a) 1, 1, 1, 1 (no spread) is one answer. **(b)** 0, 0, 10, 10 (greatest spread) is the only answer. **(c)** Any collection of equal numbers has variance 0, so (b) has 11 correct answers. The answer to (b) is unique.

1.56 Answers will vary. Typical calculators will carry only about 12 to 15 digits. Minitab (at least the version used to prepare these answers) fails at 100,000,001 (nine digits).

1.57 See Exercise 1.25 for stemplots. There is a low outlier of 4.9% (Alaska) and a high outlier of 18.6% (Florida). Because of the outliers, the five-number summary is a good choice: Min = 4.9%, Q_1 = 11.4%, M = 12.6%, Q_3 = 13.9%, Max = 18.6%.

1.58 (a) $\bar{x}$ = 1.887% and s = 7.6%. In an average month, $100 would grow to $101.89. **(b)** The low outlier is −26.6%; this would change a $100 investment to $74.40. Without the outlier, $\bar{x}$ = 2.238% and s = 6.944%—respectively higher and lower than the values with the outlier included. The median and quartiles would change very little, if at all, since they are resistant to outliers. [In fact, only Q_3 changes, from 6.7 to 6.75.]

1.59 See Exercise 1.27 for the stemplot. The survival times are skewed to the right, so the five-number summary is a good choice: Min = 43, Q_1 = 82.5, M = 102.5, Q_3 = 151.5, Max = 598 days. Half the guinea pigs lived less than 102.5 days; typical lifetimes were 82.5 to 151.5 days. The longest-lived guinea pig died just short of 600 days, while one guinea pig lived only 43 days.

1.60 See Exercise 1.29 for a stemplot; the distribution is fairly symmetric. $\bar{x}$ = 108.92, M = 110, and s = 13.17; the mean and median are close. (Although the four low scores are not outliers, they "drag down" the mean.)

1.61 The logical number to choose as the 10th percentile is 10.55% (the average of 10.2% and 10.9%—consistent with how we compute medians). Likewise, the 90th percentile is 14.85% (the average of 14.5% and 15.2%).

The top 10% are Iowa (15.2%), West Virginia (15.3%), Rhode Island (15.7%), Pennsylvania (15.9%), and Florida (18.6%). The bottom 10% are Alaska (4.9%), Utah (8.8%), Colorado and Georgia (10%), and Texas (10.2%). [Regardless of how we choose the percentiles, these answers must be the same: they are the top and bottom five states.]

1.62 Answers may vary slightly depending on the exact methods students use, but they should be similar to 101, 107, 112, 119. (Sort the numbers in order, then choose the numbers in about the 16th, 32nd, 48th, and 63rd locations.)

1.63 The five-number summaries for sodium content are below (all numbers in mg):

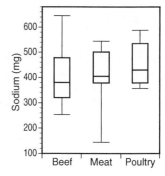

Type	Min	Q_1	M	Q_3	Max
Beef	253	320.5	380.5	478	645
Meat	144	379	405	501	545
Poultry	357	379	430	535	588

Overall, beef hot dogs have less sodium (except for the one with the most sodium: 645 mg). Even if we ignore the low outlier among meat hot dogs, meat holds a slight edge over poultry. It is difficult to make a general recommendation, but clearly, the best advice is to *avoid* poultry hot dogs; either buy beef (and hope that you don't get the worst one) or buy meat hot dogs (and hope that you get the best one).

1.64 (a) Before recentering, verbal scores were clearly lower than math scores. Both sets of scores were raised by the recentering, and the SATV scores ended up slightly higher than the SATM scores. **(b)** The two peaks (referred to Exercise 1.17) are not visible in the boxplots.

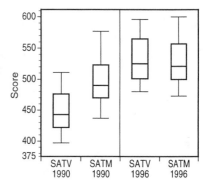

1.65 (a) $x_{\text{new}} = 746x = 746 \cdot 140 = 104,440$ watts ($a = 0$, $b = 746$). **(b)** $x_{\text{new}} = x/0.62 = 65/0.62 \doteq 104.8$ kph ($a = 0$, $b = 1/0.62 \doteq 1.61$). **(c)** $x_{\text{new}} = x - 98.6$ degrees ($a = -98.6$, $b = 1$). **(d)** $x_{\text{new}} = \frac{1}{30}x \cdot 100\% = \frac{10}{3}x\%$ ($a = 0$, $b = 10/3$).

1.66 Min $= \$17,500$, $Q_1 = \$27,500$, $M = \$32,500$, $Q_3 = \$37,500$, Max $= \$70,000$. For example: 14% of salaries are below \$25,000 and 35% are below \$30,000, so Q_1 (the 25th percentile) is \$27,500.

1.67 Variance is changed by a factor of $2.54^2 = 6.4516$; generally, for a transformation $x_{\text{new}} = a + bx$, the new variance is b^2 times the old variance.

1.68 There are 72 survival times, so to find the 10% trimmed mean, remove the highest and lowest 7 values (leaving 58). Remove the highest and lowest 14 values (leaving 44) for the 20% trimmed mean.

The mean and median for the full data set are $\bar{x} = 141.8$ and $M = 102.5$. The 10% trimmed mean is $\bar{x}^* = 118.16$, and the 20% trimmed mean is $\bar{x}^{**} = 111.68$. Since the distribution is right-skewed, removing the extremes lowers the mean.

Section 3: The Normal Distributions

1.69 (a) The curve forms a 1×1 square, which has area 1.
(b) $P(X < 0.25) = 0.25$.
(c) $P(0.1 < X < 0.9) = 0.8$.

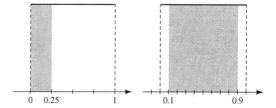

1.70 (a) The height should be $\frac{1}{2}$, since the area under the curve must be 1. The density curve is at right. **(b)** $P(X \le 1) = \frac{1}{2}$.
(c) $P(0.5 < X < 1.3) = 0.4$.

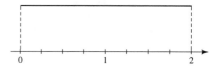

1.71 The mean and median both equal 0.5; the quartiles are $Q_1 = 0.25$ and $Q_3 = 0.75$.

1.72 (a) Mean is C, median is B (right skew pulls the mean to the right). **(b)** Mean A, Median A. **(c)** Mean A, Median B (left skew pulls the mean to the left).

For 1.73.

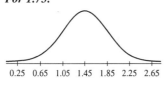

0.25 0.65 1.05 1.45 1.85 2.25 2.65

For 1.74.

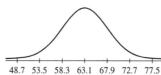

48.7 53.5 58.3 63.1 67.9 72.7 77.5

1.75 Using the 68–95–99.7 rule: $1.45 \pm 2(0.40) = 1.45 \pm 0.80$, or 0.65 to 2.25 grams per mile. Using table values: $1.45 \pm 1.96(0.40) = 1.45 \pm 0.784$, or 0.666 to 2.234 grams per mile.

1.76 The 68% interval is $63.1 \pm 4.8 = 58.3$ to 67.9 kg. 95%: $63.1 \pm 2(4.8) = 53.5$ to 72.7 kg. 99.7%: $63.1 \pm 3(4.8) = 48.7$ to 77.5 kg.

1.77 (a) $266 \pm 2(16) = 266 \pm 32$, or 234 to 298 days. **(b)** Less than 234 days; longer than 298 days.

1.78 $\bar{x} = 108.92$ and $s = 13.17$. About 70.5% (55/78) of the IQs are in the range $\bar{x} \pm s = 95.75$ to 122.09 (96–122). About 93.6% (73/78) of the IQs are in the range $\bar{x} \pm 2s = 82.58$ to 135.26 (83–135). All (100%) of the IQs are in the range $\bar{x} \pm 3s = 69.41$ to 148.43 (70–148).

1.79 Eleanor: $z = \frac{680-500}{100} = 1.8$. Gerald: $z = \frac{27-18}{6} = 1.5$. Eleanor's score is higher.

1.80 The three stand close together, an astounding four standard deviations above the typical hitter. (Williams has a slight edge, but perhaps not large enough to declare him "the best.")

Cobb	$\frac{.420-.266}{.0371} = 4.15$
Williams	$\frac{.406-.267}{.0326} = 4.26$
Brett	$\frac{.390-.261}{.0317} = 4.07$

1.81 (a) 0.9978. (b) 0.0022. (c) 0.9515. (d) $0.9515 - 0.0022 = 0.9493$.

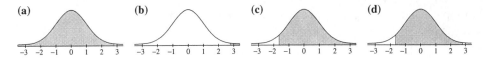

1.82 (a) 0.0122. (b) 0.9878. (c) 0.0384. (d) $0.9878 - 0.0384 = 0.9494$.

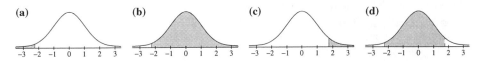

1.83 (a) -0.67 or -0.68 (software: -0.6745). (b) 0.25 (software: 0.2533).

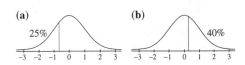

1.84 (a) 0.84 (software: 0.8416). (b) 0.38 or 0.39 (software: 0.3853).

1.85 SAT scores of 800+ correspond to z scores above 3; this is 0.15% (using the 68–95–99.7 rule).

1.86 (a) $12\% \pm 2(16.5\%) = -21\%$ to 45% (or $12\% \pm 1.96(16.5\%) = -20.34\%$ to 44.34%). (b) About 23%: $R < 0\%$ means $Z < \frac{0-12}{16.5} \doteq -0.7273$; the table gives 0.2327 for $Z < -0.73$. (b) About 21.5%: $R \geq 25\%$ means $Z \geq \frac{25-12}{16.5} \doteq 0.7879$; the table gives 0.2148 for $Z \geq 0.79$.

1.87 (a) $X > 700$ means $Z > \frac{700-544}{103} \doteq 1.5146$; the table gives 0.0655 for $Z > 1.51$.
(b) $X < 500$ means $Z < \frac{500-544}{103} \doteq -0.4272$; the table gives 0.3336 for $Z < -0.43$.
(c) $500 < X < 800$ means $-0.4272 < Z < \frac{800-544}{103} \doteq 2.4854$; this is about $0.9936 - 0.3336 = 0.6600$.

1.88 (a) About 5.21%: $P(X < 240) = P(Z < \frac{240-266}{16}) = P(Z < -1.625) = 0.0521$. This software value is also halfway between the two table values 0.0516 (for -1.63) and 0.0526 (for -1.62). (b) About 54.7%: $P(240 < X < 270) = P(-1.625 < Z < \frac{270-266}{16}) = P(-1.625 < Z < 0.25) = 0.5987 - 0.0521 = 0.5466$. (c) 279 days or longer: The 80th percentile for a standard normal distribution is 0.8416 (or 0.84 from the table), so take $266 + 0.8416(16)$.

1.89 About 6.68%: If X is her measured potassium level, then $X < 3.5$ meq/l means $Z < \frac{3.5-3.8}{0.2} = -1.5$, for which Table A gives 0.0668.

1.90 The standard score for 1.7 is $z = -1.625$, and for 2.1 it is $z = -1.125$. $P(X < 1.7) = 0.0521$; this software value is also halfway between the two table values 0.0516 (for -1.63) and 0.0526 (for -1.62). $P(1.7 < X < 2.1) = 0.1303 - 0.0521 = 0.0782$; 0.1303 is halfway between the two table values 0.1292 (for -1.13) and 0.1314 (for -1.12).

1.91 Sarah's z score is $\frac{135-110}{25} = 1$, while her mother's z score is $\frac{120-90}{25} = 1.2$, so Sarah's mother scored relatively higher. But Sarah had the higher raw score, so she does stand higher in the variable measured.

   Sarah scored at the 84th percentile (0.8413). Her mother scored at the 88.5th percentile (0.8849).

1.92 To score among 30% who are most Anglo/English: about 3.42 or more. To score among 30% who are most Mexican/Spanish: about 2.58 or less.

   For the first answer, the 70th percentile for a standard normal distribution is 0.5244 (or 0.52 from the table), so take $3 + 0.5244(0.8)$. For the second answer, use the 30th percentile for a $N(0, 1)$ distribution, which is -0.5244 (or -0.52), and take $3 - 0.5244(0.8)$.

1.93 **(a)** 50%: $P(W < 100) = P(Z < 0) = 0.5$. **(b)** $W < 80$ means $Z < \frac{80-100}{15} \doteq -1.33$; the table gives 0.0918, or 9.18%. **(c)** $W > 140$ means $Z > \frac{140-100}{15} \doteq -2.67$; the table gives 0.38%. **(d)** $100 < W < 120$ means $0 < Z < \frac{120-100}{15} \doteq 1.33$; the table gives 40.82%.

1.94 The top 5% is about 125 or higher: The 95th percentile for a $N(0, 1)$ distribution is 1.645, so take $100 + 1.645(15) = 124.675$.

   The top 1% is about 135 or higher: The 99th percentile for a $N(0, 1)$ distribution is 2.326, so take $100 + 2.326(15) = 134.89$.

1.95 **(a)** The area should be 25%, so $Q_1 \doteq -0.67$. For the third quartile, the area should be 75%, so $Q_3 \doteq 0.67$. (A more accurate value is ± 0.675). **(b)** $Q_1 = 100 - 15 \times 0.67 = 100 - 10.05 = 89.95$ (89.875 using 0.675), and $Q_3 = 110.05$ (or 110.125). **(c)** $IQR = Q_3 - Q_1 = 1.34$ (or 1.35). **(d)** $1.5 \times IQR = 2.01$ (or 2.025), so the suspected outliers are below $Q_1 - 1.5 \times IQR = -2.68$ (or -2.7), and above $Q_3 + 1.5 \times IQR = 2.68$ (or 2.7). This percentage is $2 \times 0.0037 = 0.74\%$ (or $2 \times 0.0035 = 0.70\%$).

1.96 **(a)** Software gives 1.2816 for the 90th percentile and −1.2816 for the 10th percentile. Using Table A, we would choose ±1.28. **(b)** About 245.5 and 286.5 days: Take 266 ± (1.2816)(16).

1.97 The plot does not suggest any major deviations from normality, except that the tails are less extreme than would be expected. This means extremely high and extremely low scores are "stacked up"—no one scored below 14 or above 54.

1.98 The right skewness is shown by the sharp rise at the right end; it indicates that the longest survival times are higher than what one would expect from a normal distribution.

1.99 The plot is reasonably close to a line, apart from the stair-step appearance produced by granularity—presumably due to limited accuracy of the measuring instrument.

1.100 The plot (below, left) suggests no major deviations from normality, although the three lowest measurements don't quite fall in line with the other points.

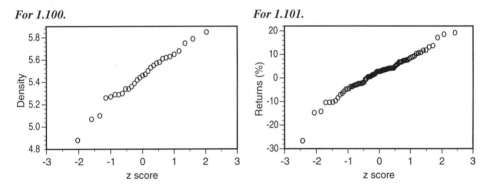

For 1.100.   *For 1.101.*

1.101 The plot (above, right) suggests that the distribution is normal (except for the low point, which was a suspected outlier—see Exercise 1.26).

1.102 See also Exercise 1.30. The left-skewness shows up as a slight curve in the normal probability plot. There are no particular outliers. The mean score is $\bar{x} = 56.96$, and the five-number summary is Min = 20, $Q_1 = 51$, $M = 59.5$, $Q_3 = 66$, Max = 80.

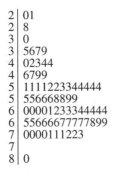

```
2 | 01
2 | 8
3 | 0
3 | 5679
4 | 02344
4 | 6799
5 | 1111223344444
5 | 556668899
6 | 00001233344444
6 | 55666677777899
7 | 0000111223
7 |
8 | 0
```

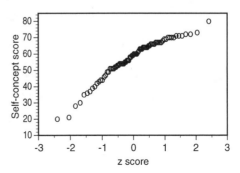

1.103 The boys' distribution seems to have two peaks, one in the low 50s and another in the high 60s/low 70s. Since both distributions are slightly skewed to the left, the five-number summaries may be more appropriate.

The stemplot and five-number summaries suggest that girls' scores do not seem to extend as high as the highest boys' scores.

Girls		Boys
1	2	0
8	2	
	3	0
975	3	6
4	4	0234
96	4	79
444	5	1111223344
8665	5	56899
444320000	6	13344
99765	6	566677778
20	7	00011123
	7	
	8	0

	$\bar{x}$	Min	Q_1	M	Q_3	Max
Boys	57.91	20	51	59	67	80
Girls	55.52	21	49	60	64	72

1.104 A stemplot from one sample is shown. Histograms will vary slightly, but should suggest a bell curve. The normal probability plot (below, left) shows something fairly close to a line, but illustrates that even for actual normal data, the tails may deviate slightly from a line.

−2	6
−2	
−1	9998877655
−1	4433332111111
−0	9998888776666555
−0	43333222211110000
0	001222223333444
0	555566666778889
1	1123444
1	5
2	0033
2	5

For 1.104.

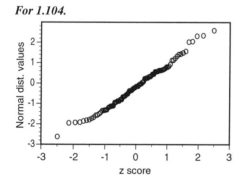

For 1.105.

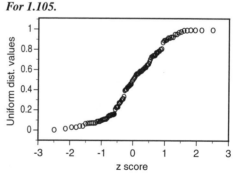

1.105 A stemplot from one sample is shown. Histograms will vary slightly, but should suggest the density curve of Figure 1.33 (but with more variation than students might expect). The normal probability plot (above, right) shows that, compared to a normal distribution, the uniform distribution does not extend as low or as high (not surprising, since all observations are between 0 and 1).

0	0123446677778899
1	001123445556
2	12337789
3	0139
4	0023446689
5	12356667889
6	001224568
7	0234447788
8	00799
9	011225577999999

Exercises

1.106 **(a)** Car makes: a bar chart or pie chart. Car age: a histogram or stemplot (or a boxplot). **(b)** Study time: a histogram or stemplot (or a boxplot). Change in study hours: a time plot (average hours studied vs. time). **(c)** A bar chart or pie chart. **(d)** A normal probability plot.

1.107 **(a)** Since a person cannot choose the day on which he or she has a heart attack, one would expect that all days are "equally likely"—no day is favored over any other. While there is *some* day-to-day variation, this expectation does seem to be supported by the chart. **(b)** Monday through Thursday are fairly similar, but there is a pronounced peak on Friday, and lows on Saturday and Sunday. Patients do have some choice about when they leave the hospital, and many probably choose to leave on Friday, perhaps so that they can spend the weekend with the family. Additionally, many hospitals cut back on staffing over the weekend, and they may wish to discharge any patients who are ready to leave before then.

1.108 No, and no: It is easy to imagine examples of many different data sets with mean 0 and standard deviation 1—e.g., $\{-1,0,1\}$ and $\{-2,0,0,0,0,0,0,0,2\}$.

Likewise, for any given five numbers $a \leq b \leq c \leq d \leq e$ (not all the same), we can create many data sets with that five number summary, simply by taking those five numbers and adding some additional numbers in between them, e.g. (in increasing order): 10, __, 20, __, __, 30, __, __, 40, __, 50. As long as the number in the first blank is between 10 and 20, etc., the five-number summary will be 10, 20, 30, 40, 50.

1.109 The 1940 distribution is skewed to the left, while the 1980 distribution is fairly symmetric and considerably less spread out than the 1940 distribution. There are few low percentages in the 1980s, reflecting increased voting by blacks.

1.110 **(a)** The stemplot below (with stems split two ways) looks fairly symmetric, but observe that the lowest observation is considerably less than the others, and the two highest are also somewhat set apart. (This is even more apparent if, e.g., we split stems five ways. This also makes the stemplot looks less symmetric.) **(b)** The lowest observation (6.75 min) and the highest two (9.75 and 10.17 min) are these unusual situations. Without them, we find $\bar{x} \doteq 8.36$ min and $s \doteq 0.4645$ min. In addition (or in place of) these numbers, we can find the five-number summary: 7.42, 7.92, 8.42, 8.67, 9.17. **(c)** Based on a normal probability plot (not shown), the distribution is reasonably normal. (The split-five-ways stemplot does not look too promising; such impressions can be misleading.) **(d)** Plot below. There is no strong indication of a trend, but the last ten days (starting a bit after Thanksgiving) are all above average.

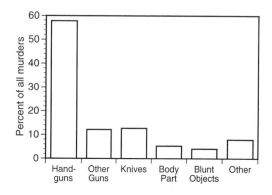

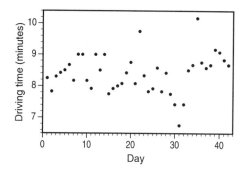

1.111 Either a bar chart or a pie chart would be appropriate; both are shown below. The pie chart labels might also show the actual percents. An "Other methods" category (with 7.9%) is needed so that the total is 100%.

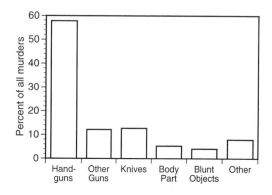

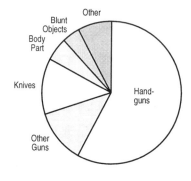

1.112 Salary distributions are right-skewed, so the mean will be higher than the median: $\bar{x} = \$1,160,000$ and $M = \$490,000$.

1.113 **(a)** $x_{\text{new}} = -50 + 2x$: $b = 2$ will change the standard deviation to 20; it also multiplies the mean by 2, so use $a = 100 - 2(75) = -50$. **(b)** $x_{\text{new}} = -49.\overline{09} + \frac{20}{11}x$. $b = \frac{20}{11}$ changes the standard deviation to 20; $a = 100 - \frac{20}{11}(82) = -49.\overline{09}$ makes the mean 100. **(c)** David: $x_{\text{new}} = -50 + 2(78) = 106$. Nancy: $x_{\text{new}} = -49.\overline{09} + \frac{20}{11}(78) = 92.\overline{72}$. David scored relatively higher. **(d)** Using either 78 from a $N(75, 10)$ distribution or 106 from $N(100, 20)$ distribution, David's score is $z = 0.3$ standard deviations above the mean, so about 61.79% of third graders score below 78. For Nancy, $z = -0.\overline{36}$, so about 35.94% (or 35.81% using software) of sixth graders score below 78.

1.114 **(a)** $P(S < 20) = P(Z < -1) = 0.1587$ (or "about 16%," using the 68–95–99.7 rule). **(b)** $P(S < 10) = P(Z < -3) = 0.0013$ (or "about 0.15%," using the 68–95–99.7 rule). **(c)** About 28.4: The 75th percentile for a standard normal distribution is 0.6745 (or 0.67 from the table), so take $25 + 0.6745(5)$.

1.115 A WISC score of 135 is $z = \frac{7}{3} = 2.\overline{3} \doteq 2.33$ standard deviations above the mean, so about 0.99% score above 135. This is about 12 or 13 (12.87) of the 1300 students.

1.116 (a) $x_{new} = 4x$: $b = 4$ multiplies both the mean and standard deviation by 4, leaving them at 100 and 20, as desired. (b) $x_{new} = 4(30) = 120$. (c) The quartiles for a standard normal distribution are ± 0.6745 (or ± 0.67 from the table), so take $100 \pm 0.6745(20) = 86.51$ and 113.49 (or 86.6 and 113.4).

1.117 The normal quantile plot indicates that the data are approximately normally distributed; the mean and standard deviation are good measures for normal distributions. The mean is $35.\overline{09}$, and the standard deviation is 11.19.

1.118 See also the stemplots in the solution to Exercise 1.22. Both normal plots appear reasonably linear, so the mean and standard deviation should be useful. For the control group: $\bar{x}_c = 366.3$ g and $s_c \doteq 50.81$ g. For the experimental group: $\bar{x}_e = 402.95$ g and $s_e \doteq 42.73$ g.

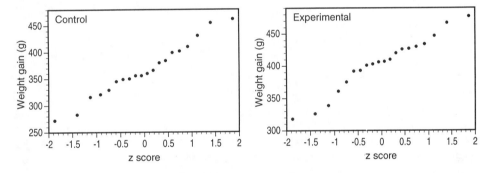

1.119 (a) Five-number summaries and boxplots below. Note in particular that the OL boxplot looks odd since $M = Q_3$ for that position. (b) The heaviest players are on the offensive line, followed by defensive linemen and tight ends. The lightest players overall are the kickers, followed by wide receivers and defensive backs. (c) The $(1.5 \times IQR)$ outlier test reveals outliers in the OL and WR positions. Specifically, the outliers are the lightest (235 lb) and heaviest (335 lb) offensive linemen and the lightest (155 lb) wide receiver.

　　Note that the outlier test can be applied "visually" to the boxplots: Take the length of the box (which is the IQR) and multiply its length by 1.5. If the boxes' "whiskers" extend more than this distance from the box, this indicates that there are outliers. With this in mind, we can easily see that only the WR and OL positions need to be examined.

	Min	Q_1	M	Q_3	Max
QB	180	185	202	207.5	210
RB	170	190	211	225	230
OL	235	275	295	295	335
WR	155	179	182.5	189	202
TE	230	235	242.5	256	260
K	160	167.5	175	184	193
DB	170	176	190	193	195
LB	205	215	220	230	237
DL	220	240	245	265	285

(All numbers in lbs)

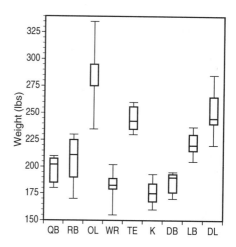

1.120 Results will vary. One set of 20 samples gave the results at the right (normal probability plots are not shown).

Means		Standard deviations	
18	589	3	8
19	00124	4	01
19	7789	4	22
20	1333	4	44455
20		4	66
21	223	4	9
21	5	5	000
		5	22
		5	45

Theoretically, $\bar{x}$ will have a $N(20, 1)$ distribution—so that about 99.7% of the time, one should find $\bar{x}$ between 17 and 23. Meanwhile, the theoretical distribution of s is nearly normal (slightly skewed) with mean $\doteq 4.9482$ and standard deviation $\doteq 0.7178$; about 99.7% of the time, s will be between 2.795 and 7.102. Note that "on the average," s underestimates σ (that is, $4.9482 < 5$). Unlike the mean $\bar{x}$, s is not an unbiased estimator of σ; in fact, for a sample of size n, the mean of s/σ is $\frac{\sqrt{2}\,\Gamma(n/2)}{\sqrt{n-1}\,\Gamma(n/2-1/2)}$. (This factor approaches 1 as n approaches infinity.) The proof of this fact is left as an exercise—for the instructor, not for the average student!

1.121 The distribution is strongly right-skewed, so the five-number summary is appropriate:

Min	\$109,000
Q_1	\$205,000
M	\$1,250,290
Q_3	\$2,300,000
Max	\$9,237,500

0	1111111122568899
1	1444577
2	0233
3	0
4	066
5	03
6	
7	
8	
9	2

The highest salary is definitely an outlier.

1.122 (a) Multiply by 1.29 franc/dollar. (b) The stemplot (or a histogram) looks similar to that of the previous exercise. (c) The values for francs can be found by multiplying the dollar values by 1.29. (d) Once again, multiply the dollar values by 1.29 to get the franc values.

```
 0 | 111111122378
 1 | 011248889
 2 | 226899
 3 | 8
 4 |
 5 | 19
 6 | 048
 7 |
 8 |
 9 |
10 |
11 | 9
```

	$\bar{x}$	Q_1	M	Q_3	s	IQR
Dollars	1,803,761	205,000	1,250,290	2,300,000	2,028,071	2,095,000
Francs	2,326,852	264,450	1,612,873	2,967,000	2,616,212	2,702,550

1.123 The stemplot shown does not include Los Angeles county—an extremely high outlier. The distribution is strongly right-skewed, so we use the five-number summary:

```
 0 | 000000000000000000000001111111111
 0 | 22223333
 0 | 445
 0 | 66777
 0 | 8
 1 | 1
 1 | 3
 1 | 455
 1 |
 1 |
 2 |
 2 |
 2 |
 2 | 66
```

Min	1,232
Q_1	44,193
M	150,816
Q_3	533,392
Max	9,127,751

With $IQR = 489,199$, the outlier test says that any population over $533,392 + 733,798.5 = 1,267,190.5$ is an outlier. This would give seven outliers, but viewing the stemplot, one is inclined to take only the three largest counties as outliers.

One division would be to include all of the top 25% of the counties (i.e., the counties with population over $Q_3 = 533,392$), some of the middle half (those with population between Q_1 and Q_3), and a small fraction of the bottom 25%.

1.124 Stemplots for both variables are at the right. H2S is slightly right-skewed, while LACTIC is more spread out and symmetric. Normal probability plots (not shown) reflect that observation: LACTIC produces a fairly straight line, while H2S is slightly curved on the ends. From the summary statistics below, $\bar{x}$ and s are appropriate for LACTIC, while the five-number summary is better for H2S.

```
 H2S              LACTIC
 2 | 9             8 | 6
 3 | 1268899       9 | 9
 4 | 17799        10 | 689
 5 | 024         11 | 56
 6 | 11679       12 | 5599
 7 | 4699        13 | 013
 8 | 7           14 | 469
 9 | 025         15 | 2378
10 | 1           16 | 38
                 17 | 248
                 18 | 1
                 19 | 09
                 20 | 1
```

	$\bar{x}$	s	Five-number summary				
H2S	5.942	2.127	2.996	3.912	5.329	7.601	10.199
Lactic	1.4420	0.3035	0.860	1.250	1.450	1.680	2.010

1.125 Men seem to have higher SATM scores than women; each number in the five-number summary is about 40 to 50 points higher than the corresponding number for women. Women generally have higher GPAs than men, but the difference is less striking; in fact, the men's median is slightly higher.

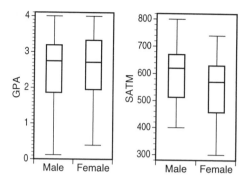

All four normal probability plots (not shown) look fairly linear, so all four data sets might be judged normal. However, both GPA sets—especially the male GPA—are somewhat left-skewed; there is some evidence of this in the long bottom tails of the GPA boxplots. Statistical tests indicate that the male GPA numbers would not be likely to come from a normal distribution.

	Min	Q_1	M	Q_3	Max
Male GPA	0.12	2.135	2.75	3.19	4.00
Female GPA	0.39	2.250	2.72	3.33	4.00
Male SATM	400	550	620	670	800
Female SATM	300	510	570	630	740

Chapter 2 Solutions

Section 1: Scatterplots

2.1 **(a)** Time spent studying is explanatory; the grade is the response variable. **(b)** Explore the relationship; there is no reason to view one or the other as explanatory. **(c)** Rainfall is explanatory; crop yield is the response variable. **(d)** Explore the relationship. **(e)** The father's class is explanatory; the son's class is the response variable.

2.2 Height at age six is explanatory, and height at age 16 is the response. Both variables are quantitative.

2.3 **(a)** The two variables are negatively related; the plot shows a clear curve, with an outlier (one car with high nitrogen oxides). **(b)** No: High carbon monoxide is associated with low nitrogen oxides, and vice versa.

2.4 **(a)** City: 11 mpg. Highway: 16 mpg. **(b)** The plot shows a fairly strong positive linear relationship. We would expect that cars which are fuel efficient (or not) in one setting would also be efficient (or not) in the other.

2.5 **(a)** At right. Alcohol from wine should be on the horizontal axis. **(b)** There is a fairly strong linear relationship. **(c)** The association is negative: Countries with high wine consumption have fewer heart disease deaths, while low wine consumption tends to go with more deaths from heart disease. This does not prove causation; there may be some other reason for the link.

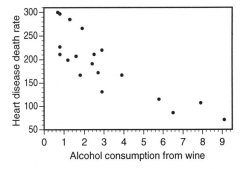

2.6 **(a)** At right. First-round score should be on the horizontal axis; horizontal and vertical scales should be the same. **(b)** There is a fairly strong positive association; since the scores are those of the same golfers on two rounds, this association is expected. **(c)** The player with 105 on the first round and 89 on the second lies outside the generally linear pattern. (The extreme point at (102, 107) lies in the pattern, so should not be considered an outlier.) We can't tell which round was unusual for the outlying player.

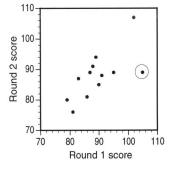

2.7 (a) At right. Flow rate is explanatory. **(b)** As the flow rate increases, the amount of eroded soil increases. Yes, the pattern is approximately linear; the association is positive.

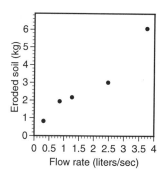

2.8 (a) At right; speed is explanatory. **(b)** The relationship is curved—low in the middle, higher at the extremes. Since low "mileage" is actually *good* (it means that we use less fuel to travel 100 km), this makes sense: moderate speeds yield the best performance. Note that 60 km/hr is about 37 mph. **(c)** Above-average values of "mileage" are found with both low and high values of "speed." **(d)** The

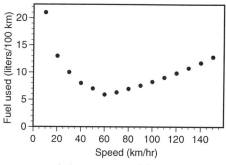

relationship is very strong—there is little scatter around the curve, and it is very useful for prediction.

2.9 (a) Franklin is marked with a + (in the lower left corner). **(b)** There is a moderately strong positive linear association. (It turns out that $r^2 = 87.0\%$.) There are no really extreme observations, though Bank 9 did rather well (its point lies slightly above the pattern of the rest), and the first three banks had high values for both variables (but fit with the overall pattern). Franklin does not look out of place.

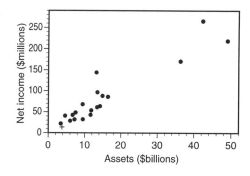

2.10 (a) Body mass is the explanatory variable. Women are marked with solid circles, men with open circles. (b) There is a moderately strong, linear, positive association. The amount of scatter appears to increase with body mass. The relationship is basically the same for both genders, but males typically have larger values for both variables.

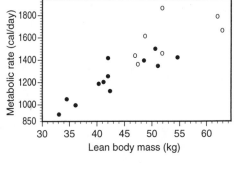

2.11 (a) Shown. Fatal cases are marked with solid circles; those who survived are marked with open circles. (b) There is no clear relationship. (c) Generally, those with short incubation periods are more likely to die. (d) Person 6—the 17-year-old with a short incubation (20 hours) who survived—merits extra attention. He or she is also the youngest in the group by far. Among the other survivors, one (person 17) had an incubation period of 28 hours, and the rest had incubation periods of 43 hours or more.

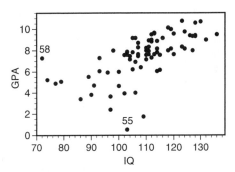

2.12 The scatterplot shows a weak positive association. Student 55, a male, has an IQ of 103 and a GPA of 0.530. Student 58, a female, has an IQ of 72 with a 7.295 GPA.

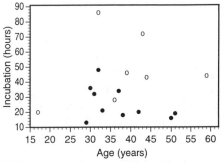

2.13 (a) $\bar{x} = \$177,330$. The distribution is left-skewed, so the five-number summary is more appropriate: Min $= \$113,000$, $Q_1 = \$149,000$, $M = \$174,900$, $Q_3 = \$188,000$, Max $= \$327,500$. (b) There is a weak positive relationship. (c) The five most expensive houses: The prices are outliers, and their points on the scatterplot lie above the general pattern.

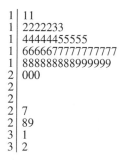

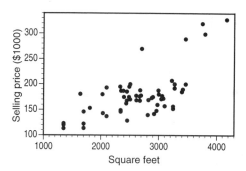

2.14 **(a)** Below, left. A strong relationship—a sort of negative association, but "angular" rather than linear. (The strength of the relationship is somewhat hard to judge because the points are so tightly packed together vertically [for the horizontal row of points] and horizontally [for the vertical column of points].) **(b)** The other scatterplot shows a reasonably linear negative relationship. (If common logarithms are used instead of natural logs, the plot will look the same, except the vertical and horizontal scales will be different.)

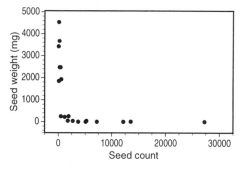

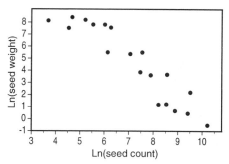

2.15 **(a)** Means: 10.65, 10.43, 5.60, and 5.45. **(b)** There is little difference in the growth when comparing 0 and 1000 nematodes, or 5000 and 10,000 nematodes—but the growth drops substantially between 1000 and 5000 nematodes.

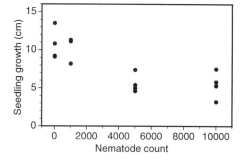

2.16 **(a)** Plot at right. The means are (in the order given) $47.1\overline{6}$, $15.\overline{6}$, 31.5, and $14.8\overline{3}$. **(b)** Yellow seems to be the most attractive, and green is second. White and blue boards are poor attractors. **(c)** Positive or negative association make no sense here because color is a categorical variable (what is an "above-average" color?).

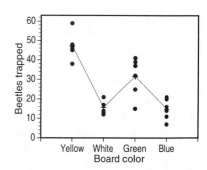

2.17 **(a)** The means (by pecking order) are 1520, 1707, 1540, and 1816 g. These are connected in the scatterplot. **(b)** Against: Pecking order 1 had the lowest mean weight, while 4 was the heaviest on the average.

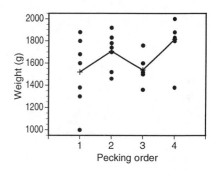

Section 2: Correlation

2.18 $\bar{x} = 58.2$ cm and $s_x \doteq 13.20$ cm (for the femur measurements); $\bar{y} = 66$ cm and $s_y \doteq 15.89$ cm (for the humerus). The standardized values are at the right; the correlation is $r = 3.97659/4 = 0.994$.

z_x	z_y	$z_x z_y$
-1.53048	-1.57329	2.40789
-0.16669	-0.18880	0.03147
0.06061	0.25173	0.01526
0.43944	0.37759	0.16593
1.19711	1.13277	1.35605
		3.97659

2.19 **(a)** See the solution to Exercise 2.10 for the plot. It appears that the correlation for men will be slightly smaller, since the men's points are more scattered. **(b)** Women: $r = 0.876$. Men: $r = 0.592$. **(c)** Women: $\bar{x} = 43.03$ kg. Men: $\bar{x} = 53.10$ kg. This has no effect on the correlation. **(d)** The correlations would remain the same.

2.20 (a) Either variable may be on the horizontal axis; both axes should have the same scale. The scatterplot suggests a positive correlation, not too close to 1. **(b)** $r = 0.565$. **(c)** r would be the same (since it is based only on the standard scores, which are unchanged if we decrease all men's heights by 6 inches). The correlation gives no information about who is taller. **(d)** Changing the units of measurement does not affect standard scores, and so does not change r. **(e)** $r = 1$ (this is a perfect straight line).

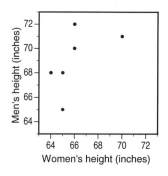

2.21 See 2.6 for the scatterplot. $r = 0.550$; without player 7, $r^* = 0.661$. Without player 7, the pattern of the scatterplot is more linear.

2.22 See 2.8 for the scatterplot. $r = -0.172$—it is close to zero because the relationship is a curve rather than a line.

2.23 (a) The solid circles in the plot. **(b)** The open circles. **(c)** $r = r^* = 0.253$. The correlations are equal, since the scale (units) of x and y does not change standard scores.

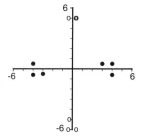

2.24 (a) Shown. **(b)** With the exception of Northern Ireland (in the upper left corner), there is a moderate positive association. **(c)** $r = 0.224$; without Northern Ireland, $r^* = 0.784$. Removing Northern Ireland makes the pattern of the scatterplot more linear.

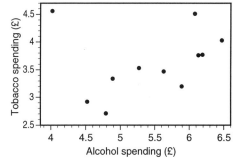

2.25 The plot shows a relatively strong negative association, hence r is negative and large (close to -1). r does not describe the curve of the plot, or the different patterns observed within the ACT and SAT states.

2.26 (a) Standard deviations measure variability; we can see that the Equity Income Fund is less variable ("volatile") than the Science & Technology Fund. Put another way, the Equity Income Fund tends to be more consistent. (Note: This does *not* indicate which gives higher yields.) **(b)** The Magellan Fund, with the higher correlation, tends to rise and fall with the S&P index. The Small Cap Stock Fund also *generally* rises and falls with the S&P index, but is not tied as closely (i.e., there are more exceptions to this "rule").

2.27 (a) The new speed and fuel consumption (respectively) values are $x^* = x \div 1.609$ and $y^* = y \times 1.609 \div 100 \div 3.785 \doteq 0.004251y$. (The factor of $1/100$ is needed since we were measuring fuel consumption in liters/100 km.) The transformed data has the same correlation as the original— $r = -0.172$—since a linear transformation does not alter the correlation. The

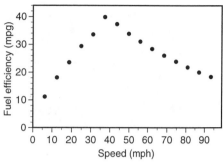

scatterplot of the transformed data is not shown here; it resembles (except for scale) the plot of 2.8. **(b)** The new correlation is $r^* = -0.043$; the new plot is even less linear than the first.

2.28 See 2.14 for the scatterplots. For the original data, $r = -0.470$, reflecting the negative association, as well as the marked nonlinearity of the scatterplot. After taking logarithms, $r^* = -0.929$; the plot of the transformed data is much more linear.

2.29 The plot shows a weak positive association; it is fairly linear. The correlation is $r = 0.542$; there is some tendency for GPAs and self-concept scores to be high (or low) together.

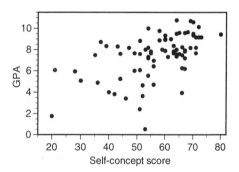

2.30 If the husband's age is y and the wife's x, the linear relationship $y = x + 2$ would hold, and hence $r = 1$.

2.31 The person who wrote the article interpreted a correlation close to 0 as if it were a correlation close to -1 (implying a negative association between teaching ability and research productivity). Professor McDaniel's findings mean there is little linear association between research and teaching—for example, knowing a professor is a good researcher gives little information about whether she is a good or bad teacher.

2.32 (a) Since sex has a nominal scale, we cannot compute the correlation between sex and anything. [There is a strong *association* between sex and income. Some writers use "correlation" as a synonym for "association." It is much better to retain the more specific meaning.] **(b)** A correlation $r = 1.09$ is impossible, since $-1 \leq r \leq 1$ always. **(c)** Correlation has no units, so $r = 0.23$ *bushels* is incorrect.

Section 3: Least-Squares Regression

2.33 (a) Below, left. The range of values on the horizontal axis may vary. **(b)** When $x = 20$, $y = 2500$ dollars. **(c)** $y = 500 + 200x$. (The slope is his rate of savings, in dollars per year).

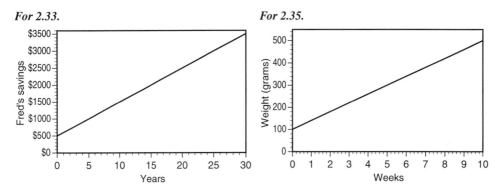

For 2.33.   *For 2.35.*

2.34 $y = 1500x$. It might be worthwhile to point out that this is simply the familiar formula "distance equals velocity times time," and that (meters/second) times (seconds) equals meters.

2.35 (a) Weight $y = 100 + 40x$ g; the slope is 40 g/week. **(b)** Above, right. **(c)** When $x = 104$, $y = 4260$ grams, or about 9.4 pounds—a rather frightening prospect. The regression line is only reliable for "young" rats; like humans, rats do not grow at a constant rate throughout their entire life.

2.36 Plot below, left. For analog service, the monthly bill is $y_1 = 19.99 + 0.85x$. For digital service, the monthly bill is $y_2 = 24.99 + 0.60x$. Digital service is cheaper for both 30 minutes ($42.99 vs. $45.49) and one hour ($60.99 vs. $70.99). In fact, digital service is cheaper for anything over 20 minutes.

For 2.36.   *For 2.37.*

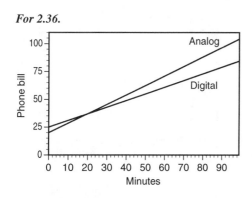

2.37 (a) Above, right. **(b)** The initial pH was 5.4247; the final pH was 4.6350. **(c)** The slope is -0.0053; the pH decreased by 0.0053 units per week (on the average).

2.38 (a) Ideally, the scales should be the same on both axes. **(b)** For every additional unit of strength after 7 days, the concrete has an additional 0.96 units of strength after 28 days. **(c)** $y = 1389 + (0.96)(3300) = 4557$ pounds per square inch.

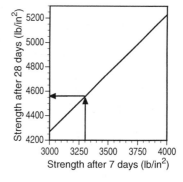

2.39 (a) The plot shows a moderately strong positive linear relationship. **(b)** $r = 0.941$; about $r^2 = 88.6\%$ of variation in manatee deaths is explained by powerboat registrations, so predictions are reasonably accurate. **(c)** $\hat{y} \doteq -41.4 + 0.125x$; when $x = 716$, $y \doteq 48$ dead manatees are predicted. **(d)** When $x = 2000$, $y \doteq 208$; extrapolation (in number of boats, as well as time) makes this prediction unreliable.

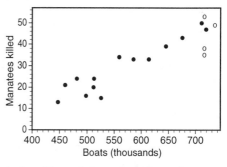

(e) The additional points are shown as open circles. Two of the points (those for 1992 and 1993) lie below the overall pattern (i.e., there were fewer actual manatee deaths than we might expect), but otherwise there is no strong indication that the measures succeeded. **(f)** The mean for those years was 42—less than our predicted mean of 48 (which *might* suggest that the measures taken showed some results).

2.40 (a) At right. (b) $\hat{y} \doteq 123+20.2x$. For
each additional degree-day per day, gas
consumption increases by about 20.2 ft^3
per day. (c) We predict $y \doteq 931$ ft^3 of
gas/day when $x = 40$ degree-days/day
(carrying out more decimal places in the
equation gives $\hat{y} = 932.1$ ft^3). Joan's
actual usage (870 ft^3) is lower, so the
insulation seems to be effective.

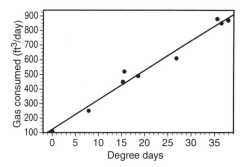

2.41 (a) At right. (b) $r = 0.507$ and
$r^2 = 0.257 = 25.7\%$. There is a positive
association between U.S. and overseas returns, but it is not very strong:
Knowing the U.S. return accounts
for only about 26% of the variation
in overseas returns. (c) The regression equation is $\hat{y} = 5.64 + 0.692x$.
(d) $\hat{y} = 12.6\%$; the residual (prediction
error) is $32.9\% - 12.6\% = 20.3\%$. Since
the correlation is so low, the predictions will not be very reliable.

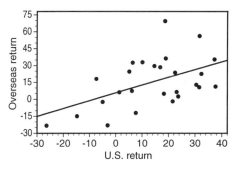

2.42 For degree-days: $\bar{x} = 21.54$ and $s_x = 13.42$. For gas consumption: $\bar{y} = 558.9$ and
$s_y = 274.4$. The correlation is $r = 0.989$.
    The slope is therefore $b = (0.989)(274.4)/13.42 \doteq 20.2$ and the intercept is $a = 558.9 - (20.2)(21.54) \doteq 123$ (there may be slight differences due to rounding).

2.43 (a) $b = r \cdot s_y/s_x = 0.16$; $a = \bar{y} - b\bar{x} = 30.2$. (b) Julie's predicted score is $\hat{y} = 78.2$.
(c) $r^2 = 0.36$; only 36% of the variability in y is accounted for by the regression, so the
estimate $\hat{y} = 78.2$ could be quite different from the real score.

2.44 $r = \sqrt{0.16} = 0.40$ (high attendance goes with high grades, so the correlation must
be positive).

2.45 The correlation is $r = 0.9670$, so $r^2 = 93.5\%$ of the variation in erosion is explained
by the relationship between flow rate and erosion.

2.46 Women's heights are the x values; men's are the y values. The slope is $b = (0.5)(2.7)/2.5 = 0.54$ and the intercept is $a = 68.5 - (0.54)(64.5) = 33.67$.

The regression equation is $\hat{y} = 33.67 + 0.54x$. Ideally, the scales should be the same on both axes. For a 67-inch tall wife, we predict the husband's height will be about 69.85 inches.

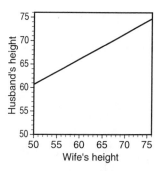

2.47 (a) Male height on female height: $\hat{y}_1 = 24 + 0.6818x$. Female height on male height: $\hat{y}_2 = 33.66 + 0.4688x$. (Note that x and y mean opposite things in these two equations.) The two slopes multiply to give $r^2 = 0.3196$, since the standard deviations cancel out. Put another way, the slopes are reciprocals—except for the factor of r attached to each. In general, the two slopes must have the same sign, since r determines whether they are positive or negative.

(b) Since regression lines always pass through $(\bar{x}, \bar{y})$, they intersect at $(66, 69)$—the first coordinate is the mean female height, while the second is the mean male height. When graphing, remember to plot the female vs. male line "sideways." That is, choose a value on the *vertical* axis as "x" (male height), then compute the corresponding "y" (female height) and find this location on the horizontal axis. Alternatively, write the second equation as $x = 33.66 + 0.4688y$ (which uses x and y in the same way as the first equation) and solve to get $y \doteq 2.133x - 71.8$.

(c) Since the slope is a ratio of heights, the conversion from inches to centimeters would have no effect (the factor of $1/2.54$ cancels out in the numerator and denominator).

2.48 Lean body mass: $\bar{m} = 46.74$, and $s_m = 8.28$ kg. Metabolic rate: $\bar{r} = 1369.5$, and $s_r = 257.5$ cal/day. The correlation is $r = 0.865$. For predicting metabolic rate from body mass, the slope is $b_1 = r \cdot s_r/s_m \doteq 26.9$ cal/day per kg. For predicting body mass from metabolic rate, the slope is $b_2 = r \cdot s_m/s_r \doteq 0.0278$ kg per cal/day.

2.49 (a) $\hat{y} = 113 + 26.9x$. For every 1 kg increase in lean body mass, the metabolic rises by about 26.9 cal/day. **(b)** $\bar{x} = 46.74$ kg, $s_x = 8.28$ kg; $\bar{y} = 1369.5$ cal/day, $s_y = 257.5$ cal/day; $r = 0.865$ (no units); $b = 26.9$ cal/day per kg, and $a = 113$ cal/day. **(c)** $\bar{x} = 102.83$ lb, $s_x = 18.23$ lb; $\bar{y}$, s_y, r, and a are unchanged; $b = 12.2$ cal/day per lb; $\hat{y} = 113 + 12.2x$.

2.50 The correlation of IQ with GPA is $r_1 = 0.634$; for self-concept and GPA, $r_2 = 0.542$. IQ does a slightly better job; it explains about $r_1^2 = 40.2\%$ of the variation in GPA, while self-concept explains about $r_2^2 = 29.4\%$ of the variation.

Section 4: Cautions about Correlation and Regression

2.51 **(a)** Below, left. **(b)** No: The pattern is not linear. **(c)** The sum is 0.01. The first two and last four residuals are negative, and those in the middle are positive. Plot below, right.

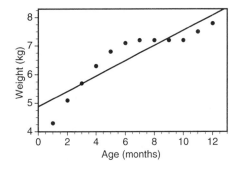
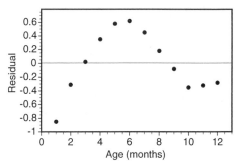

2.52 **(a)** The *Eat Slim* point is set apart from the others, but fits in reasonably well with the pattern of the rest of the plot. **(b)** With all observations, $\hat{y} = -91.2 + 3.21x$ (line 1 in the plot); without *Eat Slim*, $\hat{y} = 46.9 + 2.40x$ (line 2). *Eat Slim* is influential; it moves the line quite a bit. **(c)** Use the second equation: We estimate $\hat{y} \doteq 407$ mg of sodium for a hot dog with 150 cal.

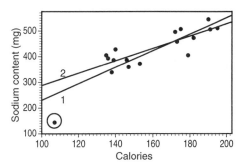

2.53 **(a)** At right. Ideally, the scales should be the same on both axes. **(b)** The first omits the outlier; it lies closer to the pattern of the other points (and farther from the omitted point).

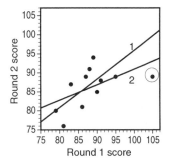

2.54 **(a)** Below, left. **(b)** The regression equation is $\hat{y} = -14.4 + 46.6x$. **(c)** Below, right. The residuals for $x = 0.25$ and $x = 20.0$ are almost all positive; all those for the middle two x values are negative.

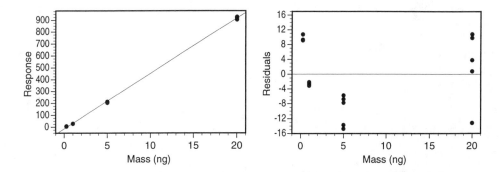

2.55 **(a)** Below, left. The relationship seems linear. **(b)** Regression line: $\hat{y} = 1.77 + 0.0803x$ (y is stride rate, x is speed). **(c)** The residuals (reported by Minitab, then rounded to 3 decimal places) are $0.011, -0.001, -0.001, -0.011, -0.009, 0.003, 0.009$. These add to 0.001. Results will vary with rounding, and also with the number of decimal places used in the regression equation. **(d)** Residuals are positive for low and high speeds, negative for moderate speeds; this suggests that a curve (like a parabola) may be a better fit. We cannot plot residuals vs. time of observation since we do not have that information.

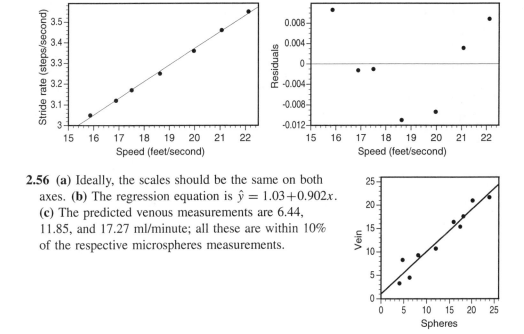

2.56 **(a)** Ideally, the scales should be the same on both axes. **(b)** The regression equation is $\hat{y} = 1.03 + 0.902x$. **(c)** The predicted venous measurements are 6.44, 11.85, and 17.27 ml/minute; all these are within 10% of the respective microspheres measurements.

2.57 **(a)** In 1986, the overseas return was 69.4%—much higher than would be expected. The residual is 50.9%. The original equation was $\hat{y} = 5.64 + 0.692x$; without this point, it is $\hat{y} = 4.13 + 0.653x$. This is not much of a change; the point is not influential.

(b) There is no obvious pattern to the residual plot (below). (The residuals shown are for the regression with all the points.)

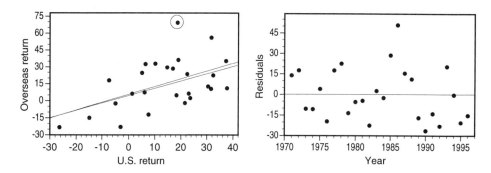

2.58 (a) The plot (below, left) suggests a weak *positive* association between price and consumption—the opposite of what we expected. **(b)** The regression equation is $\hat{y} = 44.9 + 9.50x$; regression explains $r^2 = 35.8\%$ of the variation in consumption. **(c)** The residual plot vs. time (below, right) shows a pattern of rising and falling, rather than the "random" fluctuations we expect.

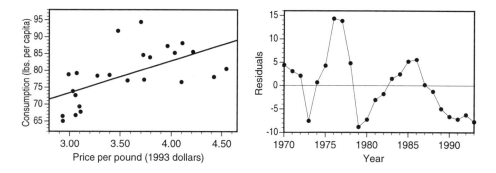

2.59 **(a)** Shown, with *three* fitted lines on the graph (the first and third are nearly identical). Equations are given above the graph. **(b)** Sea scallops are relatively expensive; the point for scallops lies far away from the rest of the points, though it does not deviate greatly from the pattern. The fitted line changes slightly (it becomes less steep) without that point. Lobsters might also be seen as outliers, though they are not as separated from the pack. Note that if we remove both

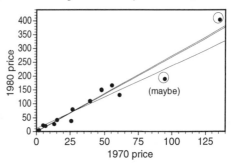

All points: $\hat{y} = -1.2 + 2.70x$
Minus scallops: $\hat{y} = 11.0 + 2.25x$
Minus scallops & lobster: $\hat{y} = 0.31 + 2.72x$

scallops and lobsters, the resulting line is almost the same as the line for all the data. **(c)** $r = 0.967$; $r^2 = 0.935 = 93.5\%$ of the variation in 1980 prices is explained by 1970 prices. **(d)** Without scallops, $r^* = 0.940$; without scallops and lobsters, $r = 0.954$. The correlation drops slightly since, in the absence of the outlier(s), the scatter of the data is less, so the scatter about a line is (relatively) greater. **(e)** Yes: The plot suggests a linear relationship.

2.60 **(a)** To three decimal places, the correlations are all approximately 0.816 (r_D actually rounds to 0.817), and the regression lines are all approximately $\hat{y} = 3.000 + 0.500x$. For all four sets, we predict $\hat{y} \doteq 8$ when $x = 10$. **(b)** Below. **(c)** For Set A, the use of the regression line seems to be reasonable—the data do seem to have a moderate linear association (albeit with a fair amount of scatter). For Set B, there is an obvious *nonlinear* relationship; we should fit a parabola or other curve. For Set C, the point (13, 12.74) deviates from the (highly linear) pattern of the other points; if we can exclude it, regression would be would very useful for prediction. For Set D, the data point with $x = 19$ is a very influential point—the other points alone give no indication of slope for the line. Seeing how widely scattered the y-coordinates of the other points are, we cannot place too much faith in the y-coordinate of the influential point; thus we cannot depend on the slope of the line, and so we cannot depend on the estimate when $x = 10$.

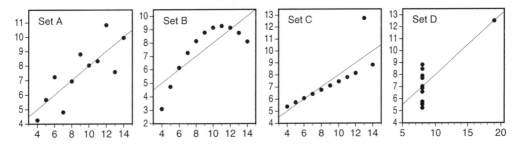

2.61 **(a)** The regression line is $\hat{y} = 11.06 - 0.01466x$, but the plot does not suggest a linear relationship. Moral: Check to see if a line is an appropriate model for the data. **(b)** The regression line is $\hat{y} = 2.72 + 0.166x$, but there is an influential point: Northern Ireland, which had much higher tobacco expenditures than one would suspect from its alcohol spending. Moral: Look for outliers and influential points.

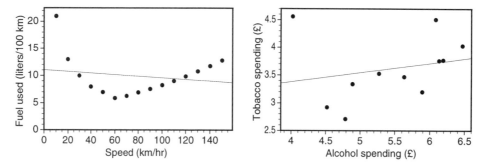

2.62 **(a)** There is *some* support for decreased mortality with higher volume (the line decreases from left to right), but the relationship is not very strong, and the wide scatter makes it difficult to judge. Hospitals with more cases tend to be less variable in mortality rate; in particular, of hospitals with more than 200 cases, almost none had mortality rates over 0.2.

However, part of this decreased scatter may be due to something else: If all hospitals had the same mortality rate, we would expect more variation in deaths among hospitals with fewer cases, for the same reason that a mean or proportion from a small sample has more variation than the same quantity from a large sample. (For example, note that a hospital with only one case would have a mortality rate of either 0 or 100%!)

(b) Above 150–200 cases, there does not seem to be strong evidence of a difference, but below that, the wide scatter at least suggests that some hospitals are better than others. For this reason, it does seem advisable to avoid hospitals with fewer than 150 cases.

2.63 **(a)** Table below, plot at right.

	Min	Q_1	M	Q_3	Max
U.S.	−26.4%	5.1%	17.5%	23.6%	37.6%
Overseas	−23.2%	2.5%	12.0%	29.6%	69.4%

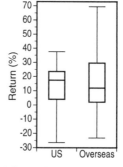

(b) Either answer is defensible: One-fourth of the time, overseas stocks did better than 29.6% (vs. 23.6% for U.S. stocks). On the other hand, half the time, U.S. stocks returned 17.5% or more (vs. 12% for overseas stocks). **(c)** Overseas stocks are more volatile—$Q_3 - Q_1 = 27.1\%$ for overseas stocks, about 50% larger than the U.S. *IQR* of 18.5%. Also, the boxplot shows a lot more spread, and the low U.S. return (−26.4%) is an outlier; not so with the overseas stocks.

2.64 (a) The plot (right) shows a strong positive linear relationship; ideally, the scales should be the same on both axes. Only one observation—$(51, 69)$—deviates from the pattern slightly. The regression line $\hat{y} = -2.580 + 1.0935x$ explains $r^2 = 95.1\%$ of the variation in the data. **(b)** Plots below. There is no striking relationship with x (rural reading); there may be an increasing spread over time. The large positive residual stands out. **(c)** The point $(108, 123)$ is a potentially influential observation (although it does not seem to deviate from the pattern of the other points). It has the second-highest residual. **(d)** When $x = 88$, we predict $\hat{y} = 93.65$. **(e)** The quantile plot (below) shows that the residuals are right-skewed.

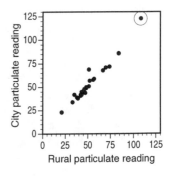

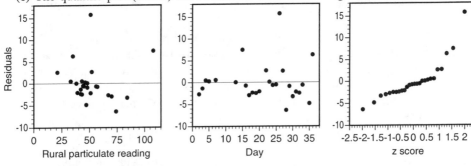

2.65 (a) Right-hand points are filled circles; left-hand points are open circles. **(b)** The right-hand points lie below the left-hand points. (This means the right-hand times are shorter, so the subject is right-handed.) There is no striking pattern for the left-hand points; the pattern for right-hand points is obscured since they are squeezed at the bottom of the plot. **(c)** Right hand:

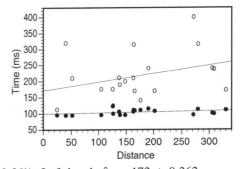

$\hat{y} = 99.4 + 0.0283x$ ($r = 0.305$, $r^2 = 9.3\%$). Left hand: $\hat{y} = 172 + 0.262x$ ($r = 0.318$, $r^2 = 10.1\%$). The left-hand regression is slightly better, but neither is very good: distance accounts for only 9.3% (right) and 10.1% (left) of the variation in time. **(d)** Neither plot shows a systematic pattern. (Plots not shown.)

2.66 The plot shown is a very simplified (and not very realistic) example—filled circles are economists in business; open circles are teaching economists. The plot should show positive association when either set of circles is viewed separately, and should show a large number of bachelor's degree economists in business and graduate degree economists in academia.

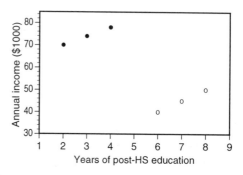

2.67 $r = 0.999$. With individual runners, the correlation would be smaller (closer to 0), since using data from individual runners would increase the "scatter" on the scatterplot, thus decreasing the strength of the relationship.

2.68 **(a)** There is clearly higher scatter for higher predicted values; the regression more accurately predicts low salaries than high salaries. **(b)** The residual plot is curved, similar to Figure 2.19(b). Salaries are typically overestimated for players who are new to the majors, and for those who have been in the majors for 15 or more years (these residuals are mostly negative). Those in for eight years will generally have their salaries underestimated; these residuals are mostly positive.

Section 5: An Application: Exponential Growth and World Oil Production

2.69 1 hour (four 15-minute periods): $2^4 = 16$. 5 hours (20 15-minute periods): $2^{20} = 1,048,576$.

2.70 **(a)** At right. **(b)** Below, left (the curve is $y = 2^{x-1}$). **(c)** The 64th square should have $2^{63} \doteq 9.22 \times 10^{18}$ grains of rice. **(d)** Below, right. Logarithms given in the table. **(e)** $y \doteq -0.30103 + 0.30103x$ (number of decimals in the answer may vary). This predicts $y \doteq 18.86$ for the logarithm of the number of grains on the 64th square—the same as $\log(2^{63})$.

Square	Grains	Logarithm
1	1	0
2	2	0.30103
3	4	0.60206
4	8	0.90309
5	16	1.20412
6	32	1.50515
7	64	1.80618
8	128	2.10721
9	256	2.40824
10	512	2.70927

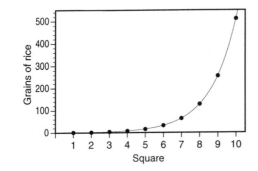

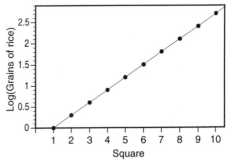

2.71 (a) At right. The bond value after x years is $500(1.075)^x$; all are rounded to 2 decimal places. **(b)** Below, left (the curve is $y = 500(1.075)^x$). **(c)** Below, right. Logarithms given in the table.

Years	Bond Value	Logarithm
1	$537.50	2.73038
2	577.81	2.76179
3	621.15	2.79320
4	667.73	2.82460
5	717.81	2.85601
6	771.65	2.88742
7	829.52	2.91883
8	891.74	2.95024
9	958.62	2.98165
10	1030.52	3.01305

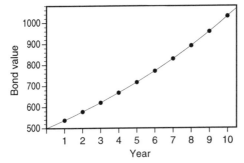

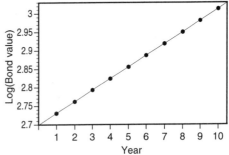

2.72 Fred's balance after x years is $500 + 100x$; Alice's balance is $500(1.075)^x$. After 25 years, Alice has more money: $3049.17 vs. $3000.00.

2.73 (a) If the investment was made at the *beginning* of 1970: $1000(1.1134)^{26} \doteq$ $16,327.95. If the investment was made at the *end* of 1970: $1000(1.1134)^{25} \doteq$ $14,664.94. **(b)** $1000(1.0562)^{25} =$ $3,923.32.

2.74 (a) Below, left. **(b)** The ratios are 3.6, $\frac{907,075}{226,260} \doteq 4.0$, and $\frac{2,826,095}{907,075} \doteq 3.1$. **(c)** Below, right. **(d)** The regression equation is $\hat{y} = -1095 + 0.556x$ (or $-38.5 + 0.556x$, if we code the years as 78, 79, etc.). The predicted value of y is 7.0302, which means we predict about $10^{7.03} \doteq 10.7$ million acres defoliated.

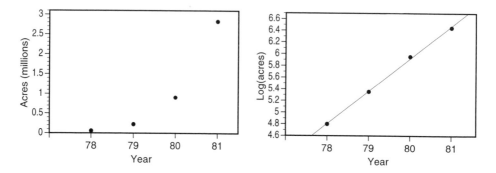

2.75 **(a)** There is a slight curve to the graph (below, left), suggesting exponential growth. **(b)** After taking logarithms, regression gives $\hat{y} = -98.753 + 0.052501x$ (plot below, right). Growth was faster from about 1965 to 1985, when the points in the scatterplot rise faster than the line. **(c)** $\log 495,710 = 5.695$, which is less than $\hat{y} \doteq 5.829$, so the actual spending was less than predicted.

Note: The problem asks students to predict 1992 spending, but comparing the logarithms may be easier. For students who can follow the switch from "log(Spending)" back to "Spending," we can observe the following: For 1992, we estimate log(Spending) = $\hat{y} \doteq 5.829$, so Spending $\doteq 10^{5.829} \doteq \$674,528$.

These answers are very sensitive to rounding; using full accuracy from software, the predicted value is \$673,585. In any case, the actual value is considerably less than the prediction.

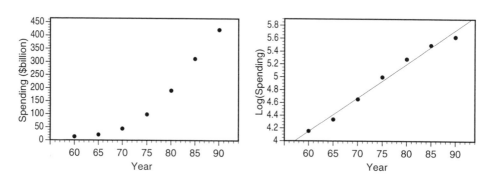

2.76 **(a)** Below, left. **(b)** Below, right. **(c)** The plot of log(population) is not linear, so growth was not exponential—or at least the rate of growth was not constant. The plot seems to be made up of two linear pieces, one for 1400–1750, the other (steeper) line from 1750–1950. The population grew more quickly after 1750.

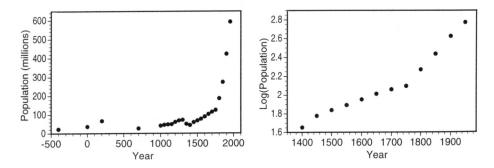

2.77 (a) Below, left. (b) Below, right. The logarithm plot has a greater slope—representing a faster growth rate—up to 1880 than after 1880. (c) $\hat{y} = -15.3815 + 0.0090210x$. When $x = 1997$, $\hat{y} = 2.633$, which corresponds to a population of 429.5 million. (Computation with "exact" values gives 429.9 million.) The actual value is much smaller than the predicted value.

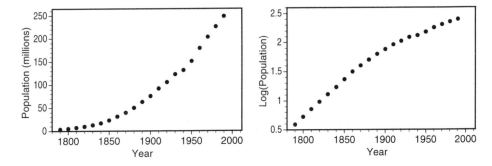

2.78 (a) Below. (b) Growth from 1950–1980 was more exponential than linear (since the log plot is fairly linear over that range). (c) The points on the log plot from 1980–1995 appear to lie on a straight line (with a lower slope), suggesting exponential growth at a lower rate. (On the other hand, the points for 1980–1995 on the first plot also seem to lie on a straight line, suggesting *linear* growth over that period. It is hard to spot minor deviations from linearity with only four points to consider.) (d) Vehicle registrations dropped during World War II.

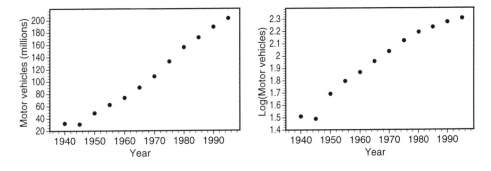

2.79 For 1945, log $y = 1.60865$, so $\hat{y} = 10^{1.60865} = 40.61$ million vehicles. For 1995, log $y = 2.43715$, so $\hat{y} = 10^{2.43715} = 273.6$ million vehicles.

2.80 Plots below. The log plot suggests exponential growth at one rate up to 1965, then at a slightly lower rate. The productivity index for 1985 is higher than the value suggested by the overall pattern.

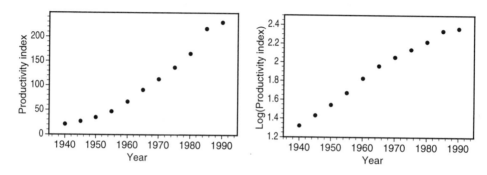

Section 6: Relations in Categorical Data

The answers for 2.81 through 2.85 are summarized in the following table, based on Table 2.15 of the text. The second entry in each cell is the *column percent* = cell entry/column total (e.g., $1.8\% \doteq \frac{36}{2017}$), and the third entry is the *row percent* = cell entry/row total (e.g., $14.6\% \doteq \frac{36}{246}$). [Thus, except for round-off error, the second entries add to 100% down the columns; the third entries add to 100% across the rows.]

Age	2-year full-time	2-year part-time	4-year full-time	4-year part-time	
Under 18	36 1.8% 14.6%	98 2.8% 39.8%	75 1.2% 30.5%	37 1.4% 15.0%	246 1.8%
18–21	1126 55.8% 21.1%	711 20.5% 13.3%	3270 54.5% 61.4%	223 8.7% 4.2%	5330 37.9%
22–34	634 31.4% 10.8%	1575 45.3% 26.9%	2267 37.8% 38.7%	1380 54.0% 23.6%	5856 41.7%
35 and up	221 11.0% 8.4%	1092 31.4% 41.7%	390 6.5% 14.9%	915 35.8% 35.0%	2618 18.6%
	2017 — 14.4%	3476 — 24.7%	6002 — 42.7%	2555 — 18.2%	14,050

2.81 (a) Adding across the bottom (total) row: 14,050 thousand, or 14,050,000. (b) At the right end of the second row of the table: $\frac{5330}{14,050} \doteq 37.9\%$. (c) Reading across the second entry of the second row above: $\frac{1126}{2017} \doteq 55.8\%$, $\frac{711}{3476} \doteq 20.5\%$, $\frac{3270}{6002} \doteq 54.5\%$, $\frac{223}{2555} \doteq 8.7\%$. (d) 18- to 21-year-olds constitute the majority of full-time students at both 2- and 4-year institutions, but make up much a smaller proportion of part-time students.

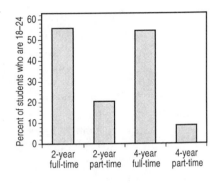

2.82 (a) There are 3476 thousand 2-year part-time students; $45.3\% \doteq \frac{1575}{3476}$ are 22 to 34 years old. (b) There are 5856 thousand 22- to-34-year-old students; $26.9\% \doteq \frac{1575}{5856}$ are enrolled part-time at 2-year colleges.

2.83 (a) These are in the right-hand "margin" of the table: Adding across the rows, we find 246 (thousand), 5330, 5856, and 2618, respectively. Dividing by 14,050 gives 1.8%, 37.9%, 41.7%, and 18.6%. (b) From the "2-year part-time" column, we divide 98, 711, 1575, and 1092 by 3476 to get 2.8%, 20.5%, 45.3%, and 31.4%. (c) Two-year part-time students are more likely to be older (over 22, and even moreso over 35) than undergraduates in general. They are also slightly more likely to be under 18, and considerably less likely to be 18 to 21.

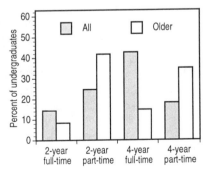

2.84 For older students, take 221, 1092, 390, and 915, and divide by 2618 to get 8.4%, 41.7%, 14.9%, and 35.0%. We might then compare these with the same percentages for the whole population: From the bottom row of the table, divide 2017, 3476, 6002, and 2555 by 14,050 to get 14.4%, 24.7%, 42.7%, and 18.2%.

From these percentages, and the bar chart at right, we can see that older students are more likely to be part-time than students in general.

2.85 For these distributions, divide the numbers in each cell by the total at the bottom of each column. (The columns in this table add to 100%.) The biggest difference is that full-time students tend to be younger—both 2- and 4-year full-time students have similar age distributions. Meanwhile, part-time students have similar distributions at both types of institutions, and are predominantly over 21, with about one-third over 35.

	2-year full-time	2-year part-time	4-year full-time	4-year part-time
<18	1.8%	2.8%	1.2%	1.4%
18–21	55.8%	20.5%	54.5%	8.7%
22–34	31.4%	45.3%	37.8%	54.0%
35+	11.0%	31.4%	6.5%	35.8%

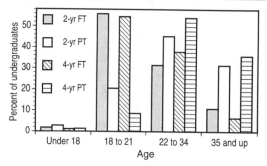

2.86 Two examples are shown at right. In general, any number from 10 to 50 can be put in the upper left corner, and then all the other entries can be determined.

30	20
30	20

50	0
10	40

2.87 **(a)** $\frac{75+119+160}{600} = 59\%$ did not respond.

(b) $\frac{75}{200} = 37.5\%$ of small businesses, $\frac{119}{200} = 59.5\%$ of medium-sized businesses, and $\frac{160}{200} = 80\%$ of large businesses did not respond. Generally, the larger the business, the less likely it is to respond. **(c)** At right. **(d)** Small: $\frac{125}{246} \doteq 50.8\%$. Medium: $\frac{81}{246} \doteq 32.9\%$. Large: $\frac{40}{246} \doteq 16.3\%$. **(e)** No: Over half of respondents were small businesses, while less than 1/6 of responses come from large businesses.

2.88 **(a)** Use column percents, e.g., $\frac{68}{225} \doteq 30.2\%$ of females are in administration, etc. See table and graph below. The biggest difference between women and men is in Administration: a higher percentage of women chose this major. Meanwhile, a greater proportion of men chose other fields, especially Finance. **(b)** There were 386 responses; $\frac{336}{722} \doteq 46.5\%$ did not respond.

	Female	Male	Overall
Accting.	30.2%	34.8%	32.1%
Admin.	40.4%	24.8%	33.9%
Econ.	2.2%	3.7%	2.8%
Fin.	27.1%	36.6%	31.1%

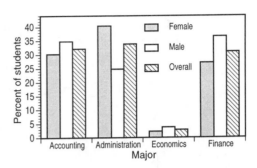

2.89 58.3% of desipramine users did not have a relapse, while 25.0% of lithium users and 16.7% of those who received placebos succeeded in breaking their addictions. Desipramine seems to be effective.

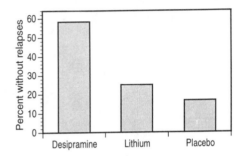

2.90 Compute column percents, e.g., $\frac{61,941}{355,265} \doteq 17.4\%$ of those U.S. degrees considered in this table are in engineering, etc. See table and graph at right. We observe that there are considerably more social science degrees, and fewer engineering degrees, in the U.S. The Western Europe and Asia distributions are similar.

Field	United States	Western Europe	Asia	Overall
Eng.	17.4%	38.3%	37.0%	32.8%
Nat. sci.	31.3%	33.7%	32.0%	32.3%
Soc. sci.	51.3%	28.0%	31.1%	34.9%

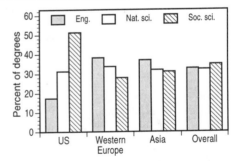

2.91 **(a)** The sum is 58,929; the difference is due to roundoff error. **(b)** Divide each column total by 99,588 to obtain the percents in the bottom margin of the table below. Bar graph below, left. **(c)** For 18 to 24 years, divide all numbers in that row by 12,613; the percentages are on the third line of the top row of the table below (73.6%, 24.1%, 0.2%, 2.1%). For 40 to 64 years, divide by 36,713 to obtain the third line of the third row of the table (6.3%, 72.7%, 6.0%, 15.0%). Among the younger women, almost three-fourths have not yet married, and those who are married have had little time to become widowed or divorced. Most of the older group are or have been married—only about 6% are still single. **(d)** 48.1% of never-married women are 18–24, 36.0% are 25–39, 11.9% are 40–

64, and 4.0% are 65 or older. The bar chart is below, right; see also the first column of the table. The target ages should be under 39.

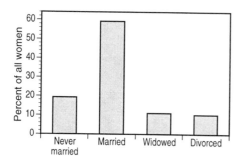 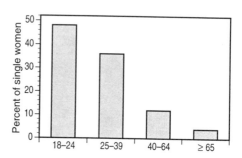

Age	Never Married	Married	Widowed	Divorced	
18–24	9,289 48.1% 73.6%	3,046 5.2% 24.1%	19 0.2% 0.2%	260 2.5% 2.1%	12,613 12.7%
25–39	6,948 36.0% 21.7%	21,437 36.4% 67.0%	206 1.9% 0.6%	3,408 33.2% 10.7%	32,000 32.1%
40–64	2,307 11.9% 6.3%	26,679 45.3% 72.7%	2,219 20.0% 6.0%	5,508 53.6% 15.0%	36,713 36.9%
≥ 65	768 4.0% 4.2%	7,767 13.2% 42.5%	8,636 77.9% 47.3%	1,091 10.6% 6.0%	18,264 18.3%
	19,312 — 19.4%	58,931 — 59.2%	11,080 — 11.1%	10,266 — 10.3%	99,588

2.92 Percents and bar graph below; for example, $64.5\% \doteq \frac{16,381}{25,415}$. Both genders use firearms more than any other method, but they are considerably more common with men (64.5% of male suicides, but only 42.0% of female suicides, used firearms). Women are more likely to use poison (34.6% vs. 14.0% for men).

	Male	Female
Firearms	64.5%	42.0%
Poison	14.0%	34.6%
Hanging	15.0%	13.2%
Other	6.5%	10.2%

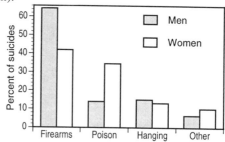

2.93 (a) At right. **(b)** $\frac{490}{700} = 70\%$ of male applicants are

	Admit	Deny
Male	490	210
Female	280	220

admitted, while only $\frac{280}{500} = 56\%$ of females are admitted.
(c) 80% of male business school applicants are admitted, compared with 90% of females; in the law school, 10% of males are admitted, compared with 33.3% of females. **(d)** A majority (6/7) of male applicants apply to the business school, which admits 83% of all applicants. Meanwhile, a majority (3/5) of women apply to the law school, which only admits 27.5% of its applicants.

2.94 (a) Alaska Airlines: $\frac{501}{3274+501} \doteq 13.3\%$.

America West: $\frac{787}{6438+787} \doteq 10.9\%$. **(b)** See
the table at the right. **(c)** Both airlines do best
at Phoenix, where America West has 72.7%
of its flights, and Alaska Airlines has only
6.2% of its flights. Seattle is the worst city
for both; Alaska West has 56.8% of its flights
there, compared with 3.6% for America West.

	Percent Delayed	
	Alaska Airlines	America West
Los Angeles	11.1%	14.4%
Phoenix	5.2	7.9
San Diego	8.6	14.5
San Francisco	16.9	28.7
Seattle	14.2	23.3

The large percentage of "good" (Phoenix) flights for America West, and the large percentage of "bad" (Seattle) flights for Alaska Airlines, makes America West look better.

2.95 Examples will vary, of course; here is one very
simplistic possibility (the two-way table is at the right;
the three-way table is below). The key is to be sure
that the three-way table has a lower percentage of
overweight people among the smokers than among the nonsmokers.

	Early Death	
	Yes	No
Overweight	4	6
Not overweight	5	5

Smoker	Early Death	
	Yes	No
Overweight	1	0
Not overweight	4	2

Nonsmoker	Early Death	
	Yes	No
Overweight	3	6
Not overweight	1	3

2.96 (a) At right. **(b)** Overall, 11.9% of white
defendants and 10.2% of black defendants get
the death penalty. However, for white victims,
the percentages are 12.6% and 17.5% (respectively); when the victim is black, they are 0% and 5.8%.

	Death Penalty?	
	Yes	No
White defendant	19	141
Black defendant	17	149

(c) In cases involving white
victims, 14% of defendants got the death penalty; when the victim was black, only
5.4% of defendants were sentenced to death. White defendants killed whites 94.3%
of the time—but are less likely to get the death penalty than blacks who killed
whites.

Section 7: The Question of Causation

2.97 Both reading ability and shoe size tend to increase with age—the lurking variable z. Diagram below.

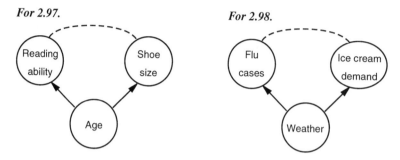

For 2.97.   *For 2.98.*

2.98 Flu tends to increase, and ice cream sales to decrease, during the winter months. Common response to weather. Diagram above.

2.99 No: The high death rate for C may occur because C is the anesthetic of choice in serious operations or for patients in poor condition.

2.100 The diagram below illustrates the confounding between exposure to chemicals and standing up.

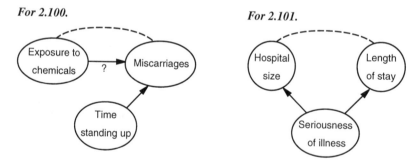

For 2.100.   *For 2.101.*

2.101 Patients suffering from more serious illnesses are more likely to go to larger hospitals (which may have more or better facilities) for treatment. They are also likely to require more time to recuperate afterwards.

2.102 Spending more time watching TV means that *less* time is spent on other activities; these may suggest lurking variables. For example, perhaps the parents of heavy TV watchers do not spend as much time at home as other parents. Also, heavy TV watchers would typically not get as much exercise.

2.103 In this case, there may be a causative effect, but in the direction opposite to the one suggested: people who are overweight are more likely to be on diets, and so choose artificial sweeteners over sugar. [Also, heavier persons are at a higher risk to develop diabetes; if they do, they are likely to switch to artificial sweeteners.]

2.104 The explanatory and response variables were "consumption of herbal tea" and "cheerfulness." The most important lurking variable is social interaction—many of the nursing home residents may have been lonely before the students started visiting.

2.105 The explanatory variable is whether or not a student has taken at least two years of foreign language, and the score on the test is the response. The lurking variable is the students' English skills *before* taking (or not taking) the foreign language: Students who have a good command of English early in their high school career are more likely to choose (or be advised to choose) to take a foreign language.

2.106 We might want to know, for example, information about proximity to power lines, tracking in our study some children who do *not* live near power lines or other electromagnetic field sources. It may also be useful to know family history for those who develop leukemia.

2.107 We need information on the type of surgery, and on the age, sex, and condition of the patient.

Exercises

2.108 **(a)** Correlation measures the strength and direction of the linear association between actual and recalled consumption; it will be high (close to 1) if there is a good match between actual and recalled consumption. ("A good match" does not necessarily mean that actual and recalled consumption are nearly the same; it only means that the subjects remember high consumption for high-quantity foods and low consumption for low-quantity foods.) The second aim of the study was to make predictions about actual consumption, so regression is the appropriate tool. **(b)** A correlation of 0.217 indicates a rather weak association. This might mean, for example, that among subjects who remembered eating a lot of beef, some really did eat a lot of beef, but others ate average or below-average quantities. **(c)** The value of r^2 is the fraction of variation in age-30 food intake accounted for by predicting with each of the other two variables (recalled intake and current intake). The higher r^2 is, the more reliable the prediction.

2.109 **(a)** Yes: The two lines appear to fit the data well. There do not appear to be any outliers or influential points. **(b)** Compare the slopes: before—0.189; after—0.157. (The units for these slopes are 100 ft^3 per degree-day/day; for students who are comfortable with units, 18.9 ft^3 vs. 15.7 ft^3 would be a better answer.) **(c)** Before: $\hat{y} = 1.089 + 0.189(35) = 7.704$. After: $\hat{y} = 0.853 + 0.157(35) = 6.348$. This amounts to an additional $(\$0.75)(7.704 - 6.348) = \$1.017$ per day, or $\$31.53$ for the month.

2.110 (a) $b = r \cdot s_y/s_x \doteq 1.1694$; $a = \bar{y} - b\bar{x} \doteq 0.3531$. The regression equation is $\hat{y} = 0.3531 + 1.1694x$; it explains $r^2 \doteq 27.6\%$ of the volatility in Philip Morris stock. **(b)** On the average, for every percentage-point rise in the S&P monthly return, Philip Morris stock returns rise about 1.17 percentage points. (And similarly, Philip Morris returns fall 1.17% for each 1% drop in the S&P index return.) **(c)** When the market is rising, the investor would like to earn money faster than the prevailing rate, and so prefers beta > 1. When the market falls, returns on stocks with beta < 1 will drop more slowly than the prevailing rate.

2.111 (a) Explanatory: weeds per meter (wpm). Response: corn yield. **(b)** The stemplots (below) give some evidence that yield decreases when there are more lamb's-quarter plants. **(c)** Scatterplot below. The regression equation is $\hat{y} = 166 - 1.10x$. Each additional lamb's-quarter per meter decreases yield by about 1.1 bushels/acre. **(d)** $\hat{y} = 166 - 1.10(6) = 159.4$ bushels/acre.

0 wpm		1 wpm		3 wpm		9 wpm	
14		14		14		14	2
14		14		14		14	
15		15		15	3	15	
15		15	7	15	69	15	
16		16	1	16		16	233
16	57	16	67	16		16	
17	2	17		17		17	
17	7	17		17	6	17	

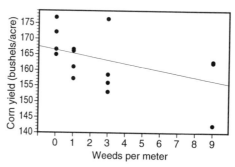

2.112 (a) Below, left. **(b)** The regression equation is $\hat{y} = 1.71 + 0.0795x$. **(c)** Below, right. The points for the residuals, like those of the original data, are split with women above the line (zero), and men below. (Men are taller on the average, so they have longer legs, and therefore longer strides. Thus, they need fewer steps per second to run at a given speed.)

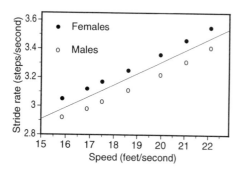

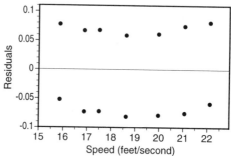

2.113 (a) At right. (b) The plot shows a negative association (longer beams are less strong), with no outliers. (c) The regression equation is $\hat{y} = 488 - 20.7x$; it is not a good match because the scatterplot does not suggest a straight line. (d) Length 5 to 9 inches: $\hat{y} = 668 - 46.9x$. Length 9 to 14 inches: $\hat{y} = 283 - 3.37x$. These two lines together describe the data fairly well.

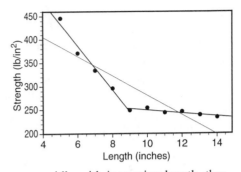

One might ask why strength at first decreases so rapidly with increasing length, then almost levels off.

2.114 (a) The first two graphs below. (b) From 0 to 6 hours (the first phase), the growth is "flat"—the colony size does not change much. From 6 to 24 hours, the log(mean colony size) plot looks like a positively sloped line, suggesting a period of exponential growth. At some point between 24 and 36 hours, the growth rate drops off (the 36-hour point is considerably below the linear pattern of the 6- to-24-hour points). (c) The regression equation is $\hat{y} = -0.594 + 0.0851x$; the prediction for $x = 10$ hours is $\hat{y} \doteq 0.257$, so the predicted mean colony size is about $10^{0.257} = 1.81$. (d) For hours 6–24 and log(mean colony size), $r = 0.9915$. For time and log(individual colony size), $r^* = 9846$. This is smaller because individual measurements have more scatter (see scatterplot below, right); the points do not cluster as tightly around a line.

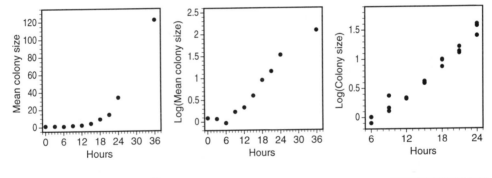

2.115 (a) $\frac{11}{20} = 55.0\%$, $\frac{68}{91} \doteq 74.7\%$, and $\frac{3}{8} = 37.5\%$. Some (but not too much) time spent in extracurricular activities seems to be beneficial. (b) No: There may be a lurking variable that affects both—e.g., a personality trait that "causes" students to do well, and also to participate in extracurricular activities in moderation.

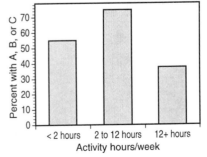

2.116 The upper part of the table shown gives the percentages of all homicides and all suicides committed with each type of firearm. This table supports the hypothesis that long guns are used more often for suicides than for homicides: We observe that handguns accounted for about 89% of homicides but only about 71% of suicides.

	Homicides	Suicides
Handgun	89.3%	70.9%
Shotgun	5.3%	12.6%
Rifle	2.9%	13.7%
Not specified	2.5%	2.9%
Handgun	79.1%	20.9%
Shotgun	56.0%	44.0%
Rifle	38.5%	61.5%
Not specified	72.2%	27.8%

It is also possible to compute the percentage of all handgun deaths which were homicides, etc. (the lower part of the table) and observe that considerably higher percentages of shotgun and rifle deaths were suicides.

Either of these sets of numbers may be used to construct a bar chart (not shown here). Note that the evidence in these tables says nothing about the accuracy of our *explanation* of this difference. Also, students may misinterpret the hypothesis as saying that we expect to see long guns used more often than handguns for suicides. Be sure they answer the right question!

2.117 Some departments pay higher salaries than others; if women are concentrated in the lower-paying disciplines, their overall median salary will be lower than that of men even if all salaries in each department are identical.

2.118 Number of firefighters and amount of damage are common responses to the seriousness of the fire.

2.119 **(a)** $\frac{68,838}{109,672} \doteq 62.8\%$, and similarly we get 61.9%, 60.9%, 55.2%, 53.5%, 52.8%, 53.3%, 50.3%, 55.1%, and 49.1%. There is a fairly steady decline in participation, with a noticeably large drop after the 1960s. **(b)** More college students became eligible to vote after 1970, and that group may be more likely to miss an election, either because of apathy or because they are away from home when elections occur.

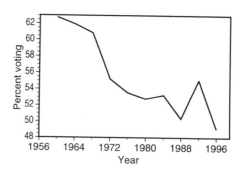

2.120 **(a)** At right. **(b)** HC and CO are positively associated; NOX is negatively associated with both HC and CO. **(c)** The HC/CO plot has no particular outliers; the two or three points in the upper right corners are nicely in line with the pattern of the rest of the plot. In the HC/NOX plot, four points (possibly more) lie above the line suggested by the rest of the points. In the NOX/CO plot, three points deviate from the overall pattern. (Note: All these answers may vary. Some students may consider more points to be outliers; some might circle fewer points.)
(d) $r_{HC,CO} = 0.9008$, $r_{HC,NOX} = -0.5588$, and $r_{NOX,CO} = -0.6851$. Without the outliers circled, $r^*_{HC,NOX} = -0.6418$ and $r^*_{NOX,CO} = -0.7406$. These answers will vary with what students considered to be outliers in (c). **(e)** The regression equations are

HC = 0.322 + 0.0288 CO
HC = 0.810 − 0.194 NOX
NOX = 1.83 − 0.0631 CO

(f) Without engines 11, 22, 24, and 32:
HC = 0.774 − 0.191 NOX
Without engines 22, 24, and 32:
NOX = 1.85 − 0.0724 CO

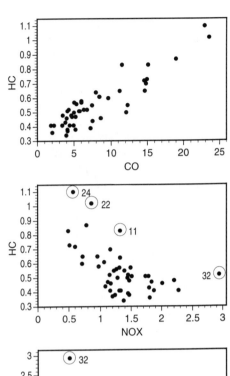

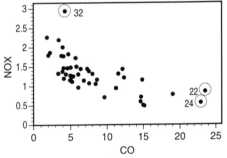

(g) The best relationship for prediction is HC/CO; the other two relationships are less linear and not as strong (the correlations are smaller, even after omitting outliers). The NOX/CO relationship *might* be good for prediction using a nonlinear function, if we omit engine 32.

2.121 **(a)** Both distributions are skewed to the right. Five-number summaries at right; stemplots below. There are no outliers for teachers' pay. Spending

	Min	Q_1	M	Q_3	Max
Pay	26.0	30.8	32.6	39.1	50.0
Spending	3.67	4.95	5.66	6.52	9.93

over $6.52+1.5(6.52-4.65) = 8.875$ thousand per student qualifies as an outlier; these states are New York, New Jersey, and Alaska (which also had high [non-outlier] pay values). **(b)** There is a moderate positive association. This makes sense since money spent for teacher salaries is part of the education budget; more money spent per pupil would typically translate to more money spent overall. **(c)** Regression equation: $\hat{y} = 14.1 + 3.53x$. For each additional $1000 spent per student, teacher salaries increase by about $3,530. Regression of pay on spending explains about 62.9% of the variation in spending. **(d)** The residuals for the three states are small (their points are close to the line). Without those states, the regression line is $\hat{y} = 12.5 + 3.82x$, which has a slightly greater slope than before—so the three points are *somewhat* influential (although we see below that the line does not change much).

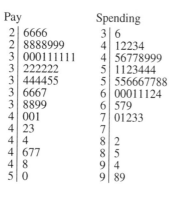

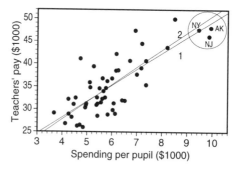

2.122 **(a)** & **(b)** The five-number summaries are

	Teachers' Pay ($1000)					Spending per Pupil ($1000)				
	Min	Q_1	M	Q_3	Max	Min	Q_1	M	Q_3	Max
Coastal	29.0	36.20	40.90	46.10	50.0	4.73	6.16	6.805	8.50	9.93
South	26.5	29.60	31.55	32.60	40.7	4.12	4.50	5.175	5.69	7.17
Midwest	26.0	31.05	35.30	37.25	47.4	4.60	5.04	5.470	5.88	7.00

The boxplots are below. Only teacher's salaries in the south and midwest states have outliers: In the south, those above $32.6 + 1.5(3) = 37.1$ are Delaware ($39.1) and Maryland ($40.7). In the midwest, Michigan ($47.4) is above $37.25 + 1.5(6.2) = 46.55$. **(c)** The coastal states are clearly higher in both salaries and spending; the midwest is slightly higher than the south in salaries, but not very different in spending per pupil. **(d)** The residuals for the south are considerably less variable, and more than three-quarters are negative. There is no striking difference between the coastal and midwest residuals.

	Min	Q_1	M	Q_3	Max
			Residuals		
Coastal	−6.69841	−2.75212	1.14705	5.02827	10.3386
South	−5.17373	−1.73138	−0.95191	−0.12244	2.9210
Midwest	−5.14927	−2.17094	−0.05066	3.34934	8.8804

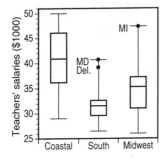
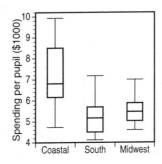
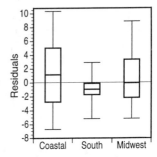

2.123 The scatterplot is not very promising. The regression equation is $\hat{y} = 1.28 + 0.00227x$; the correlation is $r = 0.252$, and the regression explains $r^2 = 6.3\%$ of the variation in GPA. By itself, SATM does not give reliable predictions of GPA.

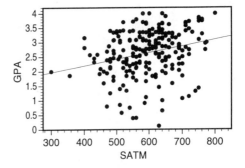

2.124 (a) There is a strong positive linear relationship, as we would expect since the two measurements should be nearly equal. Ideally, the scales should be the same on both axes. **(b)** $r = 0.9965$; the process is quite reliable. **(c)** The regression equation is $\hat{y} = -0.0333 + 1.02x$. With $\bar{x} = 1.6298$, $s_x = 0.1694$, $\bar{y} = 1.6252$, and $s_y = 0.1730$, we compute the same slope from $b = r\,s_y/s_x$.

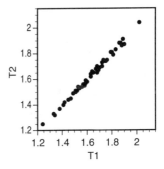

2.125 **(a)** T2 vs. T1 at right; residuals below. **(b)** The distributions of T1 and T2 (stemplots below) do not appear to have any outliers. **(c)** With the new point, $\hat{y} = -0.017 + 1.011x$; without it, $\hat{y} = -0.033 + 1.018x$. The two lines are very similar, so the point is not influential. **(d)** With the new point, $r = 0.966$; without it, $r = 0.996$.

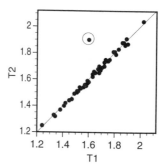

T1		T2	
12	4	12	5
12		13	233
13	334	13	7
13	8	14	024
14	12	14	59
14	579	15	011344
15	11234	15	5667889
15	678899	16	224
16	0003334	16	5567789
16	578889	17	00344
17	02234	17	559
17	569	18	113
18	013	18	6788
18	6789	19	01
19	0	19	
19		20	4
20	2		

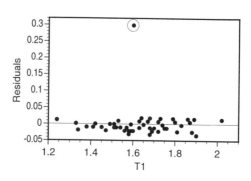

2.126 **(a)** The stemplot of T2 is nearly the same as the one above; just remove the "0" leaf from the 19 stem, and add a stem 12 and leaf 0 at the top. The stemplot of T1 is at the right; 2.2 is high (it is the leaf 0 at the bottom). **(b)** The summary measures (and original values) are $\bar{x} = 1.6410$ (1.6298), $s_x =$

12	4
13	3348
14	12579
15	11234678899
16	003334578889
17	02234569
18	0136789
19	0
20	2
21	
22	0

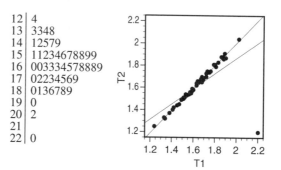

0.1858 (0.1694), $\bar{y} = 1.6169$ (1.6252), $s_y = 0.1813$ (0.1730). These values only change slightly. **(c)** The new point appears to be, and is, influential. **(d)** $r = 0.709$, compared to 0.996 without the influential point—a big change.

Chapter 3 Solutions

Section 1: First Steps

3.1 One observation could have many explanations. Were the sunflowers in the sun and the okra in the shade? Were the sunflowers upwind from the okra? Repeated trials in controlled conditions are needed.

3.2 The anecdote describes a single unusual event. We would like data on deaths and injuries for occupants wearing/not wearing restraints for many accidents.

3.3 It is an observational study: information is gathered without imposing any treatment. A voter's gender is the explanatory variable, and political party is the response variable.

3.4 **(a)** This is an experiment: a treatment is imposed. **(b)** The explanatory variable is the teaching method (computer assisted or standard), and the response variable is the increase in reading ability based on the pre- and posttests.

3.5 **(a)** Which surgery was performed is the explanatory variable, while survival time is the response. **(b)** This study uses available data; it is not an experiment because the study itself imposes no treatment on the subjects. **(c)** Any conclusions drawn from this study would have to be viewed with suspicion, because doctors may recommend treatment based on the patient's condition. Perhaps some doctors are more likely to suggest one treatment for more advanced cases; those patients would have a poorer prognosis than the patients for whom the doctors suggest the other treatment.

3.6 It was not an experiment, since we observe variables without imposing any treatments. The explanatory variable is whether or not a family had been accepted in public housing, and the response variable is "family stability" (and "other variables").

3.7 This was an experiment; the treatment was walking briskly on the treadmill. The fact that eating was not recorded limits the conclusions that can be drawn. The explanatory variable was time after exercise, and the response variable was the metabolic rate.

3.8 **(a)** The anesthetic used (the "treatment") was not imposed, but rather was chosen by the doctors caring for each patient. The nature and seriousness of the illness and the patient's overall physical condition may influence the choice of anesthetic and also influence the death rate. **(b)** The high death rate for C may occur because C is the anesthetic of choice in serious operations or for patients in poor condition. We should get information on the type of surgery, and on the age, sex, and condition of the patient.

Section 2: Design of Experiments

3.9 Subjects: 300 sickle cell patients. Factor: drug given. Treatments: hydroxyurea and placebo. Response variable: number of pain episodes.

3.10 Experimental units: pairs of pieces of package liner. Factor: temperature of jaws. Treatments: 250°F, 275°F, 300°F, 325°F. Response variable: peel strength of the seal.

3.11 Subjects: students. Factors: length of commercial, and number of repetitions. Treatments: 30 seconds repeated 1, 3, or 5 times, and 90 seconds repeated 1, 3, or 5 times. Response variables: recollection of ad, attitude about camera, and intention to buy camera.

3.12 Experimental units: chicks. Factors: corn variety and protein level. Treatments: standard at 12%, 16%, or 20% protein; opaque-2 at 12%, 16%, or 20% protein; and floury-2 at 12%, 16%, or 20% protein. Response variables: weight gain.

3.13 **(a)** Below. **(b)** A placebo allows researchers to control for the relief subjects might experience due to the psychological effect of taking a drug.

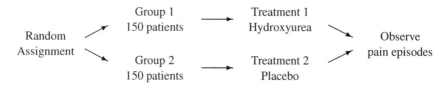

3.14 **(a)** Measure the blood pressure for all subjects, then randomly select half to get a calcium supplement, with the other half getting a placebo.

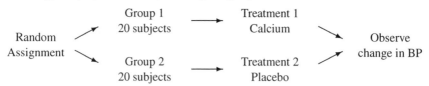

(b) If we assign labels 01 to 40 (down the columns), then choose two digits at a time from line 131, we give calcium to the subjects listed in the table below. (They are chosen in the order given, reading down the columns.) See note on page 50 about using Table B.

05–Chen	29–O'Brian	31–Plochman	02–Asihiro
32–Rodriguez	20–Imrani	18–Howard	36–Townsend
19–Hruska	16–Guillen	07–Cranston	23–Krushchev
04–Bikalis	37–Tullock	13–Fratianna	27–Marsden
25–Liang	39–Willis	33–Rosen	35–Tompkins

3.15 (a) The response variable is the company chosen.

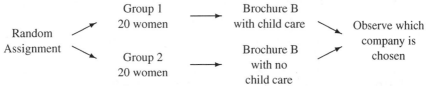

(b) If we assign labels 01 to 40 (down the columns), then choose two digits at a time beginning on line 121, we choose the subjects listed in the table below for the child-care brochure. (They are chosen in the order given, reading down the columns.) See note on page 50 about using Table B.

29–Ng	25–Lippman	09–Danielson	28–Morse
07–Cortez	13–Garcia	08–Curzakis	18–Howard
34–Sugiwara	38–Ullmann	27–McNeill	03–Afifi
22–Kaplan	15–Green	23–Kim	01–Abrams
10–Durr	05–Cansico	30–Quinones	36–Travers

3.16 Diagram below. Choose two digits at a time beginning on line 120. Group 1 will be 16, 04, 19, 07, and 10; Group 2 is 13, 15, 05, 09, and 08; Group 3 is 18, 03, 01, 06, and 11. The others are in Group 4. See note on page 50 about using Table B.

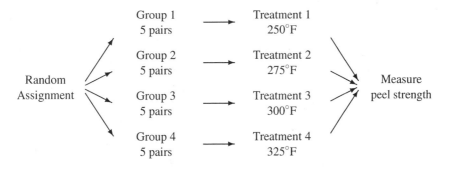

3.17 Diagram below. Assign labels 01 to 20, then choose two digits at a time beginning on line 145. Use method A in plots 19, 06, 09, 10, 16, 01, 08, 20, 02, and 07. See note on page 50 about using Table B.

01 – A	02 – A	03 – B	04 – B
05 – B	06 – A	07 – A	08 – A
09 – A	10 – A	11 – B	12 – B
13 – B	14 – B	15 – B	16 – A
17 – B	18 – B	19 – A	20 – A

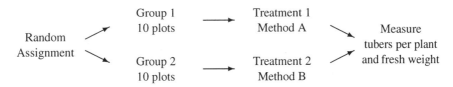

3.18 In the first design—an observational study—the men who exercise (and those who choose not to) may have other characteristics (lurking variables) which might affect their risk of having a heart attack. Since treatments are assigned to the subjects in the second design, the randomization should "wash out" these factors.

3.19 If this year is considerably different in some way from last year, we cannot compare electricity consumption over the two years. For example, if this summer is warmer, the customers may run their air conditioners more. The possible differences between the two years would confound the effects of the treatments.

3.20 **(a)** An experiment is not possible, since the explanatory variable (gender) cannot be "imposed" on the subjects. **(b)** An experiment is possible, but there may be some ethical difficulties in randomly assigning a surgical treatment to cancer patients (especially if the attending physician recommends the other treatment to the patient).

3.21 Diagram below. Assign labels 01 to 16, then choose two digits at a time beginning on line 115: use blue on poles 04, 09, 14, and 03; green on 10, 06, 11, and 16; white on 02, 07, 13, and 15; and yellow on the rest.

01	02	03	04
yellow	white	blue	blue
05	06	07	08
yellow	green	white	yellow
09	10	11	12
blue	green	green	yellow
13	14	15	16
white	blue	white	green

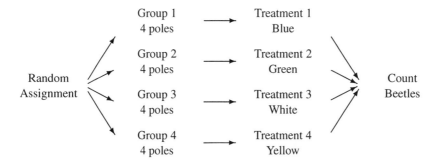

3.22 **(a)** The factors are question location (two levels: before or after text passage) and question type (three levels: simple fact, computation, word problem). This gives six treatments: before/simple fact, after/simple fact, before/computation, after/computation, before/word problem, after/word problem. **(b)** We start with 12 classes, and randomly split them into six groups of two each; see diagram below. Randomization will vary with starting line. See note on page 50 about using Table B.

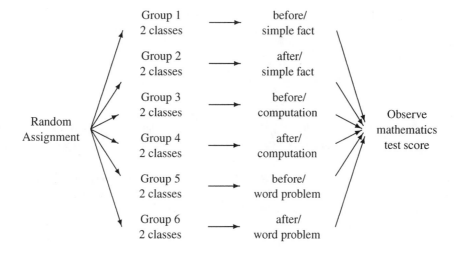

3.23 Since there are 6 treatments, we can assign 16 students to each treatment and have 4 left over. These 4 can be ignored, or each can be randomly assigned to one of the six groups.

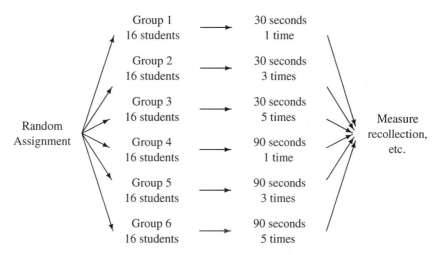

3.24 **(a)** Lack of control means that the specific effects of the meditation technique cannot be distinguished from the effect of investing a month in any activity with the expectation that it will reduce your anxiety. **(b)** The experimenter expects meditation to lower anxiety, and probably hopes to show that it does. This will unconsciously influence the diagnosis. **(c)** The control group might receive no treatment other than the before and after interview (which itself may affect anxiety) or might receive an alternative treatment such as physical exercise. Ideally the interviewer should not know the treatment received by an individual, but this is difficult in practice. An "objective" test of anxiety avoids this problem. If an interviewer is used, he or she should be an outside party with no stake in the experiment.

3.25 For each person, flip the coin to decide which hand they should use first (heads: right hand first; tails: left hand first).

3.26 The randomization will vary with the starting line in Table B.

Completely randomized design: Randomly assign 10 students to "Group 1" (which has the trend-highlighting software) and the other 10 to "Group 2" (which does not). Compare the performance of Group 1 with that of Group 2.

Matched pairs design: Each student does the activity twice, once with the software and once without. Randomly decide (for each student) whether they have the software the first or second time. Compare performance with the software and without it. (This randomization can be done by flipping a coin 20 times, or by picking 20 digits from Table B and using the software first if the digit is even, etc.)

Alternate matched pairs design: Again, all students do the activity twice. Randomly assign 10 students to Group 1 and 10 to Group 2. Group 1 uses the software the first time; Group 2 uses the software the second time.

3.27 **(a)** Ordered by increasing weight, the five blocks are

(1)	Williams	22	Festinger	24	Hernandez	25	Moses	25
(2)	Santiago	27	Kendall	28	Mann	28	Smith	29
(3)	Brunk	30	Obrach	30	Rodriguez	30	Loren	32
(4)	Jackson	33	Stall	33	Brown	34	Dixon	34
(5)	Birnbaum	35	Tran	35	Nevesky	39	Wilansky	42

(b) The exact randomization will vary with the starting line in Table B. Different methods are possible; perhaps the simplest is to number from 1 to 4 within each block, then assign the members of block 1 to a weight-loss treatment, then assign block 2, etc. For example, starting on line 133, we assign 4–Moses to treatment A, 1–Williams to B, and 3–Hernandez to C (so that 2–Festinger gets treatment D), then carry on for block 2, etc. (either continuing on the same line, or starting over somewhere else).

3.28 In each field, have two boards for each color. The diagram is below. One method of randomization would be to assign labels 1–8 (ignore 0 and 9) to each pole in field 1, then

1	2	3	4	5	6	7	8
W	B	Y	G	B	W	G	Y

1	2	3	4	5	6	7	8
B	Y	Y	B	W	G	W	G

select from line 105: 5 and 2 for blue; 4 and 7 for green; 6 and 1 for white; and the other two (3 and 8) for yellow. Proceeding on from there, in the second field we assign 1 and 4 for blue; 8 and 6 for green; 7 and 5 for white; and the other two (2 and 3) for yellow. See note on page 50 about using Table B.

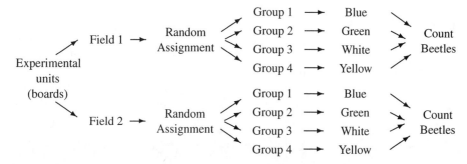

3.29 (a) Below. (b) Practically, it may take a long time until enough claims have been filed to have the information we need. Ethically, this outline suggests that we assign subjects to an insurance plan; some might object to that. Other answers are possible.

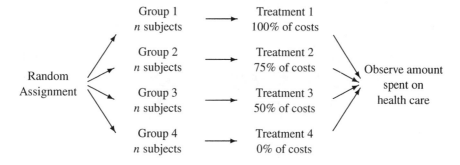

3.30 Use a block design, separately assigning the men and the women to the six treatment groups. The diagram would be quite large, but it would be modeled after Figure 3.4.

3.31 (a) False. Such regularity holds only in the long run. If it were true, you could look at the first 39 digits and know whether or not the 40th was a 0. (b) True. All pairs of digits (there are 100, from 00 to 99) are equally likely. (c) False. Four random digits have chance 1/10000 to be 0000, so this sequence will occasionally occur. 0000 is no more or less random than 1234 or 2718, or any other four-digit sequence.

3.32 The mean IQ of the whole group is $\mu = 108.92$. Logically, when we select 39 from this group, half the time the mean $\bar{x}$ of this smaller group will be more than 108.92, and half the time it will be less. The theoretical distribution of $\bar{x}$ is too difficult to find exactly, but based on 1000 simulated samples, it is approximately normal with mean 108.92 (the same as the "population" mean) and standard deviation $s_{\bar{x}} \doteq 1.54$. (Therefore, $\bar{x}$ will almost always be between 104.3 and 113.5.)

Section 3: Sampling Design

3.33 *Population:* Employed adult women. *Sample:* The 48 women who return the questionnaires. 52% did not respond.

3.34 *Population:* All words in Tom Clancy's novels. *Sample:* The 250 words recorded. *Variable:* Number of letters in a word.

3.35 **(a)** Adult U.S. residents. **(b)** U.S. households. **(c)** All regulators from the supplier, *or* the regulators in the last shipment.

3.36 *Variable:* Approval of president's job performance. *Population:* Adult citizens of the U.S., or perhaps just registered voters. *Sample:* The 1210 adults interviewed. *Possible sources of bias:* Only adults with phones were contacted. Alaska and Hawaii were omitted.

3.37 Beginning with Agarwal and going down the columns, label the people with the numbers 01 to 28. From line 139 we select
        04–Bowman, 10–Frank, 17–Liang, 19–Naber, 12–Goel, 13–Gupta
See note on page 50 about using Table B.

3.38 Labels: 000 to 439 (or 001 to 440, or two labels each). With either starting label, the first five districts from line 117 are (for one label each)
        381, 262, 183, 322, 341
With two labels each (starting with either 000/440 or 001/441), the list is
        381, 679 (= 239), 853 (= 413), 262, 183
See note on page 50 about using Table B.

3.39 Taking three-digit numbers beginning on line 125 gives the following sample:
        214, 313, 409, 306, 511
Note we can only use the numbers 101–114, 201–215, 301–317, 401–410, and 501–513.
    Alternatively, we might assign 2-digit labels 00 to 72 (or 01 to 73), rather than use the 3-digit block numbers as labels. When this is done in some order (say, numerical order of block numbers), line 125 gives
        96 (ignore), 74 (ignore), 61, 21, 49, 37, 82 (ignore), 37 (repeat—ignore), 18
See note on page 50 about using Table B.

3.40 This defeats the purpose of randomization; if we always start on the same line, our choices are no longer random.

3.41 **(a)** We will choose one of the first 40 at random and then the addresses 40, 80, 120, and 160 places down the list from it. Beginning on line 120, the addresses selected are 35, 75, 115, 155, 195. (Only the first number is chosen from the table.) **(b)** All addresses are equally likely—each has chance 1/40 of being selected. To see this, note that each of the first 40 has chance 1/40 since one is chosen at random. But each address in the second 40 is chosen exactly when the corresponding address in the first 40 is, so each of the second 40 also has chance 1/40. And so on.

This is not an SRS because the only possible samples have exactly one address from the first 25, one address from the second 25, and so on. An SRS could contain any five of the 200 addresses in the population. Note that this view of systematic sampling assumes that the number in the population is a multiple of the sample size.

3.42 Label the students 00, ..., 24 and use Table B. Then label the faculty 0, ..., 9 and use the table again. Students may try some method of choosing both samples simultaneously. We simply want to choose two separate SRSs, one from the students and one from the faculty. See note on page 50 about using Table B.

3.43 Give each name on the alphabetized lists a number: 001 to 500 for females and 0001 to 2000 for males. From line 122 of Table B, the first five females selected are 138, 159, 052, 087, and 359. Continuing on from where we left off, the first five men are 1369, 0815, 0727, 1025, and 1868.

3.44 It is not an SRS, because it is impossible to choose a sample with anything but 50 women and 200 men.

3.45 (a) Households without telephones or with unlisted numbers. Such households would likely be made up of poor individuals (who cannot afford a phone), those who choose not to have phones, and those who do not wish to have their phone number published. (b) Those with unlisted numbers would be included in the sampling frame when a random-digit dialer is used.

3.46 The higher no-answer was probably the second period—more families are likely to be gone for vacations, etc. Nonresponse of this type might underrepresent those who are more affluent (and are able to travel).

3.47 Voluntary response is the big reason. Opponents of gun control usually feel more strongly than supporters, and so are more likely to call. The sampling method also reduces response from poorer people by requiring a phone and willingness to pay for the call.

3.48 Call-in polls, and "voluntary response" polls in general, tend to attract responses from those who have strong opinions on the subject, and therefore are often not representative of the population as a whole. On the other hand, there is no reason to believe that the 500 randomly chosen adults overrepresent any particular group, so the 72% "yes" from that poll is more reliable as an estimate of the true population proportion.

3.49 Form A would draw the higher response favoring the ban. It is phrased to produce a negative reaction: "giving huge sums of money" versus "contributing," and giving "to candidates" rather than "to campaigns." Also, form B presents both sides of the issue, allowing for special interest groups to have "a right to contribute."

3.50 **(a)** The question is clear, and not particularly slanted, but some may be embarrassed to say "yes" to this. **(b)** This question is likely to elicit more responses against gun control (that is, more people will choose 2). The two options presented are too extreme; no middle position on gun control is allowed. **(c)** This is clearly slanted in favor of national health insurance. **(d)** The wording is too technical for many people to understand—and for those who *do* understand it, it is slanted because it suggests reasons why one should support recycling. It could be rewritten to something like "Do you support economic incentives to promote recycling?"

Section 4: Toward Statistical Inference

3.51 6.2% is a statistic.

3.52 2.503 cm is a parameter; 2.515 cm is a statistic.

3.53 43 is a statistic; 52% is a parameter.

3.54 Both 335 g and 289 g are statistics.

3.55 **(a)** High variability, high bias (wide scatter, many are low). **(b)** Low variability, low bias (little scatter, close to parameter). **(c)** High variability, low bias (wide scatter, neither too low nor too high). **(d)** Low variability, high bias (little scatter, but too high). Make sure that students understand that "high bias" means that the values are far from the parameter, *not* that they are too high.

3.56 The larger sample will give more precise results—that is, the results are more likely to be close to the population truth (if bias is small).

3.57 For this exercise we assume that the population proportions in all states are about the same. The effect of the population proportion on the variability will be studied further later. Additionally, we ignore finite-population corrections in this course. **(a)** No: The precision of an SRS of size 2000 is the same no matter what the population size (as long as the population is about 10 times the size of the sample or larger). **(b)** Yes: The sample sizes will vary from 32,000 (California) to 485 (Wyoming), so the precision will also vary (larger samples are less variable).

3.58 The variability would be practically the same for either population. (This makes the [certainly correct] assumption that the poll's sample size was less than 800,000—10% of the population of New Jersey.)

3.59 (a) Answers will vary. If, for example, 8 heads are observed, then $\hat{p} = \frac{8}{20} = 0.4 = 40\%$. **(b)** Note that all the leaves in the stemplot should be either 0 or 5, since all possible $\hat{p}$-values end in 0 or 5. For comparison, here is the sampling distribution (assuming p really is 0.5).

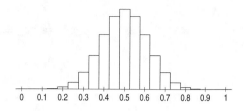

An individual student's stemplot will probably not resemble this much, but pooled efforts may be fairly close.

3.60 (a) The scores will vary depending on the starting row. Note that the smallest possible mean is 61.75 (from the sample 58, 62, 62, 65) and the largest is 77.25 (from 73, 74, 80, 82). **(b)** Answers will vary; shown below are two views of the sampling distribution. The first shows all possible values of the experiment (so the first rectangle is for 61.75, the next is for 62.00, etc.); the other shows values grouped from 61 to 61.75, 62 to 62.75, etc. (which makes the histogram less bumpy). The tallest rectangle in the first picture is 8 units; in the second, the tallest is 28 units.

Technical note: These histograms were found by considering all $\binom{10}{4} = 210$ of the possible samples. It happens that half (105) of those samples yield a mean smaller than 69.4, and half yield a greater mean. In Exercise 3.32, it was also the case that half of the samples gave means higher than μ, and half lower. In this exercise, it just happens to work out that way; in 3.32, it had to (because we were sampling half of the population).

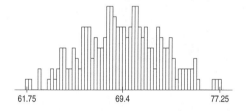

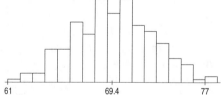

3.61 (a) We let the digits 0 and 1 represent the presence of eggs, while the other digits represent the absence of eggs. Use ten digits in each sample (one for each square yard). Answers will vary with the line chosen from Table B. **(b)** To make the stemplot, view each $\hat{p}$ value

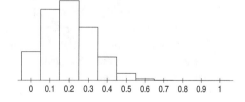

as having a 0 in the second place after the decimal—e.g., $\hat{p} = 0.20$ rather than just $\hat{p} = 0.2$—and use 0 for the leaf. For comparison, here is the sampling distribution. An individual student's stemplot will probably not resemble this much, but pooled efforts may be fairly close.

3.62 (a) We let the digits 0–3 represent "yes" responses, while the other digits represent "no." Use 20 digits in each sample. Answers will vary with the line chosen from Table B. **(b)** The mean of 10 proportions from samples of size 20 is the same as the proportion from a single sample of size 200. Almost always (99.7% of the time), this value will be in the range $0.4 \pm 3\sqrt{\frac{(0.4)(0.6)}{200}} \doteq 0.296$ and 0.504.

3.63 **(a)** $p = \frac{27}{95} \doteq 0.2842$. **(b)** Assign labels 01 through 95 to the players, then take digits two at a time. (In fact, it is easier to simply say that 01–27 correspond to offensive backs, and pay no attention to the table.) Answers will vary with the starting line in Table B; if the sample

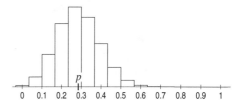

contains, say, 3 offensive backs, then $\hat{p} = \frac{3}{15} = 0.2$. **(c)** The distribution should look *roughly* normal, centered at p. For comparison, the sampling distribution of $\hat{p}$ is shown. **(d)** The mean should be fairly close to p; the lack of bias is (should be) illustrated in that the histogram is clustered around p. [The number of offensive backs has a hypergeometric distribution with parameters $N = 95$, $r = 27, n = 15$. The sampling distribution shown has standard deviation 0.1074; the average of 20 $\hat{p}$ values would be approximately $N(p, 0.024)$, so that about 99.7% of the time, $\bar{p}$ should be between 0.212 and 0.356.]

3.64 **(a)** Below is the population stemplot (which gives the same information as a histogram). The (population) mean GPA is $\mu \doteq 2.6352$ and the standard deviation is $\sigma \doteq 0.7794$. [Technically, we should take $\sigma \doteq 0.7777$, which comes

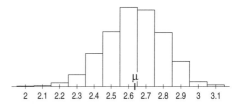

from dividing by n rather than $n - 1$, but few (if any) students would know this.] **(b)** – **(e)** These histograms are not shown; results will vary with starting line in Table B. The theoretical distribution of $\bar{x}$ is too difficult to find exactly, but based on 1000 simulated samples, it is approximately normal with mean 2.6352 (the same as μ) and standard deviation $s_{\bar{x}} \doteq 0.167$. (Therefore, $\bar{x}$ will almost always be between 2.13 and 3.14.)

The histogram shown is based on these samples. Note that it is slightly left-skewed, but less than the population distribution. Also note that the $s_{\bar{x}}$, the standard deviation of the sampling distribution, is smaller than $\sigma/\sqrt{20} \doteq 0.174$, since we are sampling without replacement.

```
0 | 134
0 | 567889
1 | 0011233444
1 | 55666678888888888999999
2 | 00000000011111111122222222223333333333444444444
2 | 555555555555666666667777777777777788888888888888999999
3 | 0000000000000011111111111222222222233333333333333333444444444
3 | 5566666666677777788889
4 | 0000
```

Exercises

3.65 It is an observational study—no treatment was imposed (clearly, there is no ethical way to impose a treatment for this kind of study).

3.66 It is an observational study—no treatment was imposed. Results of this study might establish a link between fitness and personality, but could not establish causation.

3.67 For each taster flip a coin. If heads, taste Pepsi first, then Coke. If tails, taste Coke first, then Pepsi.

3.68 The factors are whether or not the letter has a ZIP code (2 levels: yes or no) and the time of day the letter is mailed. The number of levels for the second factor may vary.

To deal with lurking variables, all letters should be the same size and should be sent to the same city, and the day on which a letter is sent should be randomly selected. Because most post offices have shorter hours on Saturdays, one may wish to give that day some sort of "special treatment" (it might even be a good idea to have the day of the week be a *third* factor in this experiment).

3.69 Answers will vary. An example: You want to compare how long it takes to walk to class by two different routes. The experiment will take 20 days. The days are labeled from 01 to 20. Using Table B, the first 10 numbers between 01 and 20 will be assigned to route A; the others will be assigned to route B. Take the designated route on each day and record the time to get to class. Note that this experiment is not blind; you know the route you take on each day.

3.70 (a) Each subject takes both tests; the order in which the tests are taken is randomly chosen. (b) Take 22 digits from Table B. If the first digit is even, subject 1 takes the BI first; if it is odd, he or she takes the ARSMA first. (Or, administer the BI first if the first digit is 0–4, the ARSMA first if it is 5–9).

3.71 (a) Below. (b) The patients are numbered from 01 to 30. Using line 125, those receiving the beta blockers are

21, 18, 23, 19, 10, 08, 03, 25, 06, 11, 15, 27, 13, 24, 28

See note on page 50 about using Table B.

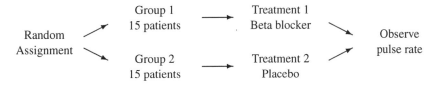

3.72 (a) Label the students from 0001 to 3478. **(b)** Taking four digits at a time beginning on line 105 gives 2940, 0769, 1481, 2975, and 1315. See note on page 50 about using Table B.

3.73 A stratified random sample would be useful here; one could select 50 faculty members from each level. Alternatively, select 25 (or 50) institutions of each size, then choose 2 (or 1) faculty members at each institution.

   If a large proportion of faculty in your state works at a particular class of institution, it may be useful to stratify unevenly. If, for example, about 50% teach at Class I institutions, you may want half your sample to come from Class I institutions.

3.74 (a) One possible population: all full-time undergraduate students in the fall term on a list provided by the Registrar. **(b)** A stratified sample with 125 students from each year is one possibility. **(c)** Mailed questionnaires might have high nonresponse rates. Telephone interviews exclude those without phones, and may mean repeated calling for those that are not home. Face-to-face interviews might be more costly than your funding will allow.

3.75 (a) Use a block design:

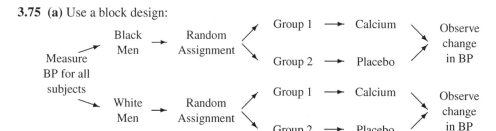

(b) A larger group gives more information—when more subjects are involved, the random differences between individuals have less influence, and we can expect the average of our sample to be a better representation of the whole population.

3.76 (a) There are two factors (temperature and stirring rate) and six treatments (temperature-stirring rate combinations). Twelve batches are needed. **(b)** Below. **(c)** From line 128, the first 10 numbers (between 01 and 12) are 06, 09, 03, 05, 04, 07, 02, 08, 10, and 11. So the 6th and 9th batches will receive treatment 1; batches 3 and 5 will be processed with treatment 2, etc.

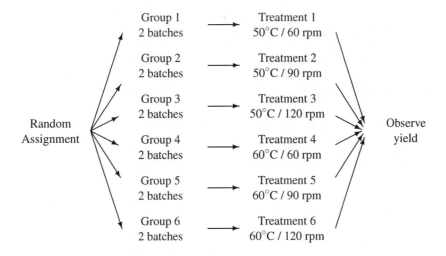

3.77 (a) Below. (b) Have each subject do the task twice, once under each temperature condition, randomly choosing which temperature comes first. Compute the difference in each subject's performances at the two temperatures.

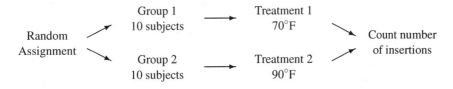

3.78 Subjects who are unwilling to have their therapy chosen for them may be systematically different from those who give their consent. In other words, they may have personality (or other) characteristics which might affect the outcome of their therapy. This would defeat the purpose of randomization, which is to have control and experimental groups that are similar (except in the treatment they receive).

3.79 The 1128 letters are a voluntary response sample, which do not necessarily reflect the opinions of her constituents, since persons with strong opinions on the subject are more likely to take the time to write.

3.80 (a) While we would expect some difference in scores between the two samples, the difference we observed was so large that it would rarely occur purely by chance (if both groups had the same mean score). (b) This observational study found an association between running and mood. It was not an experiment and so does not show that running actually changes mood. Perhaps some personality types are more likely to take up running in the first place.

3.81 Results will vary with the lines chosen in Table B, but probability computations reveal that about 95% of samples will have 3 to 7 defective rats in each sample. [The number of defective rats has a hypergeometric distribution with parameters $N = 30$, $r = 10$, $n = 15$; $P(3 \leq N \leq 7) = 0.9498$.]

3.82 Shown are the true sampling distributions (the vertical scale is the same for all three histograms). Changing p affects both the center and spread of the distributions; the spread increases as p grows (although it begins to decrease as p grows past 0.5). The difference in variability between $p = 0.3$ and $p = 0.5$ is hard to see.

A normal quantile plot for the $p = 0.5$ sample should look very much like a line.

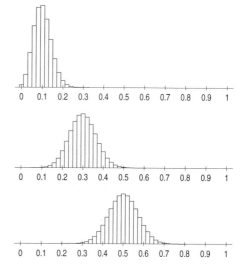

3.83 Each histogram should be centered near 0.6, with the spread decreasing as the sample size increases. Shown are the actual sampling distribution for $n = 50$ (on the bottom) and normal approximations for $n = 200$ and $n = 800$ (middle and top). When n increases by a factor of 4, note that the sampling distribution shrinks to half its former width and at the same time doubles its height.

With $n = 50$, most $\hat{p}$ values will be between 0.4 and 0.8; with $n = 200$, most will be between 0.5 and 0.7; and with $n = 800$, most will be between 0.55 and 0.65.

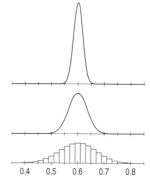

Chapter 4 Solutions

Section 1: Randomness

4.1 Long trials of this experiment often approach 40% heads. One theory attributes this surprising result to a "bottle-cap effect" due to an unequal rim on the penny. We don't know. But a teaching assistant claims to have spent a profitable evening at a party betting on spinning coins after learning of the effect.

4.3 (a) We expect probability 1/2 (for the first flip and for *any* flip of the coin). (b) The theoretical probability that the first head appears on an odd-numbered toss of a fair coin is $\frac{1}{2} + \left(\frac{1}{2}\right)^3 + \left(\frac{1}{2}\right)^5 + \cdots = \frac{2}{3}$.

4.4 Obviously, results will vary with the type of thumbtack used. If you try this experiment, note that although it is commonly done when flipping coins, we do not recommend throwing the tack in the air, catching it, and slapping it down on the back of your other hand . . . .

4.6 In the long run, of a large number of hands of five cards, about 2% (one out of 50) will contain a three of a kind. [Note: This probability is actually $\frac{88}{4165} \doteq 0.02113$.]

4.7 The theoretical probabilities are (in order) $\frac{1}{16}$, $\frac{4}{16} = \frac{1}{4}$, $\frac{6}{16} = \frac{3}{8}$, $\frac{4}{16} = \frac{1}{4}$, $\frac{1}{16}$.

4.8 (a) With $n = 20$, nearly all answers will be 0.40 or greater. With $n = 80$, nearly all answers will be between 0.58 and 0.88. With $n = 320$, nearly all answers will be between 0.66 and 0.80.

4.9 (a) Most answers will be between 35% and 65%. (b) Based on 10,000 simulated trials—more than students are expected to do—there is about an 80% chance of having a longest run of 4 or more (i.e., either making or missing 4 shots in a row), a 54% chance of getting 5 or more, a 31% chance of getting 6 or more, and a 16% chance of getting 7 or more. The average ("expected") longest run length is about 6.

4.10 (a) The theoretical probability is about 0.7190. (b) For comparison, the theoretical histogram is the first one on the right. (c) The curve furthest to the right approximates the theoretical histogram. (d) Both are (should be) centered on or near 0.73; the second histogram should be less spread out.

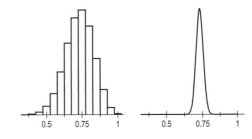

Section 2: Probability Models

4.11 (a) 0. **(b)** 1. **(c)** 0.01. **(d)** 0.6 (or 0.99, but "more often than not" is a rather weak description of an event with probability 0.99!)

4.12 (a) $S = $ {germinates, does not germinate}. **(b)** If measured in weeks, for example, $S = \{0, 1, 2, \ldots\}$. **(c)** $S = $ {A, B, C, D, F}. **(d)** $S = $ {misses both, makes one, makes both}, or $S = $ {misses both, makes first/misses second, misses first/makes second, makes both}. **(e)** $S = \{1, 2, 3, 4, 5, 6, 7\}$.

4.13 (a) $S = $ {all numbers between 0 and 24}. **(b)** $S = \{0, 1, 2, \ldots, 11\,000\}$. **(c)** $S = \{0, 1, 2, \ldots, 12\}$. **(d)** $S = $ {all numbers greater than or equal to 0}, or $S = \{0, 0.01, 0.02, 0.03, \ldots\}$. **(e)** $S = $ {all positive and negative numbers}. Note that the rats can lose weight.

4.14 $S = $ {all numbers between __ and __}. The numbers in the blanks may vary. Table 1.8 has values from 86 to 195 cal; the range of values in S should include *at least* those numbers. Some students may play it safe and say "all numbers greater than 0."

4.15 (a) The given probabilities have sum 0.96, so $P(\text{type AB}) = 0.04$. **(b)** $P(\text{type O or B}) = 0.49 + 0.20 = 0.69$.

4.16 (a) The sum of the given probabilities is 0.9, so $P(\text{blue}) = 0.1$. **(b)** The sum of the given probabilities is 0.7, so $P(\text{blue}) = 0.3$. **(c)** $P(\text{plain M\&M is red, yellow, or orange}) = 0.2 + 0.2 + 0.1 = 0.5$. $P(\text{peanut M\&M is red, yellow, or orange}) = 0.1 + 0.2 + 0.1 = 0.4$.

4.17 Model 1: Legitimate. Model 2: Legitimate. Model 3: Probabilities have sum $\frac{6}{7}$. Model 4: Probabilities cannot be negative.

4.18 (a) Legitimate. **(b)** Not legitimate, because probabilities sum to more than 1. **(c)** Not legitimate, because probabilities sum to less than 1.

4.19 No: The probabilities he describes are 0.1, 0.1, 0.3, and 0.6, which add up to 1.1.

4.20 Use the complement rule: $1 - 0.46 = 0.54$.

4.21 $P(\text{either CV disease or cancer}) = 0.45 + 0.22 = 0.67$; $P(\text{other cause}) = 1 - 0.67 = 0.33$.

4.22 (a) $P(\text{not forested}) = 1 - 0.35 = 0.65$. **(b)** $P(\text{forest or pasture}) = 0.35 + 0.03 = 0.38$. **(c)** $P(\text{neither forest nor pasture}) = 1 - 0.38 = 0.62$.

4.23 (a) The sum is 1, as we expect, since all possible outcomes are listed. **(b)** $1 - 0.41 = 0.59$. **(c)** $0.41 + 0.23 = 0.64$. **(d)** $(0.41)(0.41) = 0.1681$.

4.24 (a) $P(A) = 0.09 + 0.20 = 0.29$. $P(B) = 0.09 + 0.05 + 0.04 = 0.18$. **(b)** A^c is the event that the farm is 50 or more acres in size; $P(A^c) = 1 - 0.29 = 0.71$. **(c)** $\{A \text{ or } B\}$ is the event that a farm is either less than 50 or more than 500 acres in size; $P(A \text{ or } B) = 0.29 + 0.18 = 0.47$.

4.25 (a) The probabilities sum to 1. **(b)** Adding up the second row gives $P(\text{female}) = 0.43$. **(c)** $1 - 0.03 - 0.01 = 0.96$. **(d)** $0.11 + 0.12 + 0.01 + 0.04 = 0.28$. **(e)** $1 - 0.28 = 0.72$.

4.26 (a) $1/38$. **(b)** Since 18 slots are red, the probability of a red is $P(\text{red}) = \frac{18}{38} \doteq 0.474$. **(c)** There are 12 winning slots, so $P(\text{win a column bet}) = \frac{12}{38} \doteq 0.316$.

4.27 (a) There are 10 pairs. Just using initials: $\{(A,D), (A,J), (A,S), (A,R), (D,J), (D,S), (D,R), (J,S), (J,R), (S,R)\}$ **(b)** Each has probability $1/10 = 10\%$. **(c)** Julie is chosen in 4 of the 10 possible outcomes: $4/10 = 40\%$. **(d)** There are 3 pairs with neither Sam nor Roberto, so the probability is $3/10$.

4.28 Fight one big battle: His probability of winning is 0.6, compared to $0.8^3 = 0.512$. (Or he could choose to try for a negotiated peace.)

4.29 $(1 - 0.05)^{12} = (0.95)^{12} \doteq 0.5404$.

4.30 No: It is unlikely that these events are independent. In particular, it is reasonable to expect that college graduates are less likely to be laborers or operators.

4.31 (a) $P(A) = \frac{38,225}{166,438} \doteq 0.230$ since there are 38,225 (thousand) people who have completed 4+ years of college out of 166,438 (thousand). **(b)** $P(B) = \frac{52,022}{166,438} \doteq 0.313$. **(c)** $P(A \text{ and } B) = \frac{8,005}{166,438} \doteq 0.048$; A and B are not independent since $P(A \text{ and } B) \neq P(A)P(B)$.

4.32 $(1 - 0.02)^{20} = (0.98)^{20} \doteq 0.6676$.

4.33 Look at the first five rolls in each sequence. All have one G and four R's, so those probabilities are the same. In the first sequence, you win regardless of the sixth roll; for the second, you win if the sixth roll is G; for the third sequence, you win if it is R. The respective probabilities are $\left(\frac{2}{6}\right)^4 \left(\frac{4}{6}\right) = \frac{2}{243} \doteq 0.00823$, $\left(\frac{2}{6}\right)^4 \left(\frac{4}{6}\right)^2 = \frac{4}{729} \doteq 0.00549$, and $\left(\frac{2}{6}\right)^5 \left(\frac{4}{6}\right) = \frac{2}{729} \doteq 0.00274$.

4.34 $P(\text{first child is albino}) = \frac{1}{2} \cdot \frac{1}{2} = \frac{1}{4}$. $P(\text{both of two children are albino}) = \frac{1}{4} \cdot \frac{1}{4} = \frac{1}{16}$. $P(\text{neither is albino}) = \left(1 - \frac{1}{4}\right)^2 = \frac{9}{16}$.

4.35 (a) $(0.65)^3 \doteq 0.2746$ (under the random walk theory). **(b)** 0.35 (since performance in separate years is independent). **(c)** $(0.65)^2 + (0.35)^2 = 0.545$.

4.36 (a) $P(\text{under } 65) = 0.321 + 0.124 = 0.445$. $P(65 \text{ or older}) = 1 - 0.445 = 0.555$. **(b)** $P(\text{tests done}) = 0.321 + 0.365 = 0.686$. $P(\text{tests not done}) = 1 - 0.686 = 0.314$. **(c)** $P(A \text{ and } B) = 0.365$; $P(A)\,P(B) = (0.555)(0.686) \doteq 0.3807$. *A* and *B* are not independent; tests were done less frequently on older patients than if these events were independent.

Section 3: Random Variables

4.37 $P(\text{less than } 3) = P(1 \text{ or } 2) = \frac{2}{6} = \frac{1}{3}$.

4.38 (a) BBB, BBG, BGB, GBB, GGB, GBG, BGG, GGG. Each has probability 1/8. **(b)** Three of the eight arrangements have two (and only two) girls, so $P(X = 2) = 3/8 = 0.375$. **(c)** See table.

Value of X	0	1	2	3
Probability	1/8	3/8	3/8	1/8

4.39 (a) 1%. **(b)** All probabilities are between 0 and 1; the probabilities add to 1. **(c)** $P(X \le 3) = 0.48 + 0.38 + 0.08 = 1 - 0.01 - 0.05 = 0.94$. **(d)** $P(X < 3) = 0.48 + 0.38 = 0.86$. **(e)** Write either $X \ge 4$ or $X > 3$. The probability is $0.05 + 0.01 = 0.06$.

4.40 (a) All probabilities are between 0 and 1; the probabilities add to 1. Histogram at right. **(b)** $P(X \ge 5) = 0.07 + 0.03 + 0.01 = 0.11$. **(c)** $P(X > 5) = 0.03 + 0.01 = 0.04$. **(d)** $P(2 < X \le 4) = 0.17 + 0.15 = 0.32$. **(e)** $P(X \ne 1) = 1 - 0.25 = 0.75$. **(f)** Write either $X \ge 3$ or $X > 2$. The probability is $1 - (0.25 + 0.32) = 0.43$.

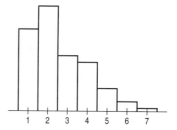

4.41 (a) 75.2%. **(b)** All probabilities are between 0 and 1; the probabilities add to 1. **(c)** $P(X \ge 6) = 1 - 0.010 - 0.007 = 0.983$. **(d)** $P(X > 6) = 1 - 0.010 - 0.007 - 0.007 = 0.976$. **(e)** Either $X \ge 9$ or $X > 8$. The probability is $0.068 + 0.070 + 0.041 + 0.752 = 0.931$.

4.42 (a) Sample space below. We must assume that we can distinguish between, e.g., "(1,2)" and "(2,1)"; otherwise the outcomes are not equally likely. **(b)** Each pair has probability 1/36. **(c)** The value of *X* is given below each pair. Histogram below, right. **(d)** $P(7 \text{ or } 11) = \frac{6}{36} + \frac{2}{36} = \frac{8}{36} = \frac{2}{9}$. **(e)** $P(\text{not } 7) = 1 - \frac{6}{36} = \frac{5}{6}$.

(1,1)	(1,2)	(1,3)	(1,4)	(1,5)	(1,6)
2	3	4	5	6	7
(2,1)	(2,2)	(2,3)	(2,4)	(2,5)	(2,6)
3	4	5	6	7	8
(3,1)	(3,2)	(3,3)	(3,4)	(3,5)	(3,6)
4	5	6	7	8	9
(4,1)	(4,2)	(4,3)	(4,4)	(4,5)	(4,6)
5	6	7	8	9	10
(5,1)	(5,2)	(5,3)	(5,4)	(5,5)	(5,6)
6	7	8	9	10	11
(6,1)	(6,2)	(6,3)	(6,4)	(6,5)	(6,6)
7	8	9	10	11	12

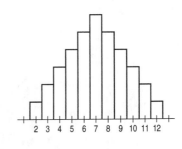

4.43 **(a)** $(0.6)(0.6)(0.4) = 0.144$. **(b)** The possible combinations are SSS, SSO, SOS, OSS, SOO, OSO, OOS, OOO

Value of X	0	1	2	3
Probability	0.216	0.432	0.288	0.064

(S = support, O = oppose). $P(\text{SSS}) = 0.6^3 = 0.216$, $P(\text{SSO}) = P(\text{SOS}) = P(\text{OSS}) = (0.6^2)(0.4) = 0.144$, $P(\text{SOO}) = P(\text{OSO}) = P(\text{OOS}) = (0.6)(0.4^2) = 0.096$, and $P(\text{OOO}) = 0.4^3 = 0.064$. **(c)** The distribution is given in the table. The probabilities are found by adding the probabilities from (b), noting that (e.g.) $P(X = 1) = P(\text{SSO or SOS or OSS})$. **(d)** Write either $X \geq 2$ or $X > 1$. The probability is $0.288 + 0.064 = 0.352$.

4.44 **(a)** $P(0 \leq X \leq 0.4) = 0.4$. **(b)** $P(0.4 \leq X \leq 1) = 0.6$. **(c)** $P(0.3 \leq X \leq 0.5) = 0.2$. **(d)** $P(0.3 < X < 0.5) = 0.2$. **(e)** $P(0.226 \leq X \leq 0.713) = 0.713 - 0.226 = 0.487$.

4.45 **(a)** $P(X \leq 0.49) = 0.49$. **(b)** $P(X \geq 0.27) = 0.73$. **(c)** $P(0.27 < X < 1.27) = P(0.27 < X < 1) = 0.73$. **(d)** $P(0.1 \leq X \leq 0.2 \text{ or } 0.8 \leq X \leq 0.9) = 0.1 + 0.1 = 0.2$. **(e)** $P(\text{not } [0.3 \leq X \leq 0.8]) = 1 - 0.5 = 0.5$. **(f)** $P(X = 0.5) = 0$.

4.46 **(a)** The height should be $\frac{1}{2}$, since the area under the curve must be 1. The density curve is at the right. **(b)** $P(y \leq 1) = \frac{1}{2}$. **(c)** $P(0.5 < y < 1.3) = 0.4$. **(d)** $P(y \geq 0.8) = 0.6$.

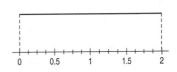

4.47 **(a)** The area of a triangle is $\frac{1}{2}bh = \frac{1}{2}(2)(1) = 1$. **(b)** $P(Y < 1) = 0.5$. **(c)** $P(Y < 0.5) = 0.125$.

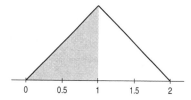
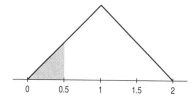

4.48 **(a)** $P(\hat{p} \geq 0.5) = P(Z \geq \frac{0.5-0.3}{0.023}) \doteq P(Z \geq 8.7) \doteq 0$. **(b)** $P(\hat{p} < 0.25) \doteq P(Z < -2.17) = 0.0150$. **(c)** $P(0.25 \leq \hat{p} \leq 0.35) \doteq P(-2.17 \leq Z \leq 2.17) = 0.9700$.

4.49 **(a)** $P(\hat{p} \geq 0.16) = P(Z \geq \frac{0.16-0.15}{0.0092}) \doteq P(Z \geq 1.09) = 0.1379$. **(b)** $P(0.14 \leq \hat{p} \leq 0.16) \doteq P(-1.09 \leq Z \leq 1.09) = 0.7242$.

Section 4: Means and Variances of Random Variables

4.50 **(a)** The payoff is either \$0 or \$3; see table. **(b)** For each \$1 bet, $\mu_X = (\$0)(0.75) + (\$3)(0.25) = \$0.75$. **(c)** The casino makes 25 cents for every dollar bet (in the long run).

Value of X	0	3
Probability	0.75	0.25

4.51 $\mu = (0)(0.10) + (1)(0.15) + (2)(0.30) + (3)(0.30) + (4)(0.15) = 2.25$.

4.52 The missing probability is 0.99058 (so that the sum is 1). This gives mean earnings $\mu_X = \$303.3525$.

4.53 The mean μ of the company's "winnings" (premiums) and their "losses" (insurance claims) is positive. Even though the company will lose a large amount of money on a small number of policyholders who die, it will gain a small amount on the majority. The law of large numbers says that the average "winnings" minus "losses" should be close to μ, and overall the company will almost certainly show a profit.

4.54 If your number is *abc*, then of the 1000 three-digit numbers, there are six— *abc, acb, bac, bca, cab, cba*—for which you will win the box. Therefore, we win nothing with probability $\frac{994}{1000} = 0.994$ and win \$83.33 with probability $\frac{6}{1000} = 0.006$. The expected payoff on a \$1 bet is $\mu = (\$0)(0.994) + (\$83.33)(0.006) = \$0.50$.

4.55 **(a)** Independent: Weather conditions a year apart should be independent. **(b)** Not independent: Weather patterns tend to persist for several days; today's weather tells us something about tomorrow's. **(c)** Not independent: The two locations are very close together, and would likely have similar weather conditions.

4.56 **(a)** Not independent: Knowing the total X of the first two cards tells us something about the total Y for three cards. **(b)** Independent: Separate rolls of the dice should be independent.

4.57 **(a)** The wheel is not affected by its past outcomes—it has no memory; outcomes are independent. So on any one spin, black and red remain equally likely. **(b)** Removing a card changes the composition of the remaining deck, so successive draws are not independent. If you hold 5 red cards, the deck now contains 5 fewer red cards, so your chance of another red decreases.

4.58 No: Assuming all "at-bat"s are independent of each other, the 35% figure applies only to the "long run" of the season, not to "short runs."

4.59 **(a)** The total mean is $11 + 20 = 31$ seconds. **(b)** No: Changing the standard deviations does not affect the means. **(c)** No: The total mean does not depend on dependence or independence of the two variables.

4.60 The total mean is $40 + 5 + 25 = 70$ minutes.

4.61 In 4.51, we had $\mu = 2.25$, so $\sigma_X^2 = (0 - 2.25)^2(0.10) + (1 - 2.25)^2(0.15) + (2 - 2.25)^2(0.30) + (3 - 2.25)^2(0.30) + (4 - 2.25)^2(0.15) = 1.3875$, and $\sigma_X = \sqrt{1.3875} \doteq 1.178$.

4.62 $\mu_X = (0)(0.03) + (1)(0.16) + (2)(0.30) + (3)(0.23) + (4)(0.17) + (5)(0.11) = 2.68$. $\sigma_X^2 = (0 - 2.68)^2(0.03) + (1 - 2.68)^2(0.16) + (2 - 2.68)^2(0.30) + (3 - 2.68)^2(0.23) + (4 - 2.68)^2(0.17) + (5 - 2.68)^2(0.11) = 1.7176$, and $\sigma_X = \sqrt{1.7176} \doteq 1.3106$.

4.63 The two histograms are superimposed at the right. Means: $\mu_H = 2.6$ and $\mu_F = 3.14$ persons. Variances: $\sigma_H^2 = 2.02$ and $\sigma_F^2 = 1.5604$. Standard deviations: $\sigma_H \doteq 1.421$ and $\sigma_F \doteq 1.249$ persons.

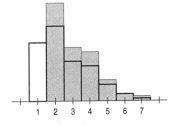

Since families must include at least two people, it is not too surprising that the average family is slightly larger (about 0.54 persons) than the average household. For large family/household sizes, the differences between the distributions are small.

4.64 $\mu_X = (\mu - \sigma)(0.5) + (\mu + \sigma)(0.5) = \mu$, and $\sigma_X = \sigma$ since $\sigma_X^2 = [\mu - (\mu - \sigma)]^2(0.5) + [\mu - (\mu + \sigma)]^2(0.5) = \sigma^2(0.5) + \sigma^2(0.5) = \sigma^2$.

4.65 Since the two times are independent, the total variance is $\sigma_{\text{total}}^2 = \sigma_{\text{pos}}^2 + \sigma_{\text{att}}^2 = 2^2 + 4^2 = 20$, so $\sigma_{\text{total}} = \sqrt{20} \doteq 4.472$ seconds.

4.66 Since the two times are independent, the total variance is $\sigma_{total}^2 = \sigma_{first}^2 + \sigma_{second}^2 = 2^2 + 1^2 = 5$, so $\sigma_{total} = \sqrt{5} \doteq 2.236$ minutes.

4.67 (a) $\sigma_Y^2 = (300 - 445)^2(0.4) + (500 - 445)^2(0.5) + (750 - 455)^2(0.1) = 19,225$ and $\sigma_Y \doteq 138.65$ units. (b) $\sigma_{X+Y}^2 = \sigma_X^2 + \sigma_Y^2 = 7,800,000 + 19,225 = 7,819,225$, so $\sigma_{X+Y} \doteq 2796.29$ units. (c) $\sigma_Z^2 = \sigma_{2000X}^2 + \sigma_{3500Y}^2 = (2000)^2\sigma_X^2 + (3500)^2\sigma_Y^2$, so $\sigma_Z \doteq \$5,606,738$.

4.68 (a) Randomly selected students would presumably be unrelated. (b) $\mu_{f-m} = \mu_f - \mu_m = 120 - 105 = 15$. $\sigma_{f-m}^2 = \sigma_f^2 + \sigma_m^2 = 28^2 + 35^2 = 2009$, so $\sigma_{f-m} \doteq 44.82$. (c) Knowing only the mean and standard deviation, we cannot find that probability (unless we assume that the distribution is normal). Many different distributions can have the same mean and standard deviation.

4.69 (a) $\mu_X = 550°$Celsius; $\sigma_X^2 = 32.5$, so $\sigma_X \doteq 5.701°$C. (b) Mean: $0°$C; standard deviation: $5.701°$C. (c) $\mu_Y = \frac{9}{5}\mu_X + 32 = 1022°$F, and $\sigma_Y = \frac{9}{5}\sigma_X \doteq 10.26°$F.

4.70 (a) $\mu_{Y-X} = \mu_Y - \mu_X = 2.001 - 2.000 = 0.001$ g. $\sigma_{Y-X}^2 = \sigma_Y^2 + \sigma_X^2 = 0.002^2 + 0.001^2 = 0.000005$, so $\sigma_{Y-X} \doteq 0.002236$ g. (b) $\mu_Z = \frac{1}{2}\mu_X + \frac{1}{2}\mu_Y = 2.0005$ g. $\sigma_Z^2 = \frac{1}{4}\sigma_X^2 + \frac{1}{4}\sigma_Y^2 = 0.00000125$, so $\sigma_Z \doteq 0.001118$ g. Z is slightly more variable than Y, since $\sigma_Y < \sigma_Z$.

4.71 $\sigma_X^2 = 94,236,826.64$, so that $\sigma_X \doteq \$9707.57$.

4.72 (a) $\mu_T = \mu_X + \mu_Y = 2\mu_X = \$606.705$. $\sigma_T = \sqrt{\sigma_X^2 + \sigma_Y^2} = \sqrt{2\sigma_X^2} = \$13,728.57$. (b) $\mu_Z = \frac{1}{2}\mu_T = \mu_X = \$303.3525$. $\sigma_Z = \sqrt{\frac{1}{4}\sigma_X^2 + \frac{1}{4}\sigma_Y^2} = \sqrt{\frac{1}{2}\sigma_X^2} = \$6864.29$. (c) With this new definition of Z: $\mu_Z = \mu_X = \$303.3525$ (unchanged). $\sigma_Z = \sqrt{\frac{1}{4}\sigma_X^2} = \frac{1}{2}\sigma_X = \$4853.78$ (smaller by a factor of $1/\sqrt{2}$).

4.73 (a) For the first program, $\mu_A = (600)\left(\frac{1}{2}\right) + (0)\left(\frac{1}{2}\right) = 300$ people. [And for the second, $\mu_B = (400)(1) = 400$.] (b) There is no difference (except in the phrasing): saving 400 is the same as losing 200. (c) No: The choice seems to be based on how the options "sound."

4.74 Below is the probability distribution for L, the length of the longest run of heads or tails. $P(\text{You win}) = P(\text{run of 1 or 2}) = \frac{89}{512} \doteq 0.1738$, so the expected outcome is $\mu = (\$2)(0.1738) + (-\$1)(0.8262) \doteq -\$0.4785$. On the average, you will lose about 48 cents each time you play. (Simulated results should be close to this exact result; how close depends on how many trials are used.)

Value of L	1	2	3	4	5	6	7	8	9	10
Probability	$\frac{1}{512}$	$\frac{88}{512}$	$\frac{185}{512}$	$\frac{127}{512}$	$\frac{63}{512}$	$\frac{28}{512}$	$\frac{12}{512}$	$\frac{5}{512}$	$\frac{2}{512}$	$\frac{1}{512}$

Section 5: General Probability Rules

4.75 $P(A \text{ or } B) = P(A) + P(B) - P(A \text{ and } B) = 0.125 + 0.237 - 0.077 = 0.285.$

4.76 $P(A \text{ or } B) = P(A) + P(B) - P(A \text{ and } B) = 0.6 + 0.4 - 0.2 = 0.8.$

4.77 **(a)** $\{A \text{ and } B\}$: household is both prosperous and educated; $P(A \text{ and } B) = 0.077$ (given).
(b) $\{A \text{ and } B^c\}$: household is prosperous but not educated; $P(A \text{ and } B^c) = P(A) - P(A \text{ and } B) = 0.048.$
(c) $\{A^c \text{ and } B\}$: household is not prosperous but is educated; $P(A^c \text{ and } B) = P(B) - P(A \text{ and } B) = 0.160.$
(d) $\{A^c \text{ and } B^c\}$: household is neither prosperous nor educated; $P(A^c \text{ and } B^c) = 0.715$ (so that the probabilities add to 1).

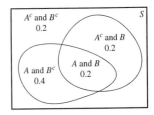

4.78 **(a)** This event is $\{A \text{ and } B\}$; $P(A \text{ and } B) = 0.2$ (given). **(b)** This is $\{A \text{ and } B^c\}$; $P(A \text{ and } B^c) = P(A) - P(A \text{ and } B) = 0.4.$ **(c)** This is $\{A^c \text{ and } B\}$; $P(A^c \text{ and } B) = P(B) - P(A \text{ and } B) = 0.2.$ **(d)** This is $\{A^c \text{ and } B^c\}$; $P(A^c \text{ and } B^c) = 0.2$ (so that the probabilities add to 1).

4.79 **(a)** $\frac{18,262}{99,585} \doteq 0.1834.$ **(b)** $\frac{7,767}{18,262} \doteq 0.4253.$ **(c)** $\frac{7,767}{99,585} \doteq 0.0780.$
(d) $P(\text{over } 65 \text{ and married}) = P(\text{over } 65) \, P(\text{married} \mid \text{over } 65) = (0.1834)(0.4253).$ (Or look at the fractions and notice the cancellation when we multiply.)

4.80 **(a)** $\frac{11,080}{99,585} \doteq 0.1113.$ **(b)** $\frac{8,636}{18,262} \doteq 0.4729.$ **(c)** $\frac{2,425}{68,709} \doteq 0.0353.$ **(d)** No: Among other reasons, if they were independent, the answers to (a) and (b) would be the same. (We would hardly expect them to be independent.)

4.81 **(a)** $\frac{3,046}{58,929} \doteq 0.0517.$ **(b)** "0.241 is the proportion of women who are *married* among those women who are *age 18 to 24*." **(c)** "0.0517 is the proportion of women who are *age 18 to 24* among those women who are *married*."

4.82 **(a)** $\frac{856}{1626} \doteq 0.5264.$ **(b)** $\frac{30}{74} \doteq 0.4054.$ **(c)** No: If they were independent, the answers to (a) and (b) would be the same.

4.83 **(a)** $\frac{770}{1626} \doteq 0.4736.$ **(b)** $\frac{529}{770} \doteq 0.6870.$ **(c)** Using the multiplication rule: $P(\text{male and bachelor's degree}) = P(\text{male}) \, P(\text{bachelor's degree} \mid \text{male}) = (0.4736)(0.6870) = 0.3254.$ (Answers will vary with how much previous answers had been rounded.) Directly: $\frac{529}{1626} \doteq 0.3253.$ [Note that the difference between these answers is inconsequential, since the numbers in the table are rounded to the nearest thousand anyway.]

4.84 There were $24,457 + 6,027 = 30,484$ suicides altogether. **(a)** $\frac{24,457}{30,484} \doteq 0.8023$. **(b)** $\frac{15,802+2,367}{30,484} \doteq 0.5960$. **(c)** Among men: $\frac{15,802}{24,457} \doteq 0.6461$. Among women: $\frac{2,367}{6,027} \doteq 0.3927$. **(d)** In choosing a suicide method, men are much more likely than women to use a firearm.

4.85 In constructing the Venn diagram, start with the numbers given for "only tea" and "all three," then determine other values. For example, $P(\text{coffee and cola, but not tea}) = P(\text{coffee and cola}) - P(\text{all three})$. **(a)** 15% drink only cola. **(b)** 20% drink none of these.

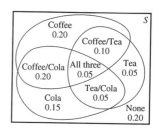

4.86 $P(A \text{ and } B) = P(A)\, P(B \mid A) = 0.1472$.

4.87 If $F = \{\text{dollar falls}\}$ and $R = \{\text{renegotiation demanded}\}$, then $P(F \text{ and } R) = P(F)\, P(R \mid F) = (0.4)(0.8) = 0.32$.

4.88 **(a)** $P(A) = 0.846$, $P(B \mid A) = 0.951$, $P(B \mid A^c) = 0.919$. **(b)** At right. **(c)** $P(A \text{ and } B) = (0.846)(0.951) \doteq 0.8045$. $P(A^c \text{ and } B) = (0.154)(0.919) \doteq 0.1415$. $P(B) \doteq 0.8045 + 0.1415 \doteq 0.9460$.

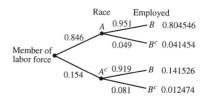

4.89 If $F = \{\text{dollar falls}\}$ and $R = \{\text{renegotiation demanded}\}$, then $P(R) = P(F \text{ and } R) + P(F^c \text{ and } R) = 0.32 + P(F^c)\, P(R \mid F^c) = 0.32 + (0.6)(0.2) = 0.44$.

4.90 $P(A \mid B) = \dfrac{P(A \text{ and } B)}{P(B)} \doteq \dfrac{0.8045}{0.9460} \doteq 0.8504$.

4.91 $P(\text{correct}) = P(\text{knows answer}) + P(\text{doesn't know, but guesses correctly}) = 0.75 + (0.25)(0.20) = 0.8$.

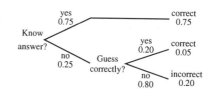

4.92 Tree diagram at right. The black candidate expects to get $12\% + 36\% + 10\% = 58\%$ of the vote.

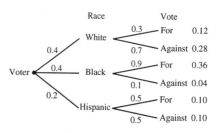

4.93 $P(\text{knows the answer} \mid \text{gives the correct answer}) = \frac{0.75}{0.80} = \frac{15}{16} = 0.9375.$

4.94 The event $\{Y < 1/2\}$ is the bottom half of the square, while $\{Y > X\}$ is the upper left triangle of the square. They overlap in a triangle with area $1/8$, so

$$P\left(Y < \tfrac{1}{2} \mid Y > X\right) = \frac{P\left(Y < \tfrac{1}{2} \text{ and } Y > X\right)}{P(Y > X)} = \frac{1/8}{1/2} = \frac{1}{4}.$$

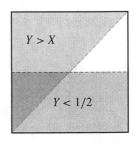

4.95 **(a)** The rat is in state A after trials 1, 2, and 3, and then changes to state B after trial 4. **(b)** $P(X = 4) = (0.8)(0.8)(0.8)(0.2) = 0.1024.$ **(c)** $P(X = x) = (0.8)^{x-1}(0.2)$ for any $x \geq 1$—the rat fails to learn from the first $x - 1$ shocks, then learns from the last shock. [This is an example of a *geometric* distribution.]

4.96 John should choose the surgery, which gives $P(A) = 0.646 + 0.073 = 0.719.$

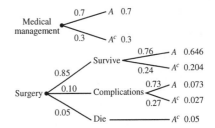

4.97 With $C = \{\text{building a plant is more profitable}\}$, we have $P(C) = 0.3078 + 0.1728 + 0.01 = 0.4906$ and $P(C^c) = 1 - P(C) = 0.5094.$ (It is also a good idea to check one's work by noting that $0.0162 + 0.4032 + 0.09 = 0.5094.$) Contracting with a Hong Kong factory has a slight edge.

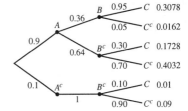

Exercises

4.98 The probability of winning with one ticket is $\frac{1+18+120+270}{100,000} = 0.00409$; the mean is

$$\mu = (\$5000)\left(\tfrac{1}{100,000}\right) + (\$200)\left(\tfrac{18}{100,000}\right) + (\$25)\left(\tfrac{120}{100,000}\right) + (\$20)\left(\tfrac{270}{100,000}\right) = \$0.17.$$

4.99 **(a)** $\mu_X = (1)(0.1) + (1.5)(0.2) + (2)(0.4) + (4)(0.2) + (10)(0.1) = 3$ million dollars. $\sigma_X^2 = (4)(0.1) + (2.25)(0.2) + (1)(0.4) + (1)(0.2) + (49)(0.1) = 503.375,$ so $\sigma_X \doteq 22.436$ million dollars. **(b)** $\mu_Y = 0.9\mu_X - 0.2 = 2.5$ million dollars, and $\sigma_Y = 0.9\sigma_X \doteq 20.192$ million dollars.

4.100 **(a)** The probability of winning nothing is $1 - \left(\frac{1}{10,000} + \frac{1}{1,000} + \frac{1}{100} + \frac{1}{20}\right) = 0.9389$.
(b) The mean is $\mu = (\$1000)\left(\frac{1}{10,000}\right) + (\$200)\left(\frac{1}{1,000}\right) + (\$50)\left(\frac{1}{100}\right) + (\$10)\left(\frac{1}{20}\right) = \$1.30$.
(c) $\sigma^2 = (\$998.70)^2 \left(\frac{1}{10,000}\right) + (\$198.70)^2 \left(\frac{1}{1,000}\right) + (\$48.70)^2 \left(\frac{1}{100}\right) + (\$8.70)^2 \left(\frac{1}{20}\right) = 168.31$, so $\sigma \doteq \$12.9734$.

4.101 **(a)** Asian stochastic beetle: $\mu = (0)(0.2) + (1)(0.3) + (2)(0.5) = 1.3$ females.
Benign boiler beetle: $\mu = (0)(0.4) + (1)(0.4) + (2)(0.2) = 0.8$ females. **(b)** When a large population of beetles is considered, each generation of Asian stochastic beetles will contain close to 1.3 times as many females as the preceding generation. So the population will grow steadily. Each generation of benign boiler beetles, on the other hand, contains only about 80% as many females as the preceding generation.

4.102 $Y = -70 + \frac{1}{20}X$: We need $b = \frac{1}{20}$ so that $\sigma_Y = b\sigma_X = 1$. Since $\mu_{a+bX} = a + b\mu_X = a + \frac{1}{20}(1400) = a + 70$, we need $a = -70$ to make $\mu_Y = 0$.

4.103 **(a)** $S = \{3, 4, 5, \ldots, 18\}$ (note these are not equally likely). **(b)** $\{X = 5\}$ means that the three dice come up $(1,1,3)$, $(1,3,1)$, $(3,1,1)$, $(1,2,2)$, $(2,1,2)$, or $(2,2,1)$. [Here we assume that there is a first, second, and third die, so we distinguish between, e.g., $(1,1,3)$ and $(1,3,1)$. This makes the computation easier.] Each of these possibilities has probability $\left(\frac{1}{6}\right)\left(\frac{1}{6}\right)\left(\frac{1}{6}\right) = \left(\frac{1}{6}\right)^3$, so $P(X = 5) = 6\left(\frac{1}{6}\right)^3 = \frac{1}{36}$. **(c)** $\mu_{X_1} = \mu_{X_2} = \mu_{X_3} = (1)\left(\frac{1}{6}\right) + (2)\left(\frac{1}{6}\right) + (3)\left(\frac{1}{6}\right) + (4)\left(\frac{1}{6}\right) + (5)\left(\frac{1}{6}\right) + (6)\left(\frac{1}{6}\right) = 3.5$, and $\sigma_{X_i}^2 = (6.25)\left(\frac{1}{6}\right) + (2.25)\left(\frac{1}{6}\right) + (0.25)\left(\frac{1}{6}\right) + (0.25)\left(\frac{1}{6}\right) + (2.25)\left(\frac{1}{6}\right) + (6.25)\left(\frac{1}{6}\right) = 2.91\overline{6}$, so $\sigma_{X_i} \doteq 1.708$. Since the three rolls of the dice are independent, $\mu_X = \mu_{X_1} + \mu_{X_2} + \mu_{X_3} = 10.5$ and $\sigma_X^2 = \sigma_{X_1}^2 + \sigma_{X_2}^2 + \sigma_{X_3}^2 = 8.75$, so that $\sigma_X \doteq 2.958$.

4.104 **(a)** $\mu_Z = 0.5\mu_X + 0.5\mu_Y = 0.065$. $\sigma_Z^2 = 0.5^2\sigma_X^2 + 0.5^2\sigma_Y^2 = 0.020225$, so $\sigma_Z \doteq 0.1422$. **(b)** For a given choice of α, $\mu_Z = \alpha\mu_X + (1-\alpha)\mu_Y = 0.02 + 0.09\alpha$ and $\sigma_Z = \sqrt{\alpha^2\sigma_X^2 + (1-\alpha)^2\sigma_Y^2} = \sqrt{0.0025 - 0.005\alpha + 0.809\alpha^2}$.

4.105 If we imagine throwing the astragali one at a time, there are 24 different ways that we could end with all four sides different ($24 = 4 \cdot 3 \cdot 2 \cdot 1$: the first astragalus can be any of the four sides, the second must be one of the other three, the third must be one of the remaining two, and the last must be the one missing side.) Any one of these 24 ways has the same probability—$(0.4)(0.4)(0.1)(0.1)$—so $P(\text{roll a Venus}) = 24(0.4)(0.4)(0.1)(0.1) = 0.0384$.

4.106 **(a)** Writing (x, y), where x is Ann's choice and y is Bob's choice, the sample space has 16 elements:

(A,A)	(A,B)	(A,C)	(A,D)	(B,A)	(B,B)	(B,C)	(B,D)
0	2	−3	0	−2	0	0	3
(C,A)	(C,B)	(C,C)	(C,D)	(D,A)	(D,B)	(D,C)	(D,D)
3	0	0	−4	0	−3	4	0

(b) The value of X is written below each entry in the table. **(c)** Below. **(d)** The mean is 0, so the game is fair. The variance is 4.75, so $\sigma_X \doteq 2.1794$.

Value of X	-4	-3	-2	0	2	3	4
Probability	$\frac{1}{16}$	$\frac{2}{16}$	$\frac{1}{16}$	$\frac{8}{16}$	$\frac{1}{16}$	$\frac{2}{16}$	$\frac{1}{16}$

4.107 (a) $P(X \geq 50) = 0.14 + 0.05 = 0.19$. **(b)** $P(X \geq 100 \mid X \geq 50) = \frac{0.05}{0.19} = \frac{5}{19}$.

4.108 If $I = \{\text{infection}\}$ and $F = \{\text{failure}\}$, then $P(I \text{ or } F) = P(I) + P(F) - P(I \text{ and } F) = 0.03 + 0.14 - 0.01 = 0.16$. The requested probability is $P(I^c \text{ and } F^c) = 1 - P(I \text{ or } F) = 0.84$.

4.109 (a) $P(\text{B or O}) = 0.13 + 0.44 = 0.57$. **(b)** $P(\text{wife has type B and husband has type A}) = (0.13)(0.37) = 0.0481$. **(c)** $P(\text{one has type A and other has type B}) = (0.13)(0.37) + (0.37)(0.13) = 0.0962$. **(d)** $P(\text{at least one has type O}) = 1 - P(\text{neither has type O}) = 1 - (1 - 0.44)(1 - 0.44) = 0.6864$.

4.110 (a) $P(\text{female} \mid A) = \frac{0.09}{0.14 + 0.09} = \frac{9}{23} \doteq 0.3913$.

(b) $P(\text{female} \mid D \text{ or } E) = \frac{0.01 + 0.04}{0.11 + 0.12 + 0.01 + 0.04} = \frac{5}{28} \doteq 0.1786$.

4.111 The response will be "no" with probability $0.35 = (0.5)(0.7)$. If the probability of plagiarism were 0.2, then $P(\text{student answers "no"}) = 0.4 = (0.5)(0.8)$. If 39% of students surveyed answered "no," then we estimate that $2 \cdot 39\% = 78\%$ have *not* plagiarized, so about 22% have plagiarized.

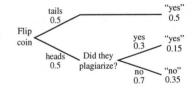

4.112 (a) At right. **(b)** $P(\text{positive}) = 0.01485 + 0.00997 = 0.02482$.

(c) $P(\text{has antibody} \mid \text{positive}) = \frac{0.00997}{0.02482} \doteq 0.4017$.

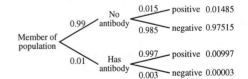

4.113 (a) The *exact* distribution is given below; the probability histogram is at the right. Actual simulation results will vary, but should have roughly this shape. **(b)** This probability is about 0.508. Based on 50 simulated trials, most answers will be between 0.30 and 0.72. **(c)** The true mean is approximately 2.8. Both computed means should be the same.

Value of X	0	1	2	3	4	5	6	7	8	9	10
Probability	$\frac{1}{1024}$	$\frac{143}{1024}$	$\frac{360}{1024}$	$\frac{269}{1024}$	$\frac{139}{1024}$	$\frac{64}{1024}$	$\frac{28}{1024}$	$\frac{12}{1024}$	$\frac{5}{1024}$	$\frac{2}{1024}$	$\frac{1}{1024}$

Chapter 5 Solutions

Section 1: Sampling Distributions for Counts and Proportions

5.1 **(a)** It may be binomial if we assume that there are no twins or other multiple births among the next 20 (this would violate requirement 2—independence—of the binomial setting), and that for all births, the probability that the baby is female is the same (requirement 4). **(b)** No: The number of observations is not fixed. **(c)** No: It is not reasonable to assume that the opinions of a husband and wife are independent.

5.2 **(a)** No: There is no fixed number of observations. **(b)** A binomial distribution is reasonable here; a "large city" will have a population over 1000 (10 times as big as the sample). **(c)** In a "Pick 3" game, Joe's chance of winning the lottery is the same every week, so assuming that a year consists of 52 weeks (observations), this would be binomial.

5.3 **(a)** Yes: It is reasonable to assume that the results for the 50 students are independent, and each has the same chance of passing. **(b)** No: Since the student receives instruction after incorrect answers, her probability of success is likely to increase. **(c)** No: Temperature may affect the outcome of the test.

5.4 **(a)** The population is three times larger than the sample; it should be at least 10 times larger. **(b)** $np = (500)(0.002) = 1$ is too small; it should be at least 10.

5.5 **(a)** There are 150 independent observations, each with probability of "success" (response) $p = 0.5$. **(b)** $\mu = np = (150)(0.5) = 75$.

Exact Prob.	Normal Approx.	Normal Approx. with CC	Table Normal	Table Normal with CC
0.2312	0.2071	0.2312	0.2061	0.2327

(c) $P(X \leq 70) = 0.2312$, or see table. **(d)** Use $n = 200$, since $(200)(0.5) = 100$.

5.6 **(a)** There are 200 responses, each independent of the others, and each with equal probability (0.4) of seeking nutritious food. **(b)** The mean is $(200)(0.4) = 80$. We could interpret "between 75

Exact Prob.	Normal Approx.	Normal Approx. with CC	Table Normal	Table Normal with CC
0.5727	0.5295	0.5727	0.5284	0.5704
0.4839	0.4363	0.4840	0.4380	0.4844
0.0026	0.0019	0.0024	0.0019	0.0025

and 85" as $P(75 \leq X \leq 85) = 0.5727$ (or see line 1 of the table); or we could exclude 75 and 85 and find $P(75 < X < 85) = P(76 \leq X \leq 84) = 0.4839$ (or see line 2). **(c)** $P(X \geq 100) = 0.0026$ (or see line 3).

5.7 (a) $\hat{p} = 0.86$ (86%). **(b)** $P(X \leq 86) = 0.1239$ (or see the table). The normal approximation can be used, since Rule of Thumb 2

Exact Prob.	Normal Approx.	Normal Approx. with CC	Table Normal	Table Normal with CC
0.1239	0.0912	0.1217	0.0918	0.1210

is *just* satisfied—$n(1 - p) = 10$. **(c)** Even when the claim is correct, there will be some variation in sample proportions. In particular, in about 12% of samples we can expect to observe 86 or fewer orders shipped on time.

5.8 (a) This is the probability that 26 to 34 people from the sample jog; $P(26 \leq X \leq 34) = 0.6273$ (or see line 1 of the table). **(b)** These probabilities (normal approximations only) are given in the last three lines of the table. As sample

Exact Prob.	Normal Approx.	Normal Approx. with CC	Table Normal	Table Normal with CC
0.6273	0.5717	0.6271	0.5704	0.6266
—	0.8869	0.8977	0.8858	0.8968
—	0.9749	0.9771	0.9750	0.9774
—	0.9985	0.9986	0.9984	0.9986

size increases, the probability that our estimate is accurate increases.

5.9 (a) Find $P(0.41 \leq \hat{p} \leq 0.47) = P(123 \leq X \leq 141) = 0.7309$ (table line 1). **(b)** For $n = 600$, $P(0.41 \leq \hat{p} \leq 0.47) = P(246 \leq X \leq 282) = 0.8719$ (table line 2). For $n = 1200$, $P(0.41 \leq \hat{p} \leq$

Exact Prob.	Normal Approx.	Normal Approx. with CC	Table Normal	Table Normal with CC
0.7309	0.7048	0.7308	0.7062	0.7286
0.8719	0.8612	0.8719	0.8612	0.8714
0.9663	0.9637	0.9662	0.9634	0.9660

$0.47) = P(492 \leq X \leq 564) = 0.9663$ (table line 3). Larger sample sizes are more likely to produce values of $\hat{p}$ close to the true value of p.

5.10 (a) It would be reduced by a factor of $1/\sqrt{2}$ to about 4.9%. **(b)** The sample would have to be four times as big: $n = 200$. A larger sample gives a more accurate estimate of the proportion we seek. [This assumes that the campus is big enough that the binomial approximation is still valid for $n = 200$; by our rule of thumb, we need at least 2000 students.]

5.11 X, the number of women in our sample who have never been married, has a binomial distribution with $n = 10$ and $p = 0.25$. **(a)** $P(X = 2) = 0.2816$. **(b)** $P(X \leq 2) = 0.5256$. **(c)** $P(10 - X \geq 8) = P(X \leq 2) = 0.5256$.

5.12 If the university's claim is true, X—the number of athletes in our sample who graduated—would have a binomial distribution with $n = 20$ and $p = 0.80$. **(a)** $P(X = 11) = 0.0074$. **(b)** $P(X \leq 11) = 0.0100$.

5.13 **(a)** $n = 4$ and $p = 1/4 = 0.25$. **(b)** The distribution is below; the histogram is at the right. **(c)** $\mu = np = 1$.

X	0	1	2	3	4
p_X	.3164	.4219	.2109	.0469	.0039

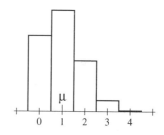

5.14 **(a)** $n = 6$ and $p = 0.65$. **(b)** The distribution is below; the histogram is at the right. **(c)** $\mu = np = 3.9$. **(d)** $\sigma = \sqrt{np(1-p)} \doteq 1.1683$; one standard deviation from μ means $P(3 \le X \le 5) = 0.8072$.

X	0	1	2	3	4	5	6
p_X	.0018	.0205	.0951	.2355	.3280	.2437	.0754

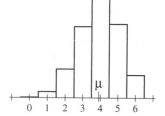

5.15 **(a)** $p = 1/4 = 0.25$. **(b)** $P(X \ge 10) = 0.0139$. **(c)** $\mu = np = 5$, $\sigma = \sqrt{np(1-p)} = \sqrt{3.75} \doteq 1.9365$. **(d)** No: The trials would not be independent, since the subject may alter his/her guessing strategy based on this information.

5.16 **(a)** Drivers in separate cars should be independent; it is reasonable to believe that all such cars have the same probability of having a male driver. **(b)** There might be different probabilities that the male is driving in each of these two situations. **(c)** X has a Bin(10, 0.85) distribution; $P(X \le 8) \doteq 0.4557$. **(d)** Y has a Bin(100, 0.85) distribution (assuming that no car is observed by more than one student); $P(Y \le 80) \doteq 0.1065$.

5.17 **(a)** The probability that all are assessed as truthful is $\binom{12}{0}(0.2)^0(0.8)^{12} \doteq 0.0687$; the probability that at least one is reported to be a liar is $1 - 0.0687 = 0.9313$. **(b)** $\mu = (12)(0.2) = 2.4$, $\sigma = \sqrt{1.92} \doteq 1.3856$. **(c)** $P(X < \mu) = P(X = 0, 1, \text{or } 2) = 0.5583$.

5.18 **(a)** $\mu = (300)(0.21) = 63$, $\sigma = \sqrt{49.77} \doteq 7.0548$. **(b)** $np = 63$ and $n(1-p) = 237$ are both more than 10. The normal approximation gives 0.0080, or 0.0097 with the continuity correction.

5.19 **(a)** $\mu = (1500)(0.12) = 180$ and $\sigma = \sqrt{158.4} \doteq 12.5857$. **(b)** $np = 180$ and $n(1-p) = 1320$ are both more than 10. Normal approximation values for $P(X \le 170)$ are in the table.

Normal Approx.	Normal Approx. with CC	Table Normal	Table Normal with CC
0.2134	0.2252	0.2148	0.2266

5.20 **(a)** $\mu = (1500)(0.7) = 1050$ and $\sigma = \sqrt{315} \doteq 17.7482$. **(b)** $P(X \ge 1000) = 0.9976$ (0.9978 with continuity correction). **(c)** $P(X > 1200) < 0.00005$ (it's *very* small). **(d)** With $n = 1700$, $P(X > 1200)$ is about 0.28 or 0.29.

5.21 (a) $P(\hat{p} \le 0.70) = P(X \le 70)$ is on line 1. **(b)** $P(\hat{p} \le 0.70) = P(X \le 175)$ is on line 2. **(c)** 400 (with $n = 100$, $\sigma = \sqrt{(0.7)(0.3)/100} \doteq 0.0458$; with $n = 400$, $\sigma = \sqrt{(0.7)(0.3)/400} \doteq 0.0229$).

Normal Approx.	Normal Approx. with CC	Table Normal	Table Normal with CC
0.1241	0.1493	0.1251	0.1492
0.0339	0.0398	0.0336	0.0401

(d) Yes: Regardless of p, n must be quadrupled to cut the standard deviation in half.

5.22 (a) $\mu_X = (1000)(0.2) = 200$ and $\sigma_X = \sqrt{160} \doteq 12.6491$. **(b)** $\mu_{\hat{p}} = p = 0.2$ and $\sigma_{\hat{p}} = \sqrt{p(1-p)/1000} = \sqrt{0.00016} \doteq 0.0126491$. **(c)** $P(\hat{p} \ge 0.24) = P(X \ge 240) = 0.0008$ (0.0009 with continuity correction). **(d)** From a standard normal distribution, $P(Z > 2.326) = 0.01$, so the subject must score 2.326 standard deviations above the mean: $\mu_{\hat{p}} + 2.326\sigma_{\hat{p}} = 0.2294$. This corresponds to 230 or more successes.

5.23 (a) $\binom{n}{n} = \frac{n!}{n!\,0!} = 1$. The only way to distribute n successes among n observations is for all observations to be successes. **(b)** $\binom{n}{n-1} = \frac{n!}{(n-1)!\,1!} = \frac{n \cdot (n-1)!}{(n-1)!} = n$. To distribute $n-1$ successes among n observations, the one failure must be either observation 1, 2, 3, ..., $n-1$, or n. **(c)** $\binom{n}{k} = \frac{n!}{k!\,(n-k)!} = \frac{n!}{(n-k)!\,[n-(n-k)]!} = \binom{n}{n-k}$. Distributing k successes is equivalent to distributing $n-k$ failures.

Section 2: The Sampling Distribution of a Sample Mean

5.24 (a) $\sigma_{\bar{x}} = \sigma/\sqrt{3} \doteq 5.7735$ mg. **(b)** Solve $\sigma/\sqrt{n} = 5$: $\sqrt{n} = 2$, so $n = 4$. The average of several measurements is more likely than a single measurement to be close to the mean.

5.25 (a) $P(X < 0) = P(Z < \frac{0-(-3.5)}{26}) = P(Z < 0.1346) = 0.5535$ (table value: 0.5517). **(b)** The mean is the population mean -3.5%. The standard deviation is $\sigma/\sqrt{n} = 26\%/\sqrt{5} = 11.628\%$. **(c)** $P(\text{average return} < 0) = P(Z < \frac{0-(-3.5)}{26/\sqrt{5}}) = P(Z < 0.3010) = 0.6183$ (table value: 0.6179). Averages of several observations are more likely to be close to μ than an individual observation.

5.26 (a) $P(X \ge 21) = P(Z \ge \frac{21-18.6}{5.9}) = P(Z \ge 0.4068) = 0.3421$ (table value: 0.3409). [Since ACT scores are reported as whole numbers, we might instead compute $P(X \ge 20.5) = P(Z \ge 0.3220) = 0.3737$ (table value: 0.3745).] **(b)** $\mu_{\bar{x}} = 18.6$ and $\sigma_{\bar{x}} = \sigma/\sqrt{50} \doteq 0.8344$. **(c)** $P(\bar{x} \ge 21) = P(Z \ge \frac{21-18.6}{5.9/\sqrt{50}}) = P(Z \ge 2.8764) = 0.0020$. [In this case, it is not appropriate to find $P(\bar{x} \ge 20.5)$, unless $\bar{x}$ is rounded to the nearest whole number.]

5.27 (a) Normal with mean 123 mg and standard deviation $\sigma_{\bar{x}} = \sigma/\sqrt{3} \doteq 0.0462$ mg. **(b)** $P(X \ge 124 \text{ mg}) = P(Z \ge \frac{124-123}{0.08/\sqrt{3}}) = P(Z \ge 21.65)$—essentially 0.

5.28 $\mu_{\bar{x}} = 40.125$ mm and $\sigma_{\bar{x}} = \sigma/\sqrt{4} = 0.001$ mm.

5.29 (a) $P(X < 295 \text{ ml}) = P(Z < \frac{295-298}{3}) = P(Z < -1) = 0.8413.$ **(b)** $\bar{x}$ has a $N(298 \text{ ml}, \sigma/\sqrt{6})$ distribution, so $P(\bar{x} < 295 \text{ ml}) = P(Z < \frac{295-298}{3/\sqrt{6}}) = P(Z < -2.4495) = 0.0072$ (table value: 0.0071).

5.30 (a) $P(X < 3.5) = P(Z < \frac{3.5-3.8}{0.2}) = P(Z < -1.5) = 0.0668.$ **(b)** $\bar{x}$ has a $N(3.8, 0.1)$ distribution, so $P(\bar{x} < 3.5) = P(Z < \frac{3.5-3.8}{0.1}) = P(Z < -3) = 0.0013.$

5.31 (a) $P(X = 1) = \frac{18}{38} = \frac{9}{19}$ and $P(X = -1) = \frac{10}{19}.$ $\mu_X = \frac{9}{19} - \frac{10}{19} = -\frac{1}{19}$ dollars, and $\sigma_X = \sqrt{360/361} \doteq \$0.9986.$ **(b)** In the long run, the gambler's average losses will be close to $-\frac{1}{19} \doteq -\$0.0526$ per bet. **(c)** $\bar{x}$ has a $N(-\frac{1}{19}, 0.1412)$ distribution. 95% of the time, the mean winnings will fall between $-\$0.3350$ and $\$0.2298$; his total winnings will be between $-\$16.75$ and $\$11.49.$ **(d)** $P(\bar{x} < 0) = P(Z < 0.3727) = 0.6453$ (table vale: 0.6443). **(e)** The total mean winnings have a $N(-\frac{1}{19}, 0.003158)$ distribution, so 95% of the time, the mean winnings are between $-\$0.05895$ and $-\$0.04632$ (using the 68–95–99.7 rule), or $-\$0.05882$ and $-\$0.04644$ (using $z^* = 1.96$). The casino winnings are between \$5895 and \$4632, or \$5882 and \$4644.

5.32 (a) Normal with $\mu_{\bar{x}} = 55,000$ miles and $\sigma_{\bar{x}} = 4500/\sqrt{8} \doteq 1591$ miles. **(b)** $P(\bar{x} \leq 51,800) = P(Z \leq -2.0113) = 0.0221$ (table value: 0.0222).

5.33 $\bar{x}$ is approximately normal with $\mu_{\bar{x}} = 1.6$ and $\sigma_{\bar{x}} = 1.2/\sqrt{200} \doteq 0.0849$ flaws. $P(\bar{x} > 2) \doteq P(Z > 4.71) = 0$ (essentially).

5.34 (a) $\bar{x}$ is approximately normal with $\mu_{\bar{x}} = 2.2$ and $\sigma_{\bar{x}} = 1.4/\sqrt{52} \doteq 0.1941$ accidents. **(b)** $P(\bar{x} < 2) \doteq P(Z < -1.0302) = 0.1515.$ **(c)** $P(N < 100) = P(\bar{x} < \frac{100}{52}) = P(Z < -1.4264) = 0.0769$ (table value: 0.0764). Alternatively, we might use the continuity correction and find $P(N < 99.5) = P(\bar{x} < \frac{99.5}{52}) = P(Z < -1.4759) = 0.0700$ (table value: 0.0694).

5.35 (a) $\bar{x}$ is approximately normal with $\mu_{\bar{x}} = 0.9$ and $\sigma_{\bar{x}} = 0.15/\sqrt{125} \doteq 0.01342$ g/mi. **(b)** $P(Z > 2.326) = 0.01$ if Z is $N(0, 1)$, so $L = 0.9 + (2.326)(0.01342) = 0.9312$ g/mi.

5.36 Over 45 years, $\bar{x}$ (the mean return) is approximately normal with $\mu_{\bar{x}} = 9\%$ and $\sigma_{\bar{x}} = 28\%/\sqrt{45} \doteq 4.1740\%.$ $P(\bar{x} > 15\%) = P(Z > 1.4375) = 0.0753$ (table value: 0.0749). $P(\bar{x} < 5\%) = P(Z < -0.9583) = 0.1690$ (table value: 0.1685).

5.37 $L = \mu - 1.645\sigma/\sqrt{n} = 12.513.$

5.38 (a) $R_1 + R_2$ is normal with mean $100 + 250 = 350\Omega$ and s.d. $\sqrt{2.5^2 + 2.8^2} \doteq 3.7537\Omega.$ **(b)** $P(345 \leq R_1 + R_2 \leq 355) = P(-1.3320 \leq Z \leq 1.3320) = 0.8172$ (table value: 0.8164).

5.39 **(a)** $\mu_{\bar{x}} = 360$ g and $\mu_{\bar{y}} = 385$ g, so $\mu_{\bar{y}-\bar{x}} = 385 - 360 = 25$ g. $\sigma_{\bar{x}} = 12.298$ g and $\sigma_{\bar{y}} = 11.180$ g, so $\sigma_{\bar{y}-\bar{x}} = \sqrt{\sigma_{\bar{y}}^2 + \sigma_{\bar{x}}^2} = \sqrt{276.25} \doteq 16.62$ g. **(b)** $\bar{x}$ is $N(360$ g, 12.298 g$)$, $\bar{y}$ is $N(385$ g, 11.180 g$)$, and $\bar{y} - \bar{x}$ is $N(25$ g, 16.62 g$)$. **(c)** $P(\bar{y} - \bar{x} \geq 25) = P(Z \geq 0) = 0.5$.

5.40 **(a)** $\bar{x}$ is normal with $\mu_{\bar{x}} = 34$ and $\sigma_{\bar{x}} = 12/\sqrt{26} \doteq 2.3534$. **(b)** $\bar{y}$ is normal with $\mu_{\bar{y}} = 37$ and $\sigma_{\bar{y}} = 11/\sqrt{24} \doteq 2.2454$. **(c)** $\bar{y} - \bar{x}$ is normal with $\mu_{\bar{y}-\bar{x}} = 37 - 34 = 3$ and $\sigma_{\bar{y}-\bar{x}} = \sqrt{\sigma_{\bar{x}}^2 + \sigma_{\bar{y}}^2} \doteq \sqrt{10.5801} \doteq 3.2527$. **(d)** $P(\bar{y} - \bar{x} \geq 4) = P(Z \geq 0.3074) = 0.3793$ (table value: 0.3783).

5.41 **(a)** $\bar{y}$ is $N(\mu_Y, \sigma_Y/\sqrt{m})$, and $\bar{x}$ is $N(\mu_X, \sigma_X/\sqrt{n})$.
(b) $\bar{y} - \bar{x}$ is $N\left(\mu_Y - \mu_X, \sqrt{\dfrac{\sigma_Y^2}{m} + \dfrac{\sigma_X^2}{n}}\right)$.

5.42 **(a)** Two standard deviations: $d_1 = 2(0.002) = 0.004$ and $d_2 = 2(0.001) = 0.002$. **(b)** $\sigma_{X+Y+Z} = \sqrt{0.002^2 + 0.001^2 + 0.001^2} \doteq 0.002449$, so $d \doteq 0.005$—considerably less than $d_1 + 2d_2 = 0.008$.

5.43 If F and L are their respective scores, then $F - L$ has a $N(0, \sqrt{2^2 + 2^2}) = N(0, 2\sqrt{2})$ distribution, so $P(|F - L| > 5) = P(|Z| > 1.7678) = 0.0771$ (table value: 0.0768).

5.44 **(a)** $X + Y$ would be normal with $\mu_{X+Y} = 25 + 25 = 50$ and $\sigma_{X+Y} = \sqrt{181} \doteq 13.4536$. **(b)** $P(X + Y \geq 60) = P(Z \geq 0.7433) = 0.2287$ (table value: 0.2296). **(c)** The mean is correct, but the standard deviation is not.

5.45 **(a)** Yes: This is always true; it does not depend on independence. **(b)** No: It is not reasonable to believe that X and Y are independent.

5.46 **(a)** Shown is a stemplot for one set of 100 means. This set had mean 139.7 and standard deviation 26.9; of course, these will vary for other samples. **(b)** For the 72 survival times, $\mu = 141.847$. **(c)** $\sigma = 108.448$. This is found by dividing by n (72) rather than $n - 1$ (71), since we are viewing the 72 survival times as a population rather than a sample. If we ignore this technical distinction, we can instead use $s = 109.209$. We expect that the standard deviation of 100 means should be close to $\sigma/\sqrt{12} = 31.3061$ (or $s/\sqrt{12} = 31.5258$). **(d)** According to the central limit theorem, the sample means will generally look a lot more normal.

8	9
9	7889
10	112346778899
11	01122456899
12	001233345889
13	114578899
14	111223344567788999
15	01222344569
16	0456789
17	25689
18	0023458
19	07
20	2

Section 3: Control Charts

5.47 The center line is at $\mu = 75°$; the control limits should be at $75° \pm 3\sigma/\sqrt{4}$, which means $74.25°$ and $75.75°$.

5.48 Center: 0.8750 inch; control limits: $\mu \pm 3\sigma/\sqrt{5} = 0.8750 \pm 0.0016$, i.e., 0.8734 inch and 0.8766 inch.

5.49 (a) Center: 11.5; control limits: 11.2 and 11.8. **(b)** Graphs at right and below. Points outside control limits are circled; the ninth point of a run of nine is marked with a square. **(c)** Set B is from the in-control process. The process mean shifted suddenly for Set A; it appears to have changed on about the 11th or 12th sample. The mean drifted gradually for the process in Set C.

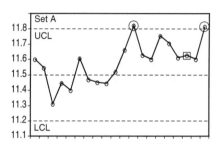

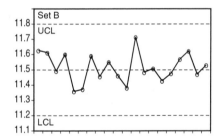

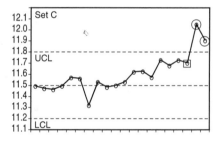

5.50 The centerline is $\mu = 2.2050$ cm, with control limits $\mu \pm 3\sigma/\sqrt{5} = 2.2037$ to 2.2063 cm. The mean of sample number 7 fell below the lower control limit; that would have been the time to correct the process. There is no run of nine.

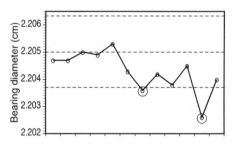

5.51 (a) Center: $\mu = 10$ psi; control limits: $\mu \pm 3\sigma/\sqrt{3} = 7.922$ and 12.078. **(b)** There are no runs that should concern us here. Lot 13 signals that the process is out of control. The two samples that follow the bad one are fine, so it may be that whatever caused the low average for the 13th sample was an isolated incident (temperature fluctuations in the oven during the baking

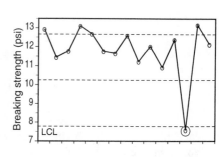

of that batch, or a bad batch of ingredients, perhaps). The operator should investigate to see if there is such an explanation, and try to remedy the situation if necessary.

5.52 (a) Center: $\bar{\bar{x}} = 3.064\%$. **(b)** Control limits: $\bar{\bar{x}} \pm 3\bar{s}/\sqrt{6} = -8.51\%$ and 14.64%. **(c)** Three of the first five returns are outside the control limits; after that, there are no out-of-control signals. After considerable fluctuation in the first few years, Wal-Mart stock has had relatively stable returns.

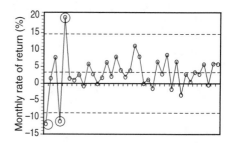

5.53 Control charts focus on ensuring that the *process* is consistent, not that the *product* is good. An in-control process may consistently produce some percentage of low-quality products. Keeping a process in control allows one to detect shifts in the distribution of the output (which may have been caused by some correctable error); it does not help in fixing problems that are inherent to the process.

5.54 Let $A = \{$at least 4 of 5 points fall above $\mu + \sigma/\sqrt{n}\}$ and $B = \{$at least 4 of 5 points fall below $\mu - \sigma/\sqrt{n}\}$. Note that $P(A \text{ and } B) = 0$.

The probability that any point falls above $\mu + \sigma/\sqrt{n}$ (or below $\mu - \sigma/\sqrt{n}$) is about 16%—half of the 32% that fall outside the central 68%—so $P(A) \doteq \binom{5}{4}(0.16)^4(0.84) + \binom{5}{5}(0.16)^5 \doteq 0.0029$. $P(B)$ also equals 0.0029, so $P(A \text{ or } B) = P(A) + P(B) = 0.0058$.

5.55 The probability that any point falls within $\mu \pm \sigma/\sqrt{n}$ is about 68%, so $P(15 \text{ points}$ within one sigma level$) \doteq (0.68)^{15} \doteq 0.0031$.

5.56 $c = 3.090$ (Looking at Table A, there appear to be three possible answers—3.08, 3.09, or 3.10. In fact, the answer is 3.090232....)

5.57 Center: 162 lbs; control limits: 159.4 and 164.6 lbs. The first five points, and the eighth, are above the upper control limit; the first 9 points are a "run of nine" above the centerline. However, the overall impression is that Joe's weight returns to being "in control"; it decreases fairly steadily, and the last eight points are between the control limits.

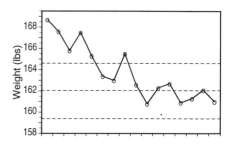

5.58 **(a)** $\bar{x} = 8.4005$ and $s = 0.6233$ min. **(b)** Control limits: $\bar{x} \pm 2s = 7.15$ to 9.65 min. **(c)** The times for October 27 and December 5 are both high, for the reasons given in the exercise. There was one day (November 28) with an extraordinarily low time (which is perhaps no cause for concern). The last 10 points are all above the centerline; ice or snow may have slowed him down on some or all of those days. There is no apparent trend.

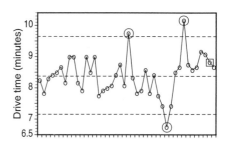

5.59 **(a)** Mean: 0.1; standard deviation: $\sqrt{\frac{p(1-p)}{400}} = 0.015$. **(b)** Approximately $N(0.1, 0.015)$. **(c)** Center: 0.1; control limits: 0.055 and 0.145. **(d)** This process is out of control. Points below the lower control limit would not be a problem here, but beginning with lot number 2, we see many points above the upper control limit, and every value of $\hat{p}$ is above the center line (with the exception of two points that fall *on* the center line). A failure rate above 0.1 is strongly indicated.

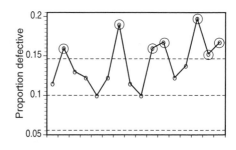

5.60 $\hat{p}$ is approximately normal with mean p and standard deviation $\sqrt{\frac{p(1-p)}{n}}$, so use centerline p and control limits $p \pm 3\sqrt{\frac{p(1-p)}{n}}$.

5.61 Center: 0.0225; control limits: $0.0225 \pm 3\sqrt{(0.0225)(0.9775)/80} = -0.02724$ and 0.07224. Since -0.02724 is a meaningless value for a proportion, the LCL may as well be set to 0, especially since we are concerned with the failure proportion being too high rather than too low.

Exercises

5.62 X, the number of free throws made, has a binomial distribution with $n = 6$ and $p = 0.7$. $P(X \leq 2) = 0.0705$; this is fairly small, which gives some reason to doubt that it was just bad luck.

5.63 **(a)** $P(Z > \frac{105-100}{15}) = P(Z > \frac{1}{3}) = 0.3694$ (table value: 0.3707). **(b)** $\mu_{\bar{x}} = 100$; $\sigma_{\bar{x}} = 15/\sqrt{60} \doteq 1.93649$. **(c)** $P(Z > \frac{105-100}{1.93649}) = P(Z > 2.5820) = 0.0049$. **(d)** The answer to (a) could be quite different; (b) would be the same (it does not depend on normality at all). The answer we gave for (c) would still be fairly reliable because of the central limit theorem.

5.64 **(a)** $\mu = np = 3025$ and $\sigma = \sqrt{np(1-p)} \doteq 51.5652$. **(b)** $P(X \geq 3500) \doteq P(Z \geq 9.21)$, which is basically 0.

5.65 No: There is no fixed number of trials. (This is called a *negative* binomial distribution.)

5.66 **(a)** $P(X = 6) = \binom{8}{6} \left(\frac{3}{4}\right)^6 \left(\frac{1}{4}\right)^2 \doteq 0.3115$. **(b)** $\mu = np = 60$. **(c)** $P(X \geq 50) = 0.9954$ (normal approximation: 0.9951, or 0.9966 with continuity correction).

5.67 $P(\frac{750}{12} < \bar{x} < \frac{825}{12}) = P(-1.732 < Z < 2.598) = 0.9537$ (table value: 0.9535).

5.68 **(a)** Binomial with $n = 500$ and $p = 0.52$. **(b)** Find $P(X \geq 250) = P(\hat{p} \geq 0.5)$; possible approximations are in the table. Use $\mu_X = 260$ and $\sigma_X \doteq 11.1714$, or $\mu_{\hat{p}} \doteq 0.52$ and $\sigma_{\hat{p}} \doteq 0.02234$.

Normal Approx.	Normal Approx. with CC	Table Normal	Table Normal with CC
0.8146	0.8264	0.8159	0.8264

5.69 **(a)** No. Possible reasons: One could never have $X = 0$. There is no fixed number of "attempts" here. Solving $np = 1.5$ and $\sqrt{np(1-p)} = 0.75$ gives $p = 0.625$ and $n = 2.4$. **(b)** No: A count assumes only whole-number values, so it cannot be normally distributed. **(c)** Approximately normal with $\mu_{\bar{x}} = 1.5$ and $\sigma_{\bar{x}} = 0.75/\sqrt{700} \doteq 0.02835$. **(d)** $700\bar{x}$ has (approximately) a $N(1050, 19.84)$ distribution; $P(700\bar{x} > 1075) = P(Z > 1.2599) = 0.1039$ (table value: 0.1038). We could also do a continuity correction for this question: $P(700\bar{x} > 1075.5) = P(Z > 1.2851) = 0.0994$ (table value: 0.0985).

5.70 Find $P(\hat{p} \geq 0.5) = P(X \geq 250)$; possible approximations are in the table. Use $\mu_X = 225$ and $\sigma_X \doteq 11.1243$, or $\mu_{\hat{p}} = 0.45$ and $\sigma_{\hat{p}} \doteq 0.02225$.

Normal Approx.	Normal Approx. with CC	Table Normal	Table Normal with CC
0.0123	0.0138	0.0122	0.0139

5.71 (a) The machine that makes the caps and the machine that applies the torque are not the same. **(b)** T (torque) is $N(7, 0.9)$ and S (cap strength) is $N(10, 1.2)$, so $T - S$ is $N(-3, \sqrt{0.9^2 + 1.2^2}) = N(-3, 1.5)$. Then $P(T > S) = P(T - S > 0) = P(Z > 2) = 0.0228$.

5.72 Center: 10 inch-lb; control limits: $10 \pm 3(1.2)/\sqrt{6} = 8.53$ and 11.47 inch-lb.

5.73 (a) $P(W < 2.8 \text{ or } W > 3.2) = P(Z < -0.1913 \text{ or } Z > 2.4472) = 1 - P(-0.1913 \leq Z \leq 2.4472) = 0.4313$ (0.4318 using table). **(b)** Center: 3.0 μm. Control limits: $3 \pm 3(0.1516)/\sqrt{5} = 2.797$ and 3.203 μm.

5.74 (a) $\bar{x}$ is $N(32, 6/\sqrt{23}) \doteq N(32, 1.2511)$, while $\bar{y}$ is $N(29, 5/\sqrt{23}) \doteq N(29, 1.0426)$. **(b)** Since the two groups are independent, $\bar{y} - \bar{x}$ is $N(29 - 32, \sqrt{(5^2 + 6^2)/23}) \doteq N(-3, 1.6285)$. **(c)** $P(\bar{y} > \bar{x}) = P(\bar{y} - \bar{x} > 0) = P(Z > 1.8421) = 0.0327$ (table value: 0.0329).

5.75 $X - Y$ is $N(0, \sqrt{0.3^2 + 0.3^2}) \doteq N(0, 0.4243)$, so $P(|X - Y| \geq 0.8) = P(|Z| \geq 1.8856) = 1 - P(|Z| \leq 1.8856) = 0.0593$ (table value: 0.0588).

Chapter 6 Solutions

Section 1: Estimating with Confidence

6.1 (a) $\sigma_{\bar{x}} = 4.5/\sqrt{24} \doteq 0.9186$ kg. (b) $\bar{x} = 61.791\bar{6}$, so the 95% confidence interval is $\bar{x} \pm 1.96\sigma_{\bar{x}} \doteq 59.99$ to 63.59 kg. Since 65 kg is well above the upper confidence limit, we have good evidence that $\mu < 65$ kg.

6.2 $\bar{x} = 123.8$ bu/acre, and $\sigma_{\bar{x}} = 10/\sqrt{15} \doteq 2.582$ bu/acre. (a)–(c) See the table; the intervals are $\bar{x} \pm z^*\sigma_{\bar{x}}$, (d) The margin of error increases with the confidence level.

Conf. Level	z^*	Interval
90%	1.645	119.6 to 128.0 bu/acre
95%	1.960	118.7 to 128.9 bu/acre
99%	2.576	117.1 to 130.5 bu/acre

6.3 (a) 1 kg is 2.2 pounds, so $\bar{x}^* = (2.2)(61.791\bar{6}) \doteq 135.942$ lbs. (b) $\sigma_{\bar{x}^*} \doteq (2.2)(0.9186) \doteq 2.021$ lbs. (c) Either compute $\bar{x}^* \pm 1.96\sigma_{\bar{x}^*}$, or convert the confidence limits from 6.1: 132.0 to 139.9 lbs.

6.4 99% confidence interval: $\bar{x} \pm 2.576\sigma_{\bar{x}} = 59.43$ to 64.16 kg. This is wider than the 95% interval; it must be wider so that we can be more confident that our interval includes μ.

6.5 With $n = 60$, $\sigma_{\bar{x}} = 10/\sqrt{60} \doteq 1.291$ bu/acre. (a) 95% confidence interval: $\bar{x} \pm 1.960\sigma_{\bar{x}} = 121.3$ to 126.3 bu/acre. (b) Smaller: with a larger sample comes more information, which in turns gives less uncertainty ("noise") about the value of μ. (c) They will also be smaller.

6.6 (a) $3.4 \pm (1.645)(0.2) = 3.071$ to 3.729. (b) $3.4 \pm (1.645)(0.2/\sqrt{3}) = 3.210$ to 3.590.

6.7 $11.78 \pm (2.576)(3.2/\sqrt{114}) \doteq 11.78 \pm 0.77$, or 11.01 to 12.55 years.

6.8 $2.36 \pm (1.960)(0.8/\sqrt{50}) \doteq 2.36 \pm 0.22$, or 2.14 to 2.58.

6.9 $35.091 \pm (1.960)(11/\sqrt{44}) \doteq 35.091 \pm 3.250$, or 31.84 to 38.34.

6.10 $n = \left(\frac{(2.576)(3.2)}{1}\right)^2 \doteq 67.95$—take $n = 68$.

6.11 (a) $1.96\sigma/\sqrt{100} = 2.352$ points. (b) $1.96\sigma/\sqrt{10} \doteq 7.438$ points. (c) $n = \left(\frac{1.96\sigma}{3}\right)^2 \doteq 61.46$—take $n = 62$, which is under the 100-student maximum.

6.12 $n = \left(\frac{(1.96)(0.2)}{0.06}\right)^2 \doteq 42.68$—take $n = 43$.

6.13 $n = \left(\frac{(1.645)(10)}{4}\right)^2 \doteq 16.91$—take $n = 17$.

6.14 **(a)** $10.0023 \pm (2.326)(0.0002/\sqrt{5}) = 10.0021$ to 10.0025 g.
(b) $n = \left(\frac{(2.326)(0.0002)}{0.0001}\right)^2 \doteq 21.64$—take $n = 22$.

6.15 $\$23,453 \pm (2.576)(\$8721/\sqrt{2621}) \doteq \$23,453 \pm \$439$, or $\$23,014$ to $\$23,892$.

6.16 Multiply the interval of 6.15 by 2621: about $\$60,320,000$ to $\$62,620,000$ (60.32 to 62.62 million dollars).

6.17 **(a)** No: We can only be 95% confident. **(b)** The interval (27% to 33%) was based on a method that gives correct results (i.e., includes the correct percentage) 95% of the time. **(c)** For 95% confidence, $z^* = 1.960$, so $\sigma_{\text{estimate}} = \frac{3\%}{1.96} \doteq 1.53\%$. **(d)** No, it only accounts for random fluctuation.

6.18 $\$34,076 \pm (1.96)(\$200) = \$33,684$ to $\$34,468$. (Note that $200 is the standard error of the sample median, not the standard deviation of the distribution of incomes. We do not divide by the sample size.)

6.19 **(a)** $(0.95)^7 \doteq 0.698 = 69.8\%$. **(b)** $\binom{7}{6}(0.95)^6(0.05) + (0.95)^7 \doteq 0.956 = 95.6\%$.

6.20 **(a)** The interval $52\% \pm 2\%$ was based on a method that gives correct results (i.e., includes the correct percentage) 95% of the time. **(b)** Although $52\% \pm 2\%$ seems to suggest that Ringel has at least 50% of the vote, we are only 95% confident in that interval; it is possible that our sample was an "unlucky" one that did not give results within 2% of the true proportion.

6.21 Probably not, because the interval is so wide: Such a large margin of error ($\pm\$2000$) would suggest either a very small sample size or a large standard deviation, but neither of these seems very likely—in particular, a large standard deviation would mean a lot of variability in first-year salaries, suggesting that some trainees start out much higher, and some start out much lower. It is more likely that this range was based on looking at the list of first-year salaries and observing that most were between $20,000 and $24,000.

6.22 **(a)** The proportion of women giving positive responses in our sample will almost certainly not be *exactly* the same as the proportion in the population; it serves only as an estimate of the population value. **(b)** The interval was based on a method that gives correct results 95% of the time. **(c)** The sample size for women was more than twice as large as that for men. Larger sample sizes lead to smaller margins of error (with the same confidence level).

6.23 No: The interval refers to the mean math score, not to individual scores, which will be much more variable (indeed, if more than 95% of students score below 470, they are not doing very well).

6.24 Since the numbers are based on a voluntary response, rather than an SRS, the methods of this section cannot be used—the interval does not apply to the whole population.

6.25 **(a)** Now $\bar{x} = 63.012$ kg and $\sigma_{\bar{x}} = 4.5/5 = 0.9$, so the interval is 61.248 to 64.776 kg. **(b)** The interval from Exercise 6.1 may be better, since 92.3 kg is an obvious outlier and may need to be excluded.

Section 2: Tests of Significance

6.26 **(a)** H_0: $\mu = 1250$ ft^2; H_a: $\mu < 1250$ ft^2. **(b)** H_0: $\mu = 30$ mpg; H_a: $\mu > 30$ mpg. **(c)** H_0: $\mu = 5$ mm; H_a: $\mu \neq 5$ mm.

6.27 **(a)** H_0: $\mu = 18$ sec; H_a: $\mu < 18$ sec. **(b)** H_0: $\mu = 50$; H_a: $\mu > 50$. **(c)** H_0: $\mu = 24$; H_a: $\mu \neq 24$

6.28 **(a)** H_0: $p_m = p_f$; H_a: $p_m > p_f$, where p_m is the proportion of males who enjoy math, and p_f is that proportion for females. **(b)** H_0: $\mu_A = \mu_B$; H_a: $\mu_A > \mu_B$, where μ_A is the mean score for group A and μ_B is the group B mean. **(c)** H_0: $\rho = 0$; H_a: $\rho > 0$, where ρ is the (population) correlation between income and percent of disposable income saved.

6.29 **(a)** H_0: $\mu = \$52,500$; H_a: $\mu > \$52,500$. **(b)** H_0: $\mu = 2.6$ hr; H_a: $\mu \neq 2.6$ hr.

6.30 Even if calcium were not effective in lowering blood pressure, there might be *some* difference in blood pressure between the two groups. However, in this case the difference was so great that it is unlikely to have occurred by chance (if we assume that calcium is not effective). Therefore we reject the assumption that calcium has no effect on blood pressure.

6.31 While we might expect *some* difference in the amount of ethnocentrism between church attenders and nonattenders, the observed difference was so large that it is unlikely to be due to chance (i.e., it would happen less than 5% of the time if there were no difference between the groups).

6.32 **(a)** Let μ_1 be the mean for the exercise group and μ_2 be the mean for the control group. We might then test H_0: $\mu_1 = \mu_2$ vs. H_a: $\mu_1 \neq \mu_2$. (The alternative might be one-sided if we have reason to believe the effect will go in one particular direction.) **(b)** No: $P = 0.87$ gives no reason to reject H_0. **(c)** There is no (or "very little") difference between the two groups' means. **(d)** E.g., sample size(s), how the study was designed, how exercise was incorporated (were students in an exercise program for the whole term, or did they just jog around the block before going to take the final?).

6.33 There almost certainly was *some* difference between the sexes and between blacks and whites; the observed difference between men and women was so large that it is unlikely to be due to chance. For black and white students, however, the difference was small enough that it could be attributed to random variation.

6.34 $z = \frac{11.2-6.9}{2.7/\sqrt{5}} \doteq 3.56$, which has $P = 0.0002$; we conclude that the means (and the authors) are different.

6.35 **(a)** $z = \frac{135.2-115}{30/\sqrt{20}} \doteq 3.01$, which gives $P = 0.0013$. We reject H_0 and conclude that the older students do have a higher mean score. **(b)** We assume the 20 students were an SRS, and that the population is (nearly) normal—near enough that the distribution of $\bar{x}$ is close to normal. The assumption that we have an SRS is more important.

6.36 $z = \frac{123.8-120}{10/\sqrt{40}} \doteq 2.40$, which gives $P = 0.0164$. This is strong evidence that this year's mean is different. Slight nonnormality will not be a problem since we have a reasonably large sample size.

6.37 **(a)** H_0: $\mu = 20$; H_a: $\mu > 20$. $z = \frac{22.1-20}{6/\sqrt{53}} \doteq 2.548$, so $P = P(Z > 2.548) \doteq 0.0054$. This is strong evidence that $\mu > 20$—the students have a higher average than past students have. **(b)** Randomly assign some (25–30) students to take the course, and compare their ACT mean score with those who did not take the course.

6.38 **(a)** H_0: $\mu = 9.5$ mg/dl; H_a: $\mu \neq 9.5$ mg/dl. **(b)** $z = \frac{9.58-9.5}{0.4/\sqrt{180}} \doteq 2.68$ and $P \doteq 0.0074$. This is strong evidence against H_0; the pregnant women's calcium level is different from 9.5 mg/dl. **(c)** $9.58 \pm (1.96)(0.4/\sqrt{180}) \doteq 9.52$ to 9.64 mg/dl.

6.39 **(a)** H_0: $\mu = 32$; H_a: $\mu > 32$. **(b)** $\bar{x} = 35.091$, so $z = \frac{35.091-32}{11/\sqrt{44}} \doteq 1.86$ and $P \doteq 0.0314$. This is fairly good evidence that children in this district have a mean score higher than the national average—observations this extreme would occur in only about 3 out of 100 samples if H_0 were true.

6.40 **(a)** $z = \frac{0.4365-0.5}{0.2887/\sqrt{100}} \doteq -2.20$. **(b)** Significant at 5% ($z < -1.960$). **(c)** Not significant at 1% ($z \geq -2.576$).

6.41 **(a)** Significant at 5% ($z > 1.645$). **(b)** Significant at 1% ($z > 2.326$).

6.42 **(a)** Not significant at 5% ($|z| \leq 1.960$). **(b)** Not significant at 1% ($|z| \leq 2.576$).

6.43 When a test is significant at the 1% level, it means that if the null hypothesis is true, outcomes similar to those seen are expected to occur less than once in 100 repetitions of the experiment or sampling. "Significant at the 5% level" means we have observed something which occurs in less than 5 out of 100 repetitions (when H_0 is true). Something that occurs "less than once in 100 repetitions" also occurs "less than 5 times in 100 repetitions," so significance at the 1% level implies significance at the 5% level (or any higher level).

6.44 Since 3.291 is close to 3.3, the P-value is close to (and slightly less than) $2(0.0005) = 0.001$.

6.45 Since $0.215 < 0.674$, $P > 0.25$. (In fact, $P = P(Z > 0.215) = 0.4149$). [This assumes that the test gave some (weak) evidence in favor of the alternative, e.g., we had H_0: $\mu = 10$ vs. H_a: $\mu > 10$. If the alternative had been, e.g., H_a: $\mu < 10$, then $P = P(Z < 0.215)$, which is even bigger—that is, it gives even less reason to reject H_0.]

6.46 (a) Reject H_0 if $z > 1.645$. (b) Reject H_0 if $|z| > 1.96$. (c) For tests at a fixed significance level (α), we reject H_0 when we observe values of our statistic that are so extreme (far from the mean, or other "center" of the sampling distribution) that they would rarely occur when H_0 is true. (Specifically, they occur with probability no greater than α.) For a two-sided alternative, we split the rejection region—this set of extreme values—into two pieces, while with a one-sided alternative, all the extreme values are in one piece, which is twice as large (in area) as either of the two pieces used for the two-sided test.

6.47 Since $1.282 < 1.37 < 1.645$, the P-value is between $2(0.05) = 0.10$ and $2(0.10) = 0.20$. From Table A, $P = 2(0.0853) = 0.1706$.

6.48 (a) The interval is $104.1\overline{3} \pm (1.96)(9/\sqrt{12}) = 99.04$ to 109.23 pci/L. (b) Test H_0: $\mu = 105$ pci/L vs. H_a: $\mu \neq 105$ pci/L; since 105 is in the interval from (a), we do not have enough evidence to reject H_0.

6.49 (a) $\bar{x} \pm 1.96\sigma_{\bar{x}} \doteq 61.79 \pm 1.80$, or 59.99 to 63.59 kg. (b) No, since 61.3 is inside the confidence interval. (c) No, since 63 is inside the confidence interval.

6.50 (a) Test H_0: $\mu = 7$ mg vs. H_a: $\mu \neq 7$ mg; since 7 is not in the interval (1.9 to 6.5 mg), we have evidence against H_0. (b) No, since 5 is in the interval.

6.51 $P = 0.1292$. Although this sample showed *some* difference in market share between pioneers with patents or trade secrets and those without, the difference was small enough that it could have arisen merely by chance. The observed difference would occur in about 13% of all samples even if there is *no* difference between the two types of pioneer companies.

6.52 (a) H_0: $p = 0.5$ vs. H_a: $p > 0.5$. (b) Binomial with parameters $n = 5$ and $p = 0.5$. (c) $P = P(X \geq 4) = 0.1875$.

Section 3: Use and Abuse of Tests

6.53 A test of significance answers question (b).

6.54 There is evidence that vitamin C is effective, but not necessarily that the effect is "strong." The large sample sizes could make even a small effect significant.

6.55 **(a)** $z = \frac{478-475}{100/\sqrt{100}} = 0.3$, so $P = P(Z > 0.3) = 0.3821$. **(b)** $z = \frac{478-475}{100/\sqrt{1000}} \doteq 0.95$, so $P = P(Z > 0.95) = 0.1711$. **(c)** $z = \frac{478-475}{100/\sqrt{10000}} = 3$, so $P = P(Z > 3) = 0.0013$.

6.56 The interval is $478 \pm (2.576)(100/\sqrt{n})$. $n = 100$: 452.24 to 503.76. $n = 1000$: 469.85 to 486.15. $n = 10,000$: 475.42 to 480.58.

6.57 **(a)** $z = 1.64 < 1.645$—not significant at 5% level ($P = 0.0505$). **(b)** $z = 1.65 > 1.645$—significant at 5% level ($P = 0.0495$).

6.58 Since the numbers are based on a voluntary response, rather than an SRS, the methods of this section cannot be used—the interval does not apply to the whole population.

6.59 **(a)** No: In a sample of size 500, we expect to see about 5 people who have a "P-value" of 0.01 or less. These four *might* have ESP, or they may simply be among the "lucky" ones we expect to see. **(b)** The researcher should repeat the procedure on these four to see if they again perform well.

6.60 Using $\alpha/6 = 0.008\overline{3}$ as the cutoff, the fourth ($P = 0.008$) and sixth ($P = 0.001$) are significant.

6.61 Using $\alpha/12 = 0.0041\overline{6}$ as the cutoff, the fifth ($P = 0.001$), sixth ($P = 0.004$), and eleventh ($P = 0.002$) are significant.

6.62 **(a)** X has a binomial distribution with $n = 77$ and $p = 0.05$. **(b)** $P(X \geq 2) = 1 - P(X \leq 1) = 1 - (0.95)^{77} - \binom{77}{1}(0.95)^{76}(0.05) \doteq 0.9027$.

Section 4: Power and Inference as a Decision

6.63 $z \geq 2.326$ is equivalent to $\bar{x} \geq 450 + 2.326(100/\sqrt{500}) \doteq 460.4$, so the power is

$$P(\text{reject } H_0 \text{ when } \mu = 460) = P(\bar{x} \geq 460.4 \text{ when } \mu = 460)$$
$$= P\left(Z \geq \frac{460.4-460}{100/\sqrt{500}}\right) = P(Z \geq 0.0894) = 0.4644.$$

This is quite a bit less than the "80% power" standard; this test is not very sensitive to a 10-point increase in the mean score.

6.64 $z \leq -1.645$ is equivalent to $\bar{x} \leq 300 - 1.645(3/\sqrt{6}) \doteq 297.99$.

(a) $P(\bar{x} \leq 297.99 \text{ when } \mu = 299) = P\left(Z \leq \frac{297.99-299}{3/\sqrt{6}}\right) = P(Z \leq -0.8287) = 0.2036$.

(b) $P(\bar{x} \leq 297.99 \text{ when } \mu = 295) = P\left(Z \leq \frac{297.99-295}{3/\sqrt{6}}\right) = P(Z \leq 2.437) = 0.9926$.

(c) The power against $\mu = 290$ would be greater—it is further from μ_0 (300), so it easier to distinguish from the null hypothesis.

6.65 We reject H_0 when $\bar{x} \leq 300 - 1.645(3/\sqrt{n})$.

(a) $P\left(Z \leq \frac{299.013-299}{3/\sqrt{25}}\right) = P(Z \leq 0.021\overline{6}) = 0.5086$.

(b) $P\left(Z \leq \frac{299.5065-299}{3/\sqrt{100}}\right) = P(Z \leq 1.688\overline{3}) = 0.9543$.

6.66 (a) We reject H_0 if $\bar{x} \leq 124.54$ or $\bar{x} \geq 131.46$; these numbers are $128 \pm (1.96)(15/\sqrt{72})$. The power against $\mu = 134$ is $1 - P\left(\frac{124.54-134}{15/\sqrt{72}} \leq Z \leq \frac{131.46-134}{15/\sqrt{72}}\right) \doteq 1 - P(-5.35 \leq Z \leq -1.43) \doteq 0.9236$. (b) Power: 0.9236 (same as (a)). Over 90% of the time, this test will detect a difference of 6 (in either the positive or negative direction). (c) The power would be higher—it is easier to detect greater differences than smaller ones.

6.67 (a) $P(\bar{x} > 0 \text{ when } \mu = 0) = P(Z > 0) = 0.50$. (b) $P(\bar{x} \leq 0 \text{ when } \mu = 0.3) = P\left(Z \leq \frac{0-0.3}{1/\sqrt{9}}\right) = P(Z \leq -0.9) = 0.1841$. (c) $P(\bar{x} \leq 0 \text{ when } \mu = 1) = P\left(Z \leq \frac{0-1}{1/\sqrt{9}}\right) = P(Z \leq -3) = 0.0013$.

6.68 $P(\text{Type I error}) = 0.05 = \alpha$. $P(\text{Type II error}) = 1 - 0.9926 = 0.0074$.

6.69 $P(\text{Type I error}) = 0.01 = \alpha$. $P(\text{Type II error}) = 1 - 0.4644 = 0.5356$.

6.70 (a) $P(\text{Type I error}) = P(X \neq 4 \text{ and } X \neq 6 \text{ when the distribution is } p_0) = 0.5$. (b) $P(\text{Type II error}) = P(X = 4 \text{ or } X = 6 \text{ when the distribution is } p_1) = 0.3$.

6.71 (a) H_0: the patient is ill (or "the patient should see a doctor"); H_a: the patient is healthy (or "the patient should not see a doctor"). A Type I error means a false negative—clearing a patient who should be referred to a doctor. A Type II error is a false positive—sending a healthy patient to the doctor. (b) One might wish to lower the probability of a false negative so that most ill patients are treated. On the other hand, if money is an issue, or there is concern about sending too many patients to see the doctor, lowering the probability of false positives might be desirable.

6.72 (b) $P(\text{lot is accepted}) = (0.1)(0.95) +$
(0.9)(0.08) = 0.167.
(c) $P(\text{lot is bad, given it was accepted}) =$
$P(\text{bad and accepted})/P(\text{accepted}) =$
(0.9)(0.08)/0.167 ≐ 0.4311.

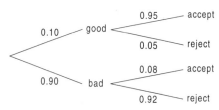

Exercises

6.73 $\bar{x} = 5.3\overline{6}$ mg/dl, so $\bar{x} \pm 1.645\sigma/\sqrt{6}$ is 4.76 to 5.97 mg/dl.

6.74 There is *some* evidence, but not strong evidence, since the confidence interval (just) includes 4.8. (An interval with a higher confidence level would overlap the 2.6–4.8 mg/dl range even more.)

6.75 (a) The plot is reasonably symmetric for such a small sample.
(b) $\bar{x} = 30.4$ μg/l; $30.4 \pm (1.96)(7/\sqrt{10})$ gives 26.06 to 34.74 μg/l.
(c) $H_0: \mu = 25$; $H_a: \mu > 25$. $z = 2.44$; so $P = 0.007$. (We knew from (b) that it had to be smaller than 0.025). This is fairly strong evidence against H_0; the beginners' mean threshold is higher than 25 μg/l.

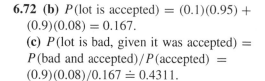

6.76 (a) Wider; raising the confidence level increases the interval size. **(b)** Yes: $35,000 falls outside the 90% confidence interval, indicating that $P < 0.10$.

6.77 Divide everything by 52.14: $653.55 ± $6.21, or $647.34 to $659.76.

6.78 (a) $145 \pm (1.645)(8/\sqrt{15})$, or 141.6 to 148.4 mg/g. **(b)** $H_0: \mu = 140$; $H_a: \mu > 140$. $z = \frac{145-140}{8/\sqrt{15}} \doteq 2.42$; the P-value is about 0.0078. This strongly supports H_a over H_0. **(c)** We must assume that the 15 cuttings in our sample are an SRS. Since our sample is not too large, the population should be normally distributed, or at least not extremely nonnormal.

6.79 $12.9 \pm (1.96)(1.6/\sqrt{26})$, or 12.3 to 13.5 g/100 ml. This assumes that the babies are an SRS from the population. The population should not be too nonnormal (although a sample of size 26 will overcome quite a bit of skewness).

6.80 (a) The intended population is probably "the American public"; the population which was actually sampled was "citizens of Indianapolis (with listed phone numbers)." **(b)** Take $\bar{x} \pm 1.96s/\sqrt{201}$. Food stores: 15.22 to 22.12. Mass merchandisers: 27.77 to 36.99. Pharmacies: 43.68 to 53.52. **(c)** The confidence intervals do not overlap at all; in particular, the *lower* confidence limit of the rating for pharmacies is higher than the *upper* confidence limit for the other stores. This indicates that the pharmacies are *really* higher.

6.81 (a) $\bar{x}$ has a $N(0, 55\%/\sqrt{104}) = N(0, 5.3932\%)$ distribution. (b) $z = \frac{6.9-0}{55/\sqrt{104}} \doteq 1.28$, so $P = 0.1003$ (or 0.1004, using software). (c) Not significant at $\alpha = 0.05$. The study gives *some* evidence of increased compensation, but it is not very strong—it would happen 10% of the time just by chance.

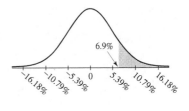

6.82 (a) The width of the interval (which equals twice the margin of error) decreases. (b) The P-value decreases (the evidence against H_0 becomes stronger). (c) The power increases (the test becomes better at distinguishing between H_0 and H_a).

6.83 H_0: $p = \frac{18}{38}$; H_a: $p \neq \frac{18}{38}$.

6.84 No: "Significant at $\alpha = 0.05$" *does* mean that the null hypothesis is unlikely, but only in the sense that the evidence (from the sample) would not occur very often if H_0 were true. There is no probability associated with H_0 [unless one is a Bayesian statistician]; it is either true or it is not.

6.85 Yes: Significance tests allow us to discriminate between random differences ("chance variation") that might occur when the null hypothesis is true, and differences that are unlikely to occur when H_0 is true.

6.86 (a) The difference observed in the study would occur in less than 1% of all samples if the two groups actually have the same proportion. (b) The interval is constructed using a method that is correct (i.e., contains the actual proportion) 95% of the time. (c) No—treatments were not randomly assigned, but instead were chosen by the mothers. Mothers who choose to attend a job training program may be more inclined to get themselves out of welfare.

6.87 For each sample, find $\bar{x}$, then take $\bar{x} \pm 1.96(5/\sqrt{5}) = \bar{x} \pm 4.383$.

We "expect" to see that 95 of the 100 intervals will include 20 (the true value of μ); binomial computations show that about 99% of the time, 90 or more of the 100 intervals will include 20.

6.88 For each sample, find $\bar{x}$, then compute $z = \frac{\bar{x}-20}{5/\sqrt{5}}$. Choose a significance level α and the appropriate cutoff point—e.g., with $\alpha = 0.10$, reject H_0 if $|z| > 1.645$; with $\alpha = 0.05$, reject H_0 if $|z| > 1.96$.

If, for example, $\alpha = 0.05$, we "expect" to reject H_0 (i.e., make the wrong decision) only 5 of the 100 times.

6.89 For each sample, find $\bar{x}$, then compute $z = \frac{\bar{x}-22.5}{5/\sqrt{5}}$. Choose a significance level α and the appropriate cutoff point (z^*)—e.g., with $\alpha = 0.10$, reject H_0 if $|z| > 1.645$; with $\alpha = 0.05$, reject H_0 if $|z| > 1.96$.

Since $Z = \frac{\bar{x}-20}{5/\sqrt{5}}$ has a $N(0, 1)$ distribution, the probability that we will accept H_0 is $P\left(-z^* < \frac{\bar{x}-22.5}{5/\sqrt{5}} < z^*\right) = P(-z^* < Z - 1.118 < z^*) = P(1.118 - z^* < Z < 1.118 + z^*)$. If $\alpha = 0.10$ ($z^* = 1.645$), this probability is 0.698; if $\alpha = 0.05$ ($z^* = 1.96$), this probability is 0.799. For smaller α, the probability will be larger. Thus we "expect" to (wrongly) accept H_0 a majority of the time, and correctly reject H_0 about 30% of the time or less.

6.90 Note to instructors: Before assigning this problem to students, it might be good to check that the software or calculator they will use makes this process relatively easy— and tell them how to do it (if they are not using Minitab). **(b)** $m = 1.96\sigma/\sqrt{n} = 1.96(100)/\sqrt{100} = 19.6$. **(d)** The number of intervals containing 460 has a binomial distribution with $n = 25$ and $p = 0.95$; about 99.3% of the time, 21 or more of the intervals should include the true mean. In separate simulations, the number of intervals containing 460 could vary; in the long run, about 95% of intervals would contain μ.

6.91 Note to instructors: Before assigning this problem to students, it might be good to check that the software or calculator they will use makes this process relatively easy— and tell them how to do it (if they are not using Minitab). **(b)** Since $\sigma_{\bar{x}} = 10$, compute $z = \frac{\bar{x}-460}{10}$. Reject H_0 if $|z| > 1.96$. **(c)** The number of rejections has a binomial distribution with parameters $n = 25$ and $p = 0.05$. Rarely (only about 0.7% of the time) would more than 4 of the 25 samples lead you to reject H_0. In the long run, about 5% of samples would wrongly reject H_0.

6.92 (b) Since $\sigma_{\bar{x}} = 10$, compute $z = \frac{\bar{x}-460}{10}$. Again use $\alpha = 0.05$, so we reject H_0 if $|z| > 1.96$. Based on the power computed in the next part, the number of rejections has a binomial distribution with parameters $n = 25$ and $p \doteq 0.516$. Most (98.4%) of the time, between 7 and 18 of the 25 samples will result in rejection. **(c)** The power is

$$P(\text{reject } H_0 \text{ when } \mu = 480) = 1 - P\left(-1.96 + \frac{460-480}{10} < Z < 1.96 + \frac{460-480}{10}\right)$$
$$= 1 - P(-3.96 < Z < -0.04) \doteq 0.5160$$

In the long run, about 51.6% of samples with $\mu = 480$ would reject H_0: $\mu = 460$.

Chapter 7 Solutions

Section 1: Inference for the Mean of a Population

7.1 **(a)** df $= 11$, $t^* = 1.796$. **(b)** df $= 29$, $t^* = 2.045$. **(c)** df $= 17$, $t^* = 1.333$.

7.2 **(a)** df $= 54$, $t^* = 2.6700$. **(b)** df $= 34$, $t^* = 1.6909$. **(c)** df $= 89$, $t^* = 1.9870$.
If software is unavailable, the answers are **(a)** df $= 50$, $t^* = 2.678$. **(b)** df $= 30$, $t^* = 1.697$. **(c)** df $= 80$, $t^* = 1.990$.

7.3 **(a)** df $= 14$. **(b)** 1.761 and 2.145. **(c)** 0.05 and 0.025 (respectively). **(d)** $0.025 < P < 0.05$. **(e)** Significant at 5%, but not at 1%. **(f)** $P = 0.0345$.

7.4 **(a)** df $= 29$. **(b)** $1.055 < 1.12 < 1.311$; these have right-tail probabilities 0.15 and 0.10 (respectively). **(d)** $0.20 < P < 0.30$. **(e)** It is not significant at either level. **(f)** $P = 0.272$.

7.5 **(a)** df $= 11$. **(b)** $0.01 < P < 0.02$. **(c)** $P = 0.0161$.

7.6 $\bar{x} = 544.75$, $s \doteq 79.7$, $\mathrm{SE}_{\bar{x}} \doteq 39.85$. A confidence interval is not really appropriate; what would it represent? If it is intended to capture the mean LSAT score for all students, then these four are certainly not a random sample.

7.7 **(a)** The stemplot shown has stems in 1000s, split 5 ways. The data are right-skewed, with a high outlier of 2433 (and possibly 1933). The quantile plot shows these two outliers, but otherwise it is not strikingly different from a line. **(b)** $\bar{x} = 926$, $s = 427.2$, $\mathrm{SE}_{\bar{x}} = 69.3$ (all in mg). **(c)** Using 30 degrees of freedom, we have $926 \pm (2.042)(69.3)$, or 784.5 to 1067.5 mg; Minitab reports 785.6 to 1066.5 mg.

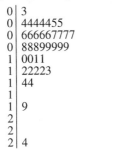
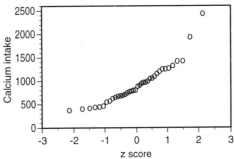

7.8 (a) Without the outliers, the stemplot shows some details not previously apparent. The normal quantile plot is essentially the same
as before (except that the two points that deviated greatly from the
line are gone). **(b)** $\bar{x} = 856.2$, $s = 306.7$, $SE_{\bar{x}} = 51.1$ (all in mg).
(c) Using 30 degrees of freedom, we have $856.2 \pm (2.042)(51.1)$, or
751.9 to 960.5 mg; Minitab reports 752.4 to 960.0 mg.

```
 3 | 7
 4 | 01346
 5 | 47
 6 | 25789
 7 | 1478
 8 | 008
 9 | 04779
10 | 56
11 | 05
12 | 0556
13 | 2
14 | 22
```

7.9 (a) The transformed data have $\bar{x} = 77.17\%$, $s = 35.6\%$, and $SE_{\bar{x}} = 5.78\%$; the
confidence interval is 65.37% to 88.97% (using $t^* = 2.042$ with df $= 30$), or 65.46%
to 88.87% (from Minitab). **(b)** After dividing the intervals from Exercise 7.7 by 12, the
intervals are the same (up to rounding error).

7.10 (a) H_0 is $\mu = 1200$; the alternative might be either H_a: $\mu \neq 1200$ or $\mu < 1200$—
the latter since we are likely more concerned with low calcium intake than with high
intake. **(b)** $t = (\bar{x} - \mu)/SE_{\bar{x}} = (926 - 1200)/69.3 \doteq -3.95$. With df $= 37$, we have
$P = 0.0003$—or half of that, for the one-sided alternative. **(c)** Whichever alternative we
use, we conclude that the daily intake is significantly different from (less than) the RDA.

7.11 (a) The stemplot (with split stems) is right-skewed with high outliers of 63 and 79.
[In fact, according to the $1.5IQR$ outlier test, 48 is an outlier, too.] The quantile plot
suggests that the distribution is not normal. **(b)** $\bar{x} = 23.56$, $s = 12.52$, $SE_{\bar{x}} = 1.77$
can openers. Using df $= 40$, we have $t^* = 2.021$ and the interval is 19.98 to 27.14 can
openers; Minitab reports 20.00 to 27.12 can openers. **(c)** With such a large sample size
(the text says we need $n \geq 40$), the t distribution is fairly good in spite of the skewness
and outliers.

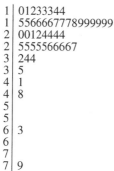

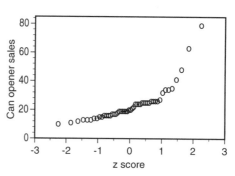

7.12 (a) Each store sells an average of 23.56 can openers, so the average profit is
$(\$2.15)(23.56) \doteq \$50.65$. **(b)** Multiply the 95% confidence interval from Exercise
7.11 by $2.15. Using df $= 40$, this gives $42.96 to $58.35. Using df $= 49$, this gives
$43.00 to $58.31.

7.13 (a) Each store averaged $50.65, giving a total of $(\$50.65)(3275) = \$165,879$.
(b) Multiply the interval from Exercise 7.12 by 3275. Using df $= 40$, this gives $140,684 to $191,100. Using df $= 49$, this gives $140,825 to $190,959.

7.14 $t^* = 2.080$ for df $= 21$, so the interval is $\$2.08 \pm (2.080)(\$0.176)$, or $1.714 to $2.446 per bushel.

7.15 For large df, use normal distribution critical values: $\bar{x} \pm 1.645\ \mathrm{SE}_{\bar{x}}$, or 87.6 to 104.4 days.

7.16 Use $t^* = 2.581$ (df $= 1000$, from the table), or $t^* = 2.5793$ (df $= 1405$, from software). Either choice—or even using the normal distribution critical value—gives the same interval: $\bar{x} \pm t^* s/\sqrt{n} = 3.83$ to 3.97.

7.17 (a) Methods of displaying will vary. Below is a stemplot where the digits are the stems, and all leaves are "0"—this is essentially the same as a histogram. The scores are slightly left-skewed. The normal quantile plot looks reasonably straight, except for the granularity of the data. **(b)** $\bar{x} = 3.618$, $s = 3.055$, $\mathrm{SE}_{\bar{x}} = 0.524$. **(c)** Using df $= 30$, we have $t^* = 2.042$ and the interval is 2.548 to 4.688. Minitab reports 2.551 to 4.684.

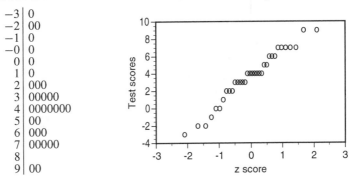

```
-3 | 0
-2 | 00
-1 | 0
-0 | 0
 0 | 0
 1 | 0
 2 | 000
 3 | 00000
 4 | 0000000
 5 | 00
 6 | 000
 7 | 00000
 8 |
 9 | 00
```

7.18 Test H_0: $\mu = 0$ vs. H_a: $\mu > 0$, where μ is the mean improvement in scores. $t = (\bar{x} - \mu)/\mathrm{SE}_{\bar{x}} = 3.618/0.524 \doteq 6.90$, which has $P < 0.0005$; we conclude that scores are higher. The confidence interval from Exercise 7.17 tells us that the mean improvement is about 2.5 to 4.7 points.

Output from Minitab:
```
Test of mu = 0.000 vs mu > 0.000
```

Variable	N	Mean	StDev	SE Mean	T	P-Value
Scores	34	3.618	3.055	0.524	6.90	0.0000

7.19 H_0: $\mu = 0$; H_a: $\mu < 0$, where μ is the mean change in vitamin C content. Subtract "After" from "Before" to give -53, -52, -57, -52, and -61 mg/100g. Then $\bar{x} = -55$, $s = 3.94$, and $\mathrm{SE}_{\bar{x}} = 1.76$ mg/100g, so $t \doteq -31.24$, which is significant for any reasonable α (using df $= 4$). Cooking does decrease the vitamin C content.

7.20 (a) The mean change is $-55 \pm (2.776)(1.76) = -59.9$ to -50.1 mg/100g. **(b)** The "After" measurements are 20.4%, 27.6%, 29.6%, 36.7%, and 17.3% of the specification. For these percents, $\bar{x} = 26.33\%$, $s = 7.68\%$, and $SE_{\bar{x}} = 3.44\%$, so the interval is 16.8% to 35.9% of the specification.

7.21 (a) H_0: $\mu = 0$; H_a: $\mu > 0$. $t = \frac{342}{108/\sqrt{250}} = 50.07$; since $P \doteq 0$, we reject H_0 and conclude that the new policy would increase credit card usage. **(b)** Using $t^* = 1.984$ (df $= 100$): \$328 to \$356. Using $t^* = 1.9695$ (df $= 249$, from software): \$329 to \$355. (The lower [upper] limits of these two intervals actually differ by only about \$0.10.) **(c)** The sample size is very large, and we are told that we have an SRS. This means that outliers are the only potential snag, and there are none. **(d)** Make the offer to an SRS of 250 customers, and choose another SRS of 250 as a control group. Compare the mean increase for the two groups.

7.22 $\bar{x} = 44.44$, $s = 20.74$, and $SE_{\bar{x}} = 9.28$ (all in μg), and $t^*2.776$, so the interval is 18.68 to 70.20 μg.

7.23 (a) $\bar{x} = 5.3\overline{6}$ mg/dl, while $s \doteq 0.6653$ so $SE_{\bar{x}} \doteq 0.2716$ mg/dl. **(b)** df $= 5$, $t^* = 2.015$, and the interval is 4.819 to 5.914 mg/dl.

7.24 (a) $\bar{x} = 1.75$ mg/dl, while $s \doteq 0.1291$ so $SE_{\bar{x}} \doteq 0.0645$ msec. **(b)** df $= 3$, $t^* = 2.353$, and the interval is 1.6 to 1.9 msec.

7.25 H_0: $\mu = 4.8$; H_a: $\mu > 4.8$ mg/dl. $t = \frac{5.3\overline{6}-4.8}{0.2716} \doteq 2.086$. For df $= 5$, we have $0.025 < P < 0.05$ (Minitab gives 0.046). This is fairly strong, though not overwhelming, evidence that the patient's phosphate level is above normal.

7.26 H_0: $\mu = 1.3$; H_a: $\mu > 1.3$ msec. $t = \frac{1.75-1.3}{0.0645} \doteq 6.98$. For df $= 3$, we have $0.0025 < P < 0.005$ (Minitab gives 0.003). This is strong evidence that the mean refractory period has increased.

7.27 (a) $114.9\pm(2.056)(9.3/\sqrt{27})$, or 111.2 to 118.6 mm Hg. **(b)** The essential assumption is that the 27 men tested can be regarded as an SRS from a population, such as all healthy white males in a stated age group. The assumption that blood pressure in this population is normally distributed is *not* essential, because $\bar{x}$ from a sample of size 27 will be roughly normal in any event, as long as the population is not too greatly skewed and has no outliers.

7.28 (a) $1.67 \pm (2.120)(0.25/\sqrt{17})$, or 1.54 to 1.80. **(b)** The essential assumption is that the 17 Mexicans tested can be regarded as an SRS from the population of all Mexicans. The assumption that ARSMA scores are normally distributed is clearly not satisfied but is not essential since scores range from 1 to 5, so there are no outliers and skewness is limited.

7.29 (a) At right. (b) H_0: $\mu = 105$; H_a: $\mu \ne 105$. $\bar{x} = 104.13$ and $s = 9.40$ pCi/l, so $t = \frac{104.13-105}{9.40/\sqrt{12}} \doteq -0.32$. With df $= 11$, we have $P > 2(0.25) = 0.50$ (Minitab reports $P = 0.76$), which gives us little reason to doubt that $\mu = 105$ pCi/l.

```
 9 | 1
 9 | 5679
10 | 134
10 | 5
11 | 1
11 | 9
12 | 2
```

7.30 $\bar{x} = 22.125$, $s \doteq 2.09$, and $\text{SE}_{\bar{x}} \doteq 1.045$. The margin of error, $1.045t^*$, varies with the choice of confidence level; note that df $= 3$. For 90% confidence, m.e. $\doteq \pm 2.46$. For 95% confidence, m.e. $\doteq \pm 2.33$. For 99% confidence, m.e. $\doteq \pm 6.11$. Explanation: The procedure we used gives results that lie within $\pm$__ of the correct mean __% of the time.

7.31 (a) "SEM" = "standard error of the mean" ($\text{SE}_{\bar{x}}$). (b) $s = \sqrt{3} \cdot \text{SE}_{\bar{x}} \doteq 0.0173$. (c) Using $t^* = 2.920$ (with df $= 2$): $0.84 \pm (2.920)(0.01)$, or about 0.81 to 0.87.

7.32 (a) H_0: $\mu = 0$ vs. H_a: $\mu < 0$ mg/100g, where μ is the change (Haiti minus Factory). (b) $t = -4.96$ with df $= 26$, which has $P < 0.0005$. The mean is significantly less than 0. (c) See the Minitab output. Note that there is no simple relationship between the Factory and Haiti confidence intervals, and the Change interval; the latter cannot be determined by looking at the first two.

Output from Minitab:

```
--- --- --- --- --- ---   Significance Test   --- --- --- --- --- ---
Test of mu = 0.00 vs mu < 0.00

Variable    N      Mean    StDev   SE Mean       T    P-Value
Change      27    -5.33     5.59      1.08    -4.96     0.0000


--- --- --- --- --- ---   Confidence Intervals   --- --- --- --- --- ---
Variable    N      Mean    StDev   SE Mean       95.0 % C.I.
Factory     27    42.852    4.793    0.923   ( 40.955,   44.749)
Haiti       27    37.519    2.440    0.469   ( 36.553,   38.484)
Change      27    -5.33     5.59     1.08    (  -7.54,    -3.12)
```

7.33 (a) For each subject, randomly select (e.g., by flipping a coin) which knob (right or left) that subject should use first. (b) H_0: $\mu = 0$ vs. H_a: $\mu < 0$, where μ is the mean of (right-thread time $-$ left-thread time). (c) $\bar{x} = -13.32$ sec; $\text{SE}_{\bar{x}} = 22.94/\sqrt{25} \doteq 4.59$ sec, so $t = -2.90$. With df $= 24$, we see that $0.0025 < P < 0.005$; Minitab reports $P = 0.0039$. We have good evidence that the mean difference really is negative, i.e., that the mean time for right-threaded knobs is less than the mean time for left-threaded knobs.

7.34 $t^* = 1.711$, so the interval for the mean difference is $-13.32 \pm (1.711)(4.59)$, or about -21.2 to -5.5 sec.

We have $\bar{x}_{\text{RH}} = 104.12$ and $\bar{x}_{\text{LH}} = 117.44$; $\bar{x}_{\text{RH}}/\bar{x}_{\text{LH}} = 88.7\%$. Right-handers working with right-handed knobs can accomplish the task in about 90% of the time needed by those working with left-handed knobs. [Note: Another way we could answer the second question is to find the mean of (right-hand time)/(left-hand time), which is 91.7%.]

7.35 (a) H_0: $\mu = 0$ vs. H_a: $\mu > 0$, where μ is the mean improvement in score (posttest − pretest). **(b)** The stemplot of the differences, with stems split 5 ways, shows that the data are slightly left-skewed, with no outliers; the t test should be reliable. **(c)** $\bar{x} = 1.450$; $SE_{\bar{x}} = 3.203/\sqrt{20} \doteq 0.716$, so $t \doteq 2.02$. With df $= 19$, we see that $0.025 < P < 0.05$; Minitab reports $P = 0.029$. This is significant at 5%, but not at 1%—we have some evidence that scores improve, but it is not overwhelming. **(d)** Minitab gives 0.211 to 2.689; using $t^* = 1.729$ and the values of $\bar{x}$ and $SE_{\bar{x}}$ above, we obtain 1.45 ± 1.238, or 0.212 to 2.688.

```
-0 | 54
-0 | 32
-0 | 11
 0 | 11
 0 | 2223333
 0 | 4455
 0 | 7
```

7.36 (a) For each subject, randomly select (e.g., by flipping a coin) which test should be administered first. **(b)** H_0: $\mu = 0$ vs. H_a: $\mu \neq 0$, where μ is the mean difference in scores (ARSMA − BI). $SE_{\bar{x}} = 0.2767/\sqrt{22} \doteq 0.05899$, so $t \doteq 4.27$. With df $= 21$, we see that $P < 0.0005$. We have good evidence that the scores differ (i.e., that the mean difference is not 0). **(c)** $0.2519 \pm (2.080)(0.05899) = 0.1292$ to 0.3746 points.

7.37 H_0: $\mu = 0$; H_a: $\mu > 0$, where μ is the mean of (variety A − variety B). $t = \frac{0.34}{0.83/\sqrt{10}} \doteq 1.295$; with df $= 9$, we see that $0.10 < P < 0.15$ (Minitab gives $P \doteq 0.11$). We do not have enough evidence to conclude that Variety A has a higher yield.

7.38 (a) Two independent samples (3). **(b)** Matched pairs (2). **(c)** Single sample (1). **(d)** Two independent samples (3).

7.39 With all 50 states listed in the table, we have information about the entire population in question; no statistical procedures are needed (or meaningful).

7.40 (a) The critical value is $t^* = 2.423$ (using df $= 40$ from the table), or 2.4049 (using df $= 49$, from software). **(b)** Reject H_0 if $t \geq t^*$, so $\bar{x} > 0 + t^*(108/\sqrt{50})$; this is either $\bar{x} \geq 37.01$ (table) or $\bar{x} \geq 36.73$ (software). **(c)** The power is

$$P(\bar{x} \geq 37.01 \text{ when } \mu = 100) = P\left(\frac{\bar{x}-100}{108/\sqrt{50}} \geq \frac{37.01-100}{108/\sqrt{50}}\right) \doteq P(Z \geq -4.12) > 0.9999.$$

Using the software t^*, the power is $P(Z \geq -4.14)$—slightly greater. A sample size of 50 will almost always detect $\mu = 100$.

7.41 (a) This is a one-sided test; we reject H_0: $\mu = 0$ if $t \geq 1.833$. This translates to $\bar{x} \geq 0 + (1.833)(0.83/\sqrt{10}) = 0.4811$. The power against $\mu = 0.5$ lb/plant is

$$P(\bar{x} \geq 0.4811 \text{ when } \mu = 0.5) = P\left(\frac{\bar{x}-0.5}{0.83/\sqrt{10}} \geq \frac{0.4811-0.5}{0.83/\sqrt{10}}\right) = P(Z \geq -0.072) \doteq 0.5279.$$

(b) We reject H_0 if $t \geq 1.711$, which translates to $\bar{x} \geq 0 + (1.711)(0.83/\sqrt{25}) = 0.2840$. The power against $\mu = 0.5$ lb/plant is

$$P(\bar{x} \geq 0.2840 \text{ when } \mu = 0.5) = P\left(\frac{\bar{x}-0.5}{0.83/\sqrt{25}} \geq \frac{0.2840-0.5}{0.83/\sqrt{25}}\right) = P(Z \geq -1.301) \doteq 0.9032.$$

7.42 (a) $t^* = 2.080$. (b) We reject H_0 if $|t| \geq 2.080$, which translates to $|\bar{x}| \geq 2.080s/\sqrt{22} \doteq 0.133$. (c) The power against $\mu = 0.2$ is

$$P(|\bar{x}| \geq 0.133 \text{ when } \mu = 0.2) = 1 - P(-0.133 \leq \bar{x} \leq 0.133)$$
$$= 1 - P\left(\frac{-0.133-0.2}{0.3/\sqrt{22}} \leq \frac{\bar{x}-0.2}{0.3/\sqrt{22}} \leq \frac{0.133-0.2}{0.3/\sqrt{22}}\right)$$
$$= 1 - P(-5.21 \leq Z \leq -1.05) \doteq 0.8531.$$

7.43 (a) H_0: population median $= 0$ vs. H_a: population median < 0, or H_0: $p = 1/2$ vs. H_a: $p < 1/2$, where p is the proportion of (right $-$ left) differences that are positive. (Equivalently one could take H_a: $p > 1/2$, where p is the proportion of negative differences.) (b) One pair of the 25 had no difference; of the remaining 24, only 5 differences were positive. If X (the number of positive differences) has a Bin(24, 1/2) distribution, the P-value is $P(X \leq 5)$, for which the normal approximation gives $P(Z < -2.86) = 0.0021$ (without the continuity correction) or $P(Z < -2.65) = 0.0040$ (with the continuity correction). [In fact, $P = 0.0033$.] In any case, this is strong evidence against H_0, indicating that the median right-threaded knob time is shorter.

Output from Minitab:
```
Sign test of median = 0.00000 versus  L.T.   0.00000

              N   BELOW  EQUAL  ABOVE   P-VALUE    MEDIAN
RH-LH        25    19      1      5     0.0033    -12.00
```

7.44 Test H_0: population median $= 0$ vs. H_a: population median > 0. Six of the 20 differences are negative. If X (the number of negative differences) has a Bin(20, 1/2) distribution, the P-value is $P(X \leq 6) = 0.0577$—which is not quite significant (if we have $\alpha = 0.05$).

Output from Minitab:
```
Sign test of median = 0.00000 versus  G.T.   0.00000

               N   BELOW  EQUAL  ABOVE   P-VALUE    MEDIAN
Post-Pre      20     6      0     14     0.0577     2.000
```

7.45 We cannot use the sign test, since we cannot determine the number of positive and negative differences in the original data.

7.46 (a) $\bar{x} \doteq 141.85$, $s \doteq 109.2$, and $SE_{\bar{x}} \doteq 12.87$ days. Use $t^* = 2.000$ (df $= 60$, from the table) or $t^* = 1.994$ (df $= 71$, from software). The former gives 116.1 to 167.6; the latter 116.2 to 167.5. (b) A stemplot and quantile plot are shown. These were based on common (base 10) logarithms; for natural logs, the quantile plot differs only in vertical scale, but the stemplot has a slightly different appearance. (c) We now have $\bar{x} \doteq 2.07205$, $s \doteq 0.243015$, and $SE_{\bar{x}} \doteq 0.028640$. For $t^* = 2.000$, the interval is 2.0148 to 2.1293; for $t^* = 1.994$, it is 2.0149 to 2.1292. (If using natural logs, these intervals are 4.6392 to 4.9030, or 4.6395 to 4.9026.)

```
16 | 35
17 | 24456
18 | 12669
19 | 000001112445566899
20 | 0000001123355788
21 | 003345669
22 | 0455689
23 | 2389
24 |
25 | 17
26 | 0
27 | 017
```

7.47 Using common (base 10) logarithms: $\bar{x} = 2.5552$, $s = 0.0653$, and $SE_{\bar{x}} = 0.0292$, giving the interval 2.4929 to 2.6175. Using natural (base e) logarithms: $\bar{x} = 5.8836$, $s = 0.1504$, and $SE_{\bar{x}} = 0.0672$, giving the interval 5.7402 to 6.0270. [Note that these intervals are equivalent; if we exponentiate to undo the logarithms, we obtain the interval 311.1 to 414.5 hours.]

Section 2: Comparing Two Means

7.48 (a) H_0: $\mu_1 = \mu_2$; H_a: $\mu_1 > \mu_2$. $\bar{x}_1 = 48.705$ and $s_1 = 1.534$ mg/100g, while $\bar{x}_2 = 21.795$ and $s_2 = 0.7707$ mg/100g; thus $t = 22.16$. Using df $= 1$, we have $0.01 < P < 0.02$ (Minitab gives 0.014). Software approximation: df $= 1.47$, and $P = 0.0039$. This is fairly strong evidence that vitamin C is lost in storage. (b) 90% confidence interval: 19.2 to 34.6 mg/100g vitamin C lost (using df $= 1$), or 22.3 to 31.5 mg/100g (using df $= 1.47$).

7.49 (a) H_0: $\mu_1 = \mu_2$; H_a: $\mu_1 > \mu_2$. $\bar{x}_1 = 95.3$ and $s_1 = 0.990$ mg/100g, while $\bar{x}_2 = 95.85$ and $s_2 = 2.19$ mg/100g. Since $\bar{x}_2 > \bar{x}_1$, we have no evidence against H_0; further analysis is not necessary. (However, just for reference, $t = -0.323$.) (b) 90% confidence interval: -11.3 to 10.2 mg/100g vitamin E lost (using df $= 1$), or -7.36 to 6.26 mg/100g (using df $= 1.39$).

7.50 Small samples may lead to rejection of H_0, if (as in Exercise 7.48) the evidence is very strong. (The weakness of small samples is that they are not very powerful; the rejection in 7.48 occurred because the evidence suggests that the true means are quite different.)

7.51 (a) Control scores are fairly symmetrical, while piano scores are slightly left-skewed. Scores in the piano group are generally higher than scores in the control group. **(b)** Below. **(c)** $H_0: \mu_1 = \mu_2$; $H_a:$ $\mu_1 > \mu_2$. $t = 5.06$. Whether df $= 33$ or df $= 61.7$, $P < 0.0001$, so we reject H_0 and conclude that piano lessons improved the test scores.

Control		Piano
0	−6	
	−5	
0	−4	
000	−3	0
00	−2	00
0000000	−1	0
00000	−0	0
000000	0	0
000000	1	0
0000000	2	000
0	3	00000
000	4	0000000
0	5	00
	6	000
	7	00000
	8	
	9	00

	n	$\bar{x}$	s	$SE_{\bar{x}}$
Piano	34	3.618	3.055	0.524
Control	44	0.386	2.423	0.365

7.52 The standard error of the difference is

$$SE_D = \sqrt{s_1^2/n_1 + s_2^2/n_2} \doteq 0.6387$$

and the interval is $(\bar{x}_1 - \bar{x}_2) \pm t^*SE_D$. Answers will vary with the degrees of freedom used; see the table.

df	t^*	Interval
30	2.042	1.928 to 4.536
33	2.0345	1.933 to 4.531
61.7	1.9992	1.955 to 4.509

7.53 Having the control group in 7.51 and 7.52 makes our conclusions more reliable, since it accounts for increases in scores that may come about simply from the passage of time. Between significance tests and confidence intervals, preferences might vary somewhat. Arguably, there is an advantage to the test since we have a one-sided alternative; the confidence interval by its nature is two-sided.

7.54 (a) The back-to-back stemplot shows a roughly normal shape for the healthy firms, while failed-firm ratios are generally lower and have a slightly less normal (skewed right) distribution. **(b)** $H_0:$ $\mu_1 = \mu_2$ vs. $H_a: \mu_1 > \mu_2$. Summary statistics for the two groups are below; the t value is 7.90, with either df $= 32$ or df $= 81.7$. Either way, $P < 0.0005$, so we conclude that failed firms' ratios are lower. **(c)** One cannot impose the "treatments" of failure or success on a firm.

Failed		Healthy
11100	0	1
22	0	2
5544	0	
6	0	66
9999988888	0	899999
111111	1	00011
33	1	2223
4	1	4445555
6	1	66666777
	1	88888889999
0	2	0000111
	2	222223
	2	455
	2	6677
	2	8
	3	01

	n	$\bar{x}$	s	$SE_{\bar{x}}$
Healthy	68	1.726	0.639	0.078
Failed	33	0.824	0.481	0.084

7.55 (a) $H_0: \mu_1 = \mu_2$; $H_a: \mu_1 \neq \mu_2$. For the low-fitness group, $\bar{x}_1 = 4.64$ and $s_1 = 0.69$. For the high-fitness group, $\bar{x}_2 = 6.43$ and $s_2 = 0.43$. $t = -8.23$, so $P < 0.0001$ (using either df $= 13$ or df $= 21.8$); this difference is significant at 5% and at 1% (and much lower). **(b)** All the subjects were college faculty members. Additionally, all the subjects volunteered for a fitness program, which could add some further confounding.

7.56 For H_0: $\mu_1 = \mu_2$ vs. H_a: $\mu_1 > \mu_2$, we have $t = 5.99$ (with df 11 or 17.6). This is significant ($P < 0.0005$), so we conclude that the treatment was effective.

	n	$\bar{x}$	s	$SE_{\bar{x}}$
Control	13	3.38	1.19	0.33
Treatment	12	1.167	0.577	0.17

7.57 **(a)** We test H_0: $\mu_1 = \mu_2$ vs. H_a: $\mu_1 < \mu_2$. $t = -7.34$, which gives $P < 0.0001$ whether df $= 133$ or df $= 140.6$. Cocaine use is associated with lower birth weights.

df	t^*	Interval
100	1.984	−489.1 to −280.9 g
133	1.9780	−488.8 to −281.2 g
140.6	1.9770	−488.7 to −281.3 g

(b) The standard error of the difference is $SE_D \doteq 52.47$, and the interval is $(\bar{x}_1 - \bar{x}_2) \pm t^*SE_D$. Answers will vary with the degrees of freedom used; see the table. **(c)** The "Other" group may include drug users, since some in it were not tested. Among drug users, there may have been other ("confounding") factors that affected birthweight. Note that in this situation, an experiment is out of the question.

7.58 **(a)** $s_1 \doteq 0.2182$ and $s_2 \doteq 0.1945$. **(b)** We test H_0: $\mu_1 = \mu_2$ vs. H_a: $\mu_1 \neq \mu_2$. $t = -17.83$, which gives $P < 0.0001$ whether df $= 44$ or df $= 97.7$. There is strong evidence that mean wheat prices differ between July and September.

7.59 $(\bar{x}_2 - \bar{x}_1) \pm t^*\sqrt{s_1^2/n_1 + s_2^2/n_2} = \$0.66 \pm t^*(\$0.037014)$, where t^* is chosen with either df $= 44$ or df $= 97.7$. Whatever choice of df is made, $t^* \doteq 2$, so the interval is about $\$0.59$ to $\$0.73$.

7.60 **(a)** $SE_D \doteq 2.1299$. Answers will vary with the df used; see the table. **(b)** Because of random fluctuations between stores, we might (just by chance) have seen a rise in the average number of units sold even if actual mean sales had remained unchanged—or even if they dropped slightly.

df	t^*	Interval
50	2.009	−1.28 to 7.28 units
52	2.0067	−1.27 to 7.27 units
121.9	1.9796	−1.22 to 7.22 units

7.61 **(a)** H_0: $\mu_A = \mu_B$; H_a: $\mu_A \neq \mu_B$; $t = -1.484$. Using $t(149)$ and $t(297.2)$ distributions, P equals 0.1399 and 0.1388, respectively; not significant in either case. The bank might choose to implement Proposal A even though the difference is not significant, since it may have a *slight* advantage over Proposal B. Otherwise, the bank should choose whichever option costs them less. **(b)** Because the sample sizes are equal and large, the t procedure is reliable in spite of the skewness.

7.62 **(a)** We test H_0: $\mu_1 = \mu_2$ vs. H_a: $\mu_1 > \mu_2$.
$t \doteq 1.654$; using $t(18)$ and $t(37.6)$ distributions,
P equals 0.0578 and 0.0532, respectively. We
have some evidence of a higher mean hemoglobin

df	t^*	Interval
18	2.101	−0.243 to 2.043
37.6	2.0251	−0.202 to 2.002

level for breast-fed infants, but not quite enough to be significant at the 5% level.
(b) $SE_D \doteq 0.5442$, and the interval is $(\bar{x}_1 - \bar{x}_2) \pm t^*SE_D$. The two possible answers
are given in the table. **(c)** We are assuming that we have two SRSs from each population, and that underlying distributions are normal. Since the sample sizes add to
42, normality is not a crucial assumption.

7.63 **(a)** H_0: $\mu_1 = \mu_2$ vs. H_a: $\mu_1 < \mu_2$, where
μ_1 is the beta-blocker population mean pulse
rate and μ_2 is the placebo mean pulse rate. We
find $t \doteq -2.4525$; with a $t(29)$ distribution, we

df	t^*	Interval
29	2.756	−10.83 to 0.63 bpm
57.8	2.6636	−10.64 to 0.44 bpm

have $0.01 < P < 0.02$ (in fact, $P = 0.01022$), which is significant at 5% but not at
1%. With a $t(57.8)$ distribution, we have $P = 0.0086$, which is significant at 5% and
at 1%. **(b)** See table at right.

7.64 **(a)** H_0 : $\mu_{\text{skilled}} = \mu_{\text{novice}}$ vs. H_a : $\mu_s > \mu_n$.
(b) The t statistic we want is the "Unequal" value:
$t = 3.1583$ with df $= 9.8$. Its P-value is 0.0052

df	t^*	Interval
9	1.833	0.4922 to 1.8535
9.8	1.8162	0.4984 to 1.8473

(half of that given). This is strong evidence against
H_0. **(c)** See table at right.

7.65 H_0: $\mu_{\text{skilled}} = \mu_{\text{novice}}$ vs. H_a: $\mu_s \neq \mu_n$ (use a two-sided alternative since we have
no preconceived idea of the direction of the difference). Use the "Unequal" values:
$t = 0.5143$ with df $= 11.8$; its P-value is 0.6165. There is no reason to reject H_0; skilled
and novice rowers seem to have (practically) the same mean weight.

7.66 With such large samples, the t distribution is practically indistinguishable from the
normal distribution, and in fact, for df $= 19,882$ or 38,786, $t^* = 2.576$. Thus the interval
is 27.915 to 32.085 points. (If one takes the conservative approach, with df $= 1000$, the
interval is 27.911 to 32.089.)

7.67 (a) Using back-to-back stemplots, we see that both distributions are slightly skewed to the right, and have one or two moderately high outliers. Normal quantile plots (not shown) are fairly linear. A t procedure may be (cautiously) used in spite of the skewness, since the sum of the sample sizes is almost 40. **(b)** H_0: $\mu_w = \mu_m$; H_a: $\mu_w > \mu_m$. Summary statistics (below) lead to $t = 2.0561$, so $P = 0.0277$ (with df = 17) or $P = 0.0235$ (with df = 35.6).

Women	stem	Men
	7	05
	8	8
	9	12
931	10	489
5	11	3455
966	12	6
77	13	2
80	14	06
442	15	1
55	16	9
8	17	
	18	07
	19	
0	20	

	n	$\bar{x}$	s
Women	18	141.056	26.4363
Men	20	121.250	32.8519

This gives fairly strong evidence—significant at 5% but not 1%—that the women's mean is higher. **(c)** For $\mu_m - \mu_w$: -36.56 to -3.05 (df = 17) or -36.07 to -3.54 (df = 35.6).

7.68 (a) A back-to-back stemplot shows no particular skewness or outliers. **(b)** H_0: $\mu_1 = \mu_2$ vs. H_a: $\mu_1 < \mu_2$. Summary statistics give $t \doteq -2.47$, so $0.01 < P < 0.02$ (with df = 19) or $P = 0.0092$ (with df = 36.9).

Control	stem	Exper.
7	2	
8	2	
1	3	1
22	3	23
55544	3	
66	3	67
988	3	99
10	4	00001
3	4	22233
5	4	4
6	4	67

	n	$\bar{x}$	s
Control	20	366.30	50.8052
Experimental	20	402.95	42.7286

This gives fairly strong evidence that the high-lysine diet leads to increased weight gain. It is significant at the 10% and 5% levels either way, and at the 1% level using the higher df. **(c)** The interval (for $\mu_2 - \mu_1$) is 5.58 to 67.72 g (df = 19) or 6.57 to 66.73 g (df = 36.9).

7.69 (a) $t = 1.604$ with df = 9 or df = 15.6; the P-value is either 0.0716 or 0.0644, respectively. Both are similar to the P-value in Example 7.20, and the conclusion is essentially the same. **(b)** With df = 9: -0.76 to 11.30 (margin of error: 6.03). With df = 15.6: -0.48 to 11.02 (margin of error: 5.75). Both margins of errors are similar to (but slightly larger than) the margin of error in Example 7.21.

7.70 (a) $SE_D \doteq 7.9895$; see table. **(b)** We know that we can reject H_0, since 0 is well outside our confidence interval. (We assume here that the alternative is two-sided, but since the interval is so far from 0, we would still reject H_0 in favor of $\mu_1 > \mu_2$.) **(c)** We assume that the hot dogs are SRSs of each population, and that the

	n	$\bar{x}$	s
Beef	20	156.850	22.6420
Poultry	17	122.471	25.4831

df	t^*	Interval
16	2.120	17.4 to 51.3 cal
32.4	2.0360	18.1 to 50.6 cal

distributions are not extremely skewed (or otherwise nonnormal). Both assumptions seem reasonable in this case.

7.71 (a) $SE_{\bar{x}_2} = 50.74/\sqrt{20} \doteq 11.35$. $SE_{\bar{x}_1 - \bar{x}_2} = \sqrt{33.89^2/10 + 50.74^2/20} \doteq 15.61$.
(b) $H_0: \mu_1 = \mu_2$ vs. $H_a: \mu_1 \neq \mu_2$; $t = 1.249$. Using $t(9)$ and $t(25.4)$ distributions, P equals 0.2431 and 0.2229, respectively; the difference is not significant. **(c)** -15.8 to 54.8 msec (df $= 9$) or -12.6 to 51.6 msec (df $= 25.4$). These intervals had to contain 0 because according to (b), the observed difference would occur in more than 22% of samples when the means are the same; thus 0 would appear in any confidence interval with a confidence level greater than about 78%.

7.72 If they did this for many separate tests, there would be a fair chance that they would wrongly reject H_0 for one or more of their tests. If they are using $\alpha = 0.05$, and do (e.g.) 20 comparisons, then even if all 20 null hypotheses are true, we "expect" to reject one of them (since $0.05 \cdot 20 = 1$).

7.73 (a) Using $t^* = 1.660$ (df $= 100$), the interval is \$412.68 to \$635.58. Using $t^* = 1.6473$ (df $= 620$), the interval is \$413.54 to \$634.72. Using $t^* = 1.6461$ (df $= 1249.2$), the interval is \$413.62 to \$634.64. **(b)** Because the sample sizes are so large (and the sample sizes are almost the same), deviations from the assumptions have little effect. **(c)** The sample is not *really* random, but there is no reason to expect that the method used should introduce any bias into the sample. **(d)** Students without employment were excluded, so the survey results can only (possibly) extend to *employed* undergraduates. Knowing the number of unreturned questionnaires would also be useful.

7.74 $t \doteq \dfrac{17.6 - 9.5}{\sqrt{\frac{6.34^2}{6} + \frac{1.95^2}{6}}} \doteq 2.99$ and df $\doteq \dfrac{\left(\frac{6.34^2}{6} + \frac{1.95^2}{6}\right)^2}{\frac{1}{5}\left(\frac{6.34^2}{6}\right)^2 + \frac{1}{5}\left(\frac{1.95^2}{6}\right)^2} \doteq 5.9$.

7.75 $s_p^2 = 27.75$, $s_p \doteq 5.2679$, and $t = 0.6489$ with df $= 293$, so $P = 0.5169$—not significant. The conclusion is similar to that in Example 7.16, where we found $P > 0.5$.

7.76 (a) We test $H_0: \mu_1 = \mu_2$ vs. $H_a: \mu_1 > \mu_2$. $s_p^2 \doteq 3.0475$, $s_p \doteq 1.7457$, and $t \doteq 1.663$ with df $= 40$, so $P = 0.0520$ (similar to the values from Exercise 7.62). We have some evidence of a higher mean hemoglobin level for breast-fed infants, but not quite enough to be significant at the 5% level. **(b)** Using $t^* = 2.021$, the interval is $(\bar{x}_1 - \bar{x}_2) \pm t^* s_p \sqrt{\frac{1}{23} + \frac{1}{19}} = -0.194$ to 1.994.

7.77 With equal variances, $t = 0.5376$ (df $= 16$), which gives $P = 0.5982$. As before, there is no reason to reject H_0; skilled and novice rowers seem to have (practically) the same mean weight.

7.78 (a) We test $H_0: \mu_1 = \mu_2$ vs. $H_a: \mu_1 \neq \mu_2$. $s_p^2 \doteq 2116.18$, $s_p \doteq 46.002$, and $t \doteq 1.094$ with df $= 28$, so $P = 0.2831$. The difference is not significant. **(b)** Using $t^* = 2.048$, the interval is $(\bar{x}_1 - \bar{x}_2) \pm t^* s_p \sqrt{\frac{1}{10} + \frac{1}{20}} = -17.0$ to 56.0 msec. **(c)** The t- and P-values are similar to those in Exercise 7.71, where we had $t = 1.249$ and P equals either 0.2431 (df $= 9$) or 0.2229 (df $= 25.4$). The t-value is smaller here because $s_p \sqrt{\frac{1}{10} + \frac{1}{20}} \doteq 17.82$

is slightly bigger than $SE_D \doteq 15.61$; this correspondingly makes P larger. The larger standard error also makes the confidence interval wider—in 7.71, we had -15.8 to 54.8 msec (df $= 9$) or -12.6 to 51.6 msec (df $= 25.4$)

Section 3: Optional Topics in Comparing Distributions

7.79 (a) From an $F(9, 20)$ distribution, $F^* = 2.39$. (b) P is between $2(0.025) = 0.05$ and $2(0.05) = 0.10$; $F = 2.45$ is significant at the 10% level but not at the 5% level.

7.80 (a) Comparing to an $F(20, 25)$ distribution, we find that $F^* = 2.30$ for $p = 0.025$ (the critical value for a 5% two-sided test). Since $2.88 > F^*$, this is significant. (b) P is between $2(0.001) = 0.002$ and $2(0.01) = 0.02$. With Minitab or other software, we find $P = 2(0.0067) = 0.0134$.

7.81 H_0: $\sigma_1 = \sigma_2$; H_a: $\sigma_1 \neq \sigma_2$. $F = 3.055^2/2.423^2 \doteq 1.59$; referring to an $F(33, 43)$ distribution, we find $P = 0.1529$ (from the table, use an $F(30, 40)$ distribution and observe that $P > 0.1$). We do not have enough evidence to conclude that the standard deviations are different.

7.82 Test H_0: $\sigma_1 = \sigma_2$ vs. H_a: $\sigma_1 \neq \sigma_2$. $F = (90 \cdot 0.023^2)/(45 \cdot 0.029^2) \doteq 1.258$; comparing to an $F(89, 44)$ distribution, we find $P = 0.4033$ (from the table, use an $F(60, 40)$ distribution and observe that $P > 0.1$). We cannot conclude that the standard deviations are different.

7.83 (a) An $F(1, 1)$ distribution; with a two-sided alternative, we need the critical value for $p = 0.025$: $F^* = 647.79$. This is a very low-power test, since large differences between σ_1 and σ_2 would rarely be detected. (b) H_0: $\sigma_1 = \sigma_2$ vs. H_a: $\sigma_1 \neq \sigma_2$. $F = (s_1^2/s_2^2) = (1.534^2/0.7707^2) \doteq 3.963$. Not surprisingly, we do not reject H_0.

7.84 (a) H_0: $\sigma_1 = \sigma_2$; H_a: $\sigma_1 \neq \sigma_2$. (b) Put the larger standard deviation on top: $F = (s_2^2/s_1^2) = (0.95895^2/0.47906^2) \doteq 4.007$. Comparing to an $F(7, 9)$ distribution, we find $0.05 < P < 0.10$; Minitab gives 0.0574. There is some evidence of inequality, but not quite enough to reject H_0 (at the 5% level).

7.85 (a) H_0: $\sigma_1 = \sigma_2$; H_a: $\sigma_1 \neq \sigma_2$. (b) Put the larger standard deviation on top: $F \doteq 2.196$ from an $F(7, 9)$ distribution, so $P > 0.20$ (in fact, $P = 0.2697$).

7.86 $F = (87/74)^2 \doteq 1.382$; this comes from an $F(19882, 19936)$ distribution, so we compare to $F(1000, 1000)$ and find $P < 0.002$. (In fact, P is a *lot* smaller than that.) With such large samples, the estimated standard deviations are very accurate, so if $\sigma_1 = \sigma_2$, then s_1 and s_2 should be nearly equal (and F should be *very* close to 1).

7.87 (a) H_0: $\sigma_m = \sigma_w$; H_a: $\sigma_m > \sigma_w$. (b) $F = (32.8519/26.4363)^2 \doteq 1.544$ from an $F(19, 17)$ distribution. (c) Using the $F(15, 17)$ entry in the table, we find $P > 0.10$ (in fact, $P = 0.1862$). We do not have enough evidence to conclude that men's SSHA scores are more variable.

7.88 For testing H_0: $\sigma_1 = \sigma_2$ vs. H_a: $\sigma_1 \neq \sigma_2$, we have $F = (50.74/33.89)^2 \doteq 2.242$ from an $F(19, 9)$ distribution. Using the $F(15, 9)$ entry in the table, we find $P > 0.20$ (in fact, $P = 0.2152$). The difference is standard deviations is not significant.

7.89 df $= 198$; we reject H_0 if $t > 1.660$ (from the table, with df $= 100$), or $t > 1.6526$ (using df $= 198$). The noncentrality parameter is $\delta \doteq 3.2636$; the power is about 95% (actually, 0.946), regardless of which t^* value is used. (The normal approximation agrees nicely with the "true" answer in this case.)

Output from G•Power:
```
Post-hoc analysis for "t-Test (means)", one-tailed:
Alpha: 0.0500
Power (1-beta): 0.9460
Effect size "d": 0.4615
Total sample size: 200 (n 1:100, n 2: 100)
Critical value: t(198) = 1.6526
Delta: 3.2636
```

7.90 $\delta = 300/(650\sqrt{2/n} \doteq 0.32636\sqrt{n}$. The table shows the values of δ, the t^* values (for df $= 48, 98, 148, 198,$ and 248), and the power computed using the normal approximation ("Power^1") and the G•Power software ("Power^2").

n	δ	t^*	Power^1	Power^2
25	1.6318	1.6772	0.4819	0.4855
50	2.3077	1.6606	0.7412	0.7411
75	2.8263	1.6546	0.8794	0.8787
100	3.2636	1.6526	0.9464	0.9460
125	3.6488	1.6510	0.9771	0.9769

To reliably detect a difference of 300 g, we should choose at least $n = 75$. (This number will vary based on what we consider to be "reliable.")

7.91 The standard error is $650\sqrt{2/n}$, and df $= 2n - 2$. The critical values and margins of error are given in the table. Graph not shown; plot margin of error vs. sample size.

n	t^*	m.e.
25	2.0106	369.6
50	1.9845	258.0
75	1.9761	209.8
100	1.9720	181.3
125	1.9696	161.9

7.92 Note: One might reasonably do this computation with a two-sided H_a (since the original alternative of Exercise 7.55 was two-sided), or a one-sided H_a (since the data in that exercise suggested that $\mu_2 > \mu_1$). Both answers are shown.

Two-sided H_a: (a) df $= 38$; we reject H_0 if $|t| > 2.750$ (from the table, with df $= 30$), or $|t| > 2.7116$ (using df $= 38$). The noncentrality parameter is $\delta \doteq 2.2588$. Note that since H_a is two-sided, the power is $P(|T| > t^*) = P(T < -t^*$ or $T > t^*)$; the normal approximation would therefore be $P(Z < -t^* - \delta$ or $Z > t^* - \delta)$.

G•Power reports that power $\doteq 0.3391$ (see output below). The normal approximation gives $P(Z < -5.01$ or $Z > 0.4912) \doteq 0.3116$ (using $t^* = 2.750$), or $P(Z < -4.97$ or $Z > 0.4528) \doteq 0.3253$ ($t^* = 2.7116$). Regardless of the method used, we conclude that we will detect a difference of 0.5 only about one-third of the time. **(b)** df = 58; we reject H_0 if $|t| > 2.009$ (df = 50), or $|t| > 2.0017$ (df = 58). The noncentrality parameter is $\delta \doteq 2.7664$. G•Power reports power $\doteq 0.7765$ (see output below). The normal approximation gives $P(Z < -4.78$ or $Z > -0.7574) \doteq 0.7756$ ($t^* = 2.009$), or $P(Z < -4.77$ or $Z > -0.7647) \doteq 0.7778$ ($t^* = 2.0017$). We will detect a difference of 0.5 about three-fourths of the time.

One-sided H_a: **(a)** With H_a: $\mu_1 < \mu_2$, $t^* = 2.457$ (df = 30) or $t^* = 2.4286$ (df = 38), and the power is 0.4412 (G•Power), with normal approximations 0.4214 (df = 30) or 0.4326 (df = 38). **(b)** $t^* = 1.676$ (df = 50) or $t^* = 1.6716$ (df = 58), and the power is 0.8619 (G•Power), with normal approximations 0.8622 (df = 50) or 0.8632 (df = 58).

Output from G•Power:
```
-------------- 20 players, 1% significance  --------------
Post-hoc analysis for "t-Test (means)", two-tailed:
Alpha: 0.0100
Power (1-beta): 0.3391
Effect size "d": 0.7143
Total sample size: 40 (n 1:20, n 2: 20)
Critical value: t(38) = 2.7116
Delta: 2.2588
-------------- 30 players, 5% significance  --------------
Post-hoc analysis for "t-Test (means)", two-tailed:
Alpha: 0.0500
Power (1-beta): 0.7765
Effect size "d": 0.7143
Total sample size: 60 (n 1:30, n 2: 30)
Critical value: t(58) = 2.0017
Delta: 2.7664
```

Exercises

7.93 Back-to-back stemplots below. The distributions appear similar; the most striking difference is the relatively large number of boys with

	n	GPA $\bar{x}$	GPA s	IQ $\bar{x}$	IQ s
Boys	47	7.2816	2.3190	110.96	12.121
Girls	31	7.6966	1.7208	105.84	14.271

low GPAs. Testing the difference in GPAs, we obtain $SE_D \doteq 0.4582$ and $t = -0.91$, which is not significant, regardless of whether we use df = 30 ($0.15 < P < 0.20$) or 74.9 ($P = 0.1811$). For the difference in IQs, we find $SE_D \doteq 3.1138$ and $t = 1.64$, which is fairly strong evidence, although it is not quite significant at the 5% level: $0.05 < P < 0.10$ (df = 30), or $P = 0.0503$ (df = 56.9).

GPA:

Girls		Boys
	0	5
	1	7
	2	4
4	3	689
7	4	068
952	5	0
4200	6	019
988855432	7	1124556666899
998731	8	001112238
95530	9	1113445567
17	10	57

IQ:

Girls		Boys
42	7	
	7	79
	8	
96	8	
31	9	03
86	9	77
433320	10	0234
875	10	556667779
44422211	11	00001123334
98	11	556899
0	12	03344
8	12	67788
20	13	
	13	6

7.94 The table below gives means and standard deviations for the two groups, as well as 95% confidence intervals. For H_0: $\mu_{OL} = \mu_{DL}$ vs. H_a: $\mu_{OL} \neq \mu_{DL}$, we have $SE_D \doteq 7.1446$, and $t \doteq 5.19$, which is significant ($P < 0.0005$ whether we use df = 14 or df = 28.1). We conclude that offensive linemen are heavier (on the average).

Based on the confidence intervals, we believe that the mean weight of offensive linemen is about 20 to 50 lb more than that of defensive linemen.

OL		DL
	22	0
5	23	055
	24	000555
	25	00
	26	05
500	27	5
44	28	005
555550	29	
50	30	
	31	
	32	
5	33	

	n	$\bar{x}$	s	df	t^*	Interval
OL	15	288.2	21.627	14	2.145	21.8 to 52.4 lb
DL	18	251.1	18.908	28.1	2.0480	22.5 to 51.7 lb

7.95 Both distributions have two high outliers. When we include those houses, $SE_D \doteq \$12,160.0$ and $t \doteq -0.5268$. For testing H_0: $\mu_3 = \mu_4$ vs. H_a: $\mu_3 < \mu_4$, $P \doteq 0.3$ whether we take df = 21 or df = 35.8, so we have little reason to reject H_0. The 95% confidence interval for the difference $\mu_3 - \mu_4$ is about $-\$31,694$ to $\$18,882$ (df = 21) or $-\$31,073$ to $\$18,261$ (df = 35.8).

Without the outliers, $SE_D \doteq \$7,448.37$ and $t \doteq -0.1131$, so we have little reason to believe that $\mu_3 < \mu_4$ ($P \doteq 0.455$ with either df = 19 or df = 34.5). The 95% confidence interval for the difference $\mu_3 - \mu_4$ is about $-\$16,432$ to $\$14,747$ (df = 19) or $-\$15,971$ to $\$14,286$ (df = 34.5).

3BR		4BR
1	1	1
3322	1	222
55554444	1	445
777777666	1	667777
9999888888	1	88899
	2	00
	2	
	2	
7	2	
9	2	8
	3	1

	With outliers			Without outliers		
	n	$\bar{x}$	s	n	$\bar{x}$	s
3BR	34	\$171,717	\$36,382.3	32	\$164,668	\$22,881.5
4BR	22	\$178,123	\$48,954.4	20	\$165,510	\$27,970.3

7.96 Let μ_1 and μ_2 be the "true mean number of deaths" in 1989 and 1990, respectively. (Understanding what this means might make for good class discussion.) The standard error of the difference $n_1 - n_2$ (the counts in 1989 and 1990, respectively) would be $\sqrt{50 + 47} = \sqrt{97}$, and for testing H_0: $\mu_1 = \mu_2$ vs. H_a: $\mu_1 > \mu_2$, we find $z = (50 - 47)/\sqrt{97} \doteq 0.30$, which is not significant. The confidence interval for $\mu_1 - \mu_2$ is $(50 - 47) \pm 2\sqrt{97} = -16.7$ to 22.7 deaths.

    Note for instructors: In case you are interested, the assumption underlying this exercise is that manatee deaths in a given year are a Poisson process (see a probability text for a description). A Poisson distribution with parameter μ has mean μ and standard deviation $\sqrt{\mu}$; since we have a single observation n from this distribution, our best estimate for the mean is n, and our best estimate for the standard deviation is $\sqrt{n}$.

7.97 It is reasonable to have a prior belief that people who evacuated their pets would score higher, so we test H_0: $\mu_1 = \mu_2$ vs. H_a: $\mu_1 > \mu_2$. We find $\mathrm{SE}_D \doteq 0.4630$ and $t = 3.65$, which gives $P < 0.0005$ no matter how we choose degrees of freedom (115 or 237.0). As one might suspect, people who evacuated their pets have a higher mean score.

    One might also compute a 95% confidence interval for the difference: 0.77 to 2.61 points (df = 115) or 0.78 to 2.60 (df = 237.0).

7.98 **(a)** We are interested in weight change; the pairs are the "before" and "after" measurements. **(b)** The mean weight change was a loss. The exact amount lost is not specified, but it was big enough that it would rarely happen by chance for an ineffective weight-loss program. **(c)** Comparing to a $t(40)$ distribution, we find $P < 0.0005$.

7.99 We test H_0: $\mu_1 = \mu_2$ vs. H_a: $\mu_1 < \mu_2$. $\mathrm{SE}_D \doteq 305.817$ and $t \doteq -0.7586$, which is not significant regardless of df (in fact $P = 0.2256$ with df = 57.3). There is not enough evidence to conclude that nitrites decrease amino acid uptake.

7.100 **(a)** We test H_0: $\mu_1 = \mu_2$ vs. H_a: $\mu_1 < \mu_2$. $\mathrm{SE}_D \doteq 0.2457$ and $t \doteq -8.95$, which is significant ($P < 0.0005$) for either df = 411 or df = 933.8. The mean for the experienced workers is greater. **(b)** With large sample sizes the t procedure can be used. **(c)** For a normal distribution, about 95% of all observations fall with 2 standard deviations of the mean; we can (cautiously) use this in spite of the skewness: $37.32 \pm 2(3.83) = 29.66$ to 44.98—about 30 to 45. **(d)** The side-by-side boxplots show that the 15th-minute distribution is more symmetric, more spread out, and generally higher than the first minute.

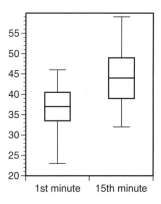

7.101 (a) The stemplot (after truncating the decimal) shows that the data are left-skewed; there are some low observations, but no particular outliers. (b) $\bar{x} = 59.5\overline{8}$ percent, $SE_{\bar{x}} \doteq 6.255/\sqrt{9} \doteq 2.085$, and for df $= 8$, $t^* = 2.306$, so the interval is 54.8% to 64.4%.

```
4 | 9
5 | 1
5 |
5 | 4
5 |
5 |
6 | 0
6 | 33
6 | 445
```

7.102 (a) "s. e." is standard error (of the mean). To find s, multiply by $\sqrt{n}$. (b) No: $SE_D \doteq 65.1153$ and $t \doteq -0.3532$, so $P = 0.3624$ (df $= 82$) or 0.3622 (df $=$

	n	Calories $\bar{x}$	Calories s	Alcohol $\bar{x}$	Alcohol s
Drivers	98	2821	435.58	0.24	0.59397
Conductors	83	2844	437.30	0.39	1.00215

173.9)—in either case, there is little evidence against H_0. (c) Not very significant—$SE_D \doteq 0.1253$, $t \doteq -1.1971$, and $P = 0.2346$ (df $= 82$) or 0.2334 (df $= 128.4$). (d) $0.39 \pm t^*(0.11) = 0.207$ to 0.573—whether we use $t^* = 1.664$ (df $= 80$) or $t^* = 1.6636$ (df $= 82$). (e) -0.3119 to 0.0119 (using $t(82)$) or -0.3114 to 0.0114 (using $t(128.4)$).

7.103 The similarity of the sample standard deviations suggests that the population standard deviations are likely to be similar. The pooled standard deviation is $s_p \doteq 436.368$, and $t \doteq -0.3533$, so $P = 0.3621$ (df $= 179$)—still not significant.

7.104 (a) The large sample sizes make the t procedure usable. (b) The F test is not robust against nonnormality, so it should not be used with this distribution.

7.105 No: Counties in California could scarcely be considered an SRS of counties in Indiana.

7.106 (a) Testing H_0: $\mu = 86$ vs. H_a: $\mu < 86$, we find $t = \frac{83-86}{10/\sqrt{40}} \doteq -1.897$. With df $= 39$, we estimate $0.025 < P < 0.05$ (software gives 0.0326). This is fairly strong evidence that the mean is lower. (b) E.g., take several soil samples; use the standard method on half, and the new method on the other half; do a matched pairs analysis on the differences.

7.107 (a) Test H_0: $\mu_1 = \mu_2$ vs. H_a: $\mu_1 > \mu_2$; $SE_D \doteq 16.1870$ and $t \doteq 1.1738$, so $P = 0.1265$ (using df $= 22$) or 0.1235 (df $= 43.3$). Not enough evidence to reject H_0. (b) -14.57 to 52.57 mg/dl (df $= 22$), or -13.64 to 51.64 mg/dl (df $= 43.3$). (c) $193 \pm (2.060)(68/\sqrt{26}) = 165.53$ to 220.47 mg/dl. (d) We are assuming that we have two SRSs from each population, and that underlying distributions are normal. It is unlikely that we have random samples from either population, especially among pets.

7.108 (a) H_0: $\mu_r = \mu_c$; H_a: $\mu_r < \mu_c$. (b) Use a matched pairs procedure on the (city $-$ rural) differences. (c) There were 26 days when readings were available from both locations; the stemplot of these differences shows two high outliers. (d) We drop the outliers and find $\bar{x} = 1$ and $s \doteq 2.106$, so $t \doteq 2.33$ (df $= 23$, $P = 0.015$). This is good evidence that the rural mean is lower (especially given that we have removed the two strongest individual pieces of evidence against H_0). If we use the t procedures in spite of the outliers, we get $\bar{x} = 2.192$, $s = 4.691$, and $t \doteq 2.38$ (df $= 25$, $P = 0.013$). (e) Without the outliers, the 90% confidence interval is 0.263 to 1.737; with them, it is 0.621 to 3.764.

```
-0 | 32
-0 | 11110
 0 | 01111111
 0 | 2222222
 0 | 5
 0 | 7
 0 |
 1 |
 1 |
 1 | 5
 1 |
 1 | 8
```

7.109 We test H_0: population median $= 0$ vs. H_a: population median > 0, or H_0: $p = 1/2$ vs. H_a: $p > 1/2$, where p is the proportion of (city $-$ rural) differences that are positive. Ignoring missing values and the two "zero" differences, there are 6 negative differences and 18 positive differences. If X (the number of positive differences) has a Bin(24, 1/2) distribution, the P-value is $P(X \leq 6) = 0.0113$; the normal approximation gives $P(Z < -2.45) = 0.0072$ (without the continuity correction) or $P(Z < -2.25) = 0.0124$ (with the continuity correction). In any case, this is strong evidence against H_0, indicating that the median city level is higher.

Output from Minitab:
```
Sign test of median = 0.00000 versus  G.T.   0.00000

                N    N*   BELOW  EQUAL  ABOVE   P-VALUE    MEDIAN
City-Rur       26    10       6      2     18    0.0113     1.000
```

7.110 The stemplot shows the distribution to be fairly symmetric, with a slightly low outlier of 4.88 (it is not an "official" outlier). There is nothing to keep us from using the t procedure. $\bar{x} \doteq 5.4479$ and $s \doteq 0.2209$; 5.4479 serves as our best estimate of the earth's density, with margin of error $t^*s/\sqrt{29}$ (this is 0.084 for 95% confidence, for example).

```
48 | 8
49 |
50 | 7
51 | 0
52 | 6799
53 | 04469
54 | 2467
55 | 03578
56 | 12358
57 | 59
58 | 5
```

7.111 Note that SE$_D \doteq 0.9501$ for abdomen skinfolds, while SE$_D \doteq 0.7877$ for thigh measurements. With 95% confidence intervals, for example, the mean abdomen skinfold difference is between 11.62 and 15.38 mm (using df $= 103.6$). With the same df, the mean thigh skinfold difference is between 9.738 and 12.86 mm.

7.112 **(a)** There is a high outlier (2.94 g/mi), but the distribution looks reasonably normal. **(b)** See the table. Intervals marked with an asterisk (*)

	n	$\bar{x}$	s	Interval
All points	46	1.3287	0.4844	1.1366 to 1.5208
				or 1.1356 to 1.5218*
No outlier	45	1.2929	0.4239	1.1227 to 1.4630
				or 1.1220 to 1.4638*

were computed using the table value $t^* = 2.704$ for df $= 40$. **(c)** We test H_0: $\mu = 1$; H_a: $\mu > 1$. If we include the outlier, $t \doteq 4.60$; without it, $t \doteq 4.64$. Either way the P value is very small. To the supervisor, we explain that if the mean NOX emissions were only 1 g/mi, we would almost never see average emissions as high as these. Therefore, we must conclude that mean emissions are higher than 1 g/mi; based on the evidence, we believe that the mean is between about 1.1 and 1.5 g/mi.

```
0 | 455
0 | 6777
0 | 899
1 | 0011111
1 | 222223333333
1 | 4444445
1 | 777
1 | 888
2 | 0
2 | 22
2 |
2 |
2 | 9
```

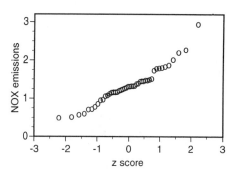

7.113 **(a)** Back-to-back stemplots and summary statistics below. With a pooled variance, $s_p \doteq 83.6388$, $t \doteq 3.9969$ with df $= 222$, so $P < 0.0001$. With unpooled variances, $SE_D \doteq 11.6508$, $t \doteq 4.0124$ with df $= 162.2$, and again $P < 0.0001$ (or, with df $= 78$, we conclude that $P < 0.0005$). The test for equality of standard deviations gives $F \doteq 1.03$ with df 144 and 78; the P-value is 0.9114, so the pooled procedure should be appropriate. In either case, we conclude that male mean SATM scores are higher than female mean SATM scores. A 99% confidence interval for the male − female difference (using s_p) is 16.36 to 77.13.

(b) Back-to-back stemplots and summary statistics below. With a pooled variance, $s_p \doteq 92.6348$, $t \doteq 0.9395$ with df $= 222$, so $P = 0.3485$. With unpooled variances, $SE_D \doteq 12.7485$, $t \doteq 0.9547$ with df $= 162.2$, so $P = 0.3411$ (or, with df $= 78$, $P = 0.3426$). The test for equality of standard deviations gives $F \doteq 1.11$ with df 144 and 78; the P-value is 0.6033, so the pooled procedure should be appropriate. In either case, we cannot see a difference between male and female mean SATV scores. A 99% confidence interval for the male − female difference (using s_p) is −21.49 to 45.83.

(c) The results may generalize fairly well to students in different years, less well to students at other schools, and probably not very well to college students in general.

	n	SATM $\bar{x}$	SATM s	SATV $\bar{x}$	SATV s
Men	145	611.772	84.0206	508.841	94.3485
Women	79	565.025	82.9294	496.671	89.3849

Men's SATM		Women's SATM
	3	0
	3	5
400	4	1334
99999888776	4	56777888999
444443333322222211000	5	0111123334
99999998888887776655555555555	5	5555555666777778889999
4444444444433333332222222211100000000	6	00011222233334444
999999987777776666655555	6	55555789
3222211100000	7	1124
77766655555	7	
0	8	

Men's SATV		Women's SATV
98	2	9
4322	3	33
9999988766	3	55669
44444444443321111100000	4	0122223333444
99999888888888877777666666555	4	566666677777788888899999
444443333322221110000000000000	5	01111122334
99888877777666666555	5	566777777889
433333332111100000	6	0000
9987775	6	668
420	7	00
6	7	5

7.114 (a) A stemplot of the differences (right) shows no outliers (although it also does not look very normal). $\bar{D} \doteq 0.0046$ and $s \doteq 0.01487$. (b) With df = 49, $t^* = 2.0096$, giving the interval 0.00037 to 0.00883. With df = 40 and $t^* = 2.021$, we get 0.00035 to 0.00885. (c) Testing H_0: $\mu = 0$ vs. H_a: $\mu \neq 0$, we find $t \doteq 2.19$, which has $0.02 < P < 0.04$ (using df = 40) or $P \doteq 0.034$ (using df = 49). There is fairly strong evidence that the mean difference is not 0.

−2	0000000
−1	0000000
−0	0000
0	00000
1	0000000000000
2	00000000000
3	000

7.115 (a) We test H_0: $\mu_B = \mu_D$ vs. H_a: $\mu_B < \mu_D$. Pooling is appropriate; $s_p \doteq 6.5707$. [If we do not pool, $SE_D \doteq 1.9811$.] Whether or not we pool, $t \doteq 2.87$ with df = 42 [or 21, or 39.3], so

	n	$\bar{x}$	s
Basal	22	41.0455	5.63558
DRTA	22	46.7273	7.38842
Strat	22	44.2727	5.76675

$P = 0.0032$ [or 0.0046, or 0.0033]. We conclude that the mean score using DRTA is higher than the mean score with the Basal method. The difference in the average scores is 5.68; a 95% confidence interval for the difference in means is about 1.7 to 9.7 points.

(b) We test H_0: $\mu_B = \mu_S$ vs. H_a: $\mu_B < \mu_S$. Pooling is appropriate; $s_p \doteq 5.7015$. [If we do not pool, $SE_D \doteq 1.7191$.] Whether or not we pool, $t \doteq 1.88$ with df = 42 [or 21, or 42.0], so $P = 0.0337$ [or 0.0372, or 0.0337]. We conclude that the mean score using

Strat is higher than the Basal mean score. The difference in the average scores is 3.23; a 95% confidence interval for the difference in means is about -0.24 to 6.7 points.

7.116 Answers will vary with choice of α, and with whether H_a is one- or two-sided. See the table for some combinations.

	H_a: $\mu_b < \mu_g$	H_a: $\mu_b \neq \mu_g$
$\alpha = 0.05$	484	615
$\alpha = 0.01$	786	915

We would reject H_0: $\mu_b = \mu_g$ in favor of H_a: $\mu_b \neq \mu_g$ if $|t| \geq t^*$, or $|\bar{x}_g - \bar{x}_b| \geq t^* \sigma \sqrt{2/n}$, where t^* varies with our choice of α, and with df $= 2n - 2$. The power against the (two-sided) alternative $d = |\mu_g - \mu_b| = 0.4$ is $P(|T| > t^*) = P(T < -t^*$ or $T > t^*)$; the normal approximation would therefore be $P(Z < -t^* - \delta$ or $Z > t^* - \delta)$. The noncentrality parameter is $\delta = 0.4/(\sigma \sqrt{1/n + 1/n}) = 0.16 \sqrt{n/2}$.

From this point, one must either use special software (like G•Power—output below) or trial and error to find the appropriate n. Since sample sizes end up being fairly large, the normal approximation is quite good—both for estimating the power, and also for approximating t^* using z^* from a normal distribution. For example, with $\alpha = 0.05$, $t^* \doteq z^* = 1.96$, and we find for $n = 613$,

$$\text{Power} \doteq P(Z < -4.7611 \text{ or } Z > -0.8411) \doteq 0.7999$$

while for $n = 614$,

$$\text{Power} \doteq P(Z < -4.7634 \text{ or } Z > -0.8434) \doteq 0.8005$$

If we use the one-sided alternative H_a, the power is $P(T > t^*)$ and the normal approximation is $P(Z > t^* - \delta)$. For example, with $\alpha = 0.05$ and $n = 483$, $t^* \doteq z^* = 1.645$, and Power $\doteq P(Z > -4.7382) \doteq 0.79995$, and with $n = 484$, Power $\doteq P(Z > -4.7405) \doteq 0.80067$.

Note that G•Power reports the *total* sample size; divide this by 2 to get n.

Output from G•Power:
```
A priori analysis for "t-Test (means)", two-tailed:
Alpha: 0.0500
Power (1-beta): 0.8000
Effect size "d": 0.1600
Total sample size: 1230
Actual power: 0.8005
Critical value: t(1228) = 1.9619
Delta: 2.8057

A priori analysis for "t-Test (means)", one-tailed:
Alpha: 0.0500
Power (1-beta): 0.8000
Effect size "d": 0.1600
Total sample size: 968
Actual power: 0.8002
Critical value: t(966) = 1.6464
Delta: 2.4890
```

7.117 The table and plot (below) show the power computed by G•Power for $|\mu_1 - \mu_2|$ varying between 0.01 and 0.10.

These values can also be approximated using the normal distribution; e.g., for a difference of 0.05, we will reject H_0 if $|t| > 2.0244$ (with a two-sided alternative). The noncentrality parameter is $\delta \doteq 2.2588$; the power is approximately

$$P(Z < -t^* - \delta \text{ or } Z > t^* + \delta) = 0.5927$$

or about 60%.

Diff	δ	One-sided Power	Two-sided Power
0.01	0.4518	0.1149	0.0725
0.02	0.9035	0.2244	0.1425
0.03	1.3553	0.3769	0.2620
0.04	1.8070	0.5517	0.4214
0.05	2.2588	0.7168	0.5954
0.06	2.7105	0.8454	0.7522
0.07	3.1623	0.9279	0.8690
0.08	3.6140	0.9715	0.9408
0.09	4.0658	0.9905	0.9773
0.10	4.5175	0.9974	0.9927

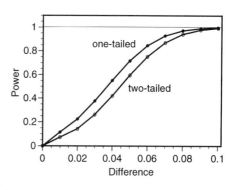

7.118 Some software handles this task more easily than others. Shown (below, left) is one possible graph; note that the critical values for df ≤ 5 are missing from the graph, in order to show the detail. We see that the critical values get closer to 1.96 as df grows.

For 7.118.

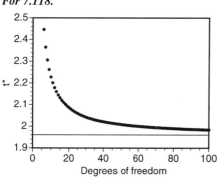

For 7.119.

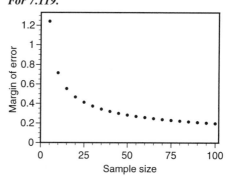

7.119 Plot above, right. The margin of error is $t^* s/\sqrt{n} = t^*/\sqrt{n}$, taking t^* from t distributions with 4, 9, 14, ..., 99 degrees of freedom. For df ≤ 29, these values are in the table; in order to get all the t^* values, software is needed. For reference, $t^* = 2.7764$ with df $= 4$ and $t^* = 1.9842$ with df $= 99$; the margin of error gradually decreases from 1.2416 when $n = 5$ to 0.19842 when $n = 100$.

Chapter 8 Solutions

Section 1: Inference for a Single Proportion

8.1 **(a)** No: $n(1 - \hat{p}) = 30(0.1) = 3$ is less than 10. **(b)** Yes: $n\hat{p} = n(1 - \hat{p}) = 25(0.5) = 12.5$. **(c)** No: $n\hat{p} = 100(0.04) = 4$ is less than 10. **(d)** Yes: $n\hat{p} = (600)(0.6) = 360$ and $n(1 - \hat{p}) = 600(0.4) = 240$.

8.2 **(a)** $\hat{p} = \frac{15}{84} \doteq 0.1786$, and $\mathrm{SE}_{\hat{p}} = \sqrt{\hat{p}(1 - \hat{p})/84} \doteq 0.0418$. **(b)** $\hat{p} \pm 1.645\,\mathrm{SE}_{\hat{p}} = 0.1098$ to 0.2473.

8.3 No: Some of those who lied about having a degree may also have lied about their major. *At most* 24 applicants lied about having a degree or about their major.

8.4 **(a)** $\hat{p} = \frac{542}{1711} \doteq 0.3168$; about 31.7% of 15+ year-old bicyclists killed between 1987 and 1991 had alcohol in their systems at the time of the accident. **(b)** $\mathrm{SE}_{\hat{p}} = \sqrt{\hat{p}(1 - \hat{p})/1711} \doteq 0.01125$; the interval is $\hat{p} \pm 1.960\,\mathrm{SE}_{\hat{p}} = 0.2947$ to 0.3388. **(c)** No: We do not know, for example, what percentage of cyclists who were *not* involved in fatal accidents had alcohol in their systems.

8.5 $\hat{p} = \frac{386}{1711} \doteq 0.2256$, and $\mathrm{SE}_{\hat{p}} = \sqrt{\hat{p}(1 - \hat{p})/1711} \doteq 0.0101$, so the 95% confidence interval is $0.2256 \pm (1.96)(0.0101)$, or 0.2058 to 0.2454.

8.6 **(a)** $\hat{p} = \frac{421}{500} = 0.842$, and $\mathrm{SE}_{\hat{p}} = \sqrt{\hat{p}(1 - \hat{p})/500} \doteq 0.0163$. **(b)** $0.842 \pm (1.96)(0.0163)$, or 0.8100 to 0.8740.

8.7 $\hat{p} = \frac{86}{100} = 0.86$, and $\mathrm{SE}_{\hat{p}} = \sqrt{\hat{p}(1 - \hat{p})/100} \doteq 0.0347$, so the 95% confidence interval is $0.86 \pm (1.96)(0.0347)$, or 0.7920 to 0.9280.

8.8 $\hat{p} = \frac{41}{216} \doteq 0.1898$, and $\mathrm{SE}_{\hat{p}} = \sqrt{\hat{p}(1 - \hat{p})/216} \doteq 0.0267$, so the 99% confidence interval is $0.1898 \pm (2.576)(0.0267)$, or 0.1211 to 0.2585.

8.9 $\hat{p} = \frac{132}{200} = 0.66$, and $\mathrm{SE}_{\hat{p}} = \sqrt{\hat{p}(1 - \hat{p})/200} \doteq 0.0335$, so the 95% confidence interval is $0.66 \pm (1.96)(0.0335)$, or 0.5943 to 0.7257.

8.10 **(a)** No: $np_0 = 4$ is less than 10. **(b)** Yes: $np_0 = 60$ and $n(1 - p_0) = 40$. **(c)** No: $n(1 - p_0) = 4$ is less than 10. **(d)** Yes: $np_0 = 150$ and $n(1 - p_0) = 350$.

8.11 We want to know if p is significantly different from 36%, so we test H_0: $p = 0.36$ vs. H_a: $p \neq 0.36$. We have $\hat{p} = 0.38$; under H_0, $\sigma_{\hat{p}} = \sqrt{(0.36)(0.64)/500} \doteq 0.0215$, so $z = \frac{0.38-0.36}{0.0215} = 0.9317$. This is clearly not significant (in fact, $P \doteq 0.35$).

8.12 **(a)** We want to know if p (the proportion of urban respondents) is significantly different from 64%, so we test H_0: $p = 0.64$ vs. H_a: $p \neq 0.64$. **(b)** We have $\hat{p} = 0.62$; under H_0, $\sigma_{\hat{p}} = \sqrt{(0.64)(0.36)/500} \doteq 0.0215$, so $z = \frac{0.62 - 0.64}{0.0215} = -0.9317$. This is clearly not significant (in fact, $P \doteq 0.35$). **(c)** The results are the same as the previous exercise; in general, performing a test on a proportion p will give the same results as the equivalent test on $p' = 1 - p$.

8.13 **(a)** $\hat{p} = \frac{750}{1785} \doteq 0.4202$, and $\mathrm{SE}_{\hat{p}} = \sqrt{\hat{p}(1 - \hat{p})/200} \doteq 0.0117$, so the 99% confidence interval is $0.4202 \pm (2.576)(0.0117)$, or 0.3901 to 0.4503. **(b)** Yes—the interval does not include 0.50 or more. **(c)** $n = \left(\frac{2.576}{0.01}\right)^2 (0.4202)(0.5798) \doteq 16166.9$—use $n = 16, 167$.

8.14 $n = \left(\frac{1.96}{0.03}\right)^2 (0.44)(0.56) \doteq 1051.7$—use $n = 1052$.

8.15 $\hat{p} = \frac{13}{75} = 0.17\overline{3}$, and $\mathrm{SE}_{\hat{p}} = \sqrt{\hat{p}(1 - \hat{p})/75} \doteq 0.0437$, so the 95% confidence interval is $0.17\overline{3} \pm (1.96)(0.0437)$, or 0.0877 to 0.2590.

8.16 We want to know if p (the proportion of respondents with no children) is significantly different from 48%, so we test H_0: $p = 0.48$ vs. H_a: $p \neq 0.48$. We have $\hat{p} = 0.44$; under H_0, $\sigma_{\hat{p}} = \sqrt{(0.48)(0.52)/500} \doteq 0.0223$, so $z = \frac{0.44 - 0.48}{0.0223} \doteq -1.79$. This has $P \doteq 2(0.0367) = 0.0734$; we don't have quite enough evidence to conclude that the telephone survey reached households without children in a different proportion than such households are found in the population.

8.17 **(a)** Testing H_0: $p = 0.5$ vs. H_a: $p \neq 0.5$, we have $\hat{p} = \frac{5067}{10000} = 0.5067$, and $\sigma_{\hat{p}} = \sqrt{(0.5)(0.5)/10000} = 0.005$, so $z = \frac{0.0067}{0.005} = 1.34$. This is not significant at $\alpha = 0.05$ (or even $\alpha = 0.10$). **(b)** $\mathrm{SE}_{\hat{p}} = \sqrt{\hat{p}(1 - \hat{p})/10000} \doteq 0.005$, so the 95% confidence interval is $0.5067 \pm (1.96)(0.005)$, or 0.4969 to 0.5165.

8.18 **(a)** We test H_0: $p = 0.5$ vs. H_a: $p > 0.5$; $\hat{p} = \frac{31}{50} = 0.62$, and $\sigma_{\hat{p}} = \sqrt{(0.5)(0.5)/50} \doteq 0.0707$, so $z = \frac{0.12}{0.0707} \doteq 1.70$, and $P = 0.0446$. This is significant at the 5% level—but just barely. If one more person had preferred instant, the results would not have been significant. **(b)** $\mathrm{SE}_{\hat{p}} = \sqrt{\hat{p}(1 - \hat{p})/50} \doteq 0.0686$, so the 90% confidence interval is $0.62 \pm (1.645)(0.0686)$, or 0.5071 to 0.7329.

8.19 **(a)** H_0: $p = 0.384$ vs. H_a: $p > 0.384$. **(b)** $\hat{p} = \frac{25}{40} = 0.625$, and $\sigma_{\hat{p}} = \sqrt{(0.384)(0.616)/40} \doteq 0.0769$, so $z = \frac{0.625 - 0.384}{0.0769} \doteq 3.13$. **(c)** Reject H_0 since $z > 1.645$; $P = 0.0009$. **(d)** $\mathrm{SE}_{\hat{p}} = \sqrt{\hat{p}(1 - \hat{p})/40} \doteq 0.0765$, so the 90% confidence interval is $0.625 \pm (1.645)(0.0765)$, or 0.4991 to 0.7509. There is strong evidence that Leroy has improved. **(e)** We assume that the 40 free throws are an SRS; more specifically, each shot represents an independent trial with the same probability of success, so the number of free throws made has a binomial distribution. To use the normal approximation, we also need (for the test) $np_0 = 15.36 > 10$ and $n(1 - p_0) = 24.64 > 10$, and (for the confidence interval) $n\hat{p} = 25 > 10$ and $n(1 - \hat{p}) = 15 > 10$.

8.20 $n = \left(\frac{1.96}{0.05}\right)^2 (0.35)(0.65) \doteq 349.6$—use $n = 350$.

8.21 $n = \left(\frac{1.96}{0.05}\right)^2 (0.2)(0.8) \doteq 245.9$—use $n = 246$.

8.22 **(a)** Higher: For more confidence, we need more information. **(b)** Higher: For more precision, we need more information. **(c)** Lower: Standard errors are smaller for more extreme p^* values (close to 0 or 1). **(d)** Same: This has no effect on margin of error.

8.23 $n = \left(\frac{1.645}{0.04}\right)^2 (0.7)(0.3) \doteq 355.2$—use $n = 356$. With $\hat{p} = 0.5$, $\text{SE}_{\hat{p}} \doteq 0.0265$, so the true margin of error is $(1.645)(0.0265) = 0.0436$.

8.24 $n = \left(\frac{2.576}{0.015}\right)^2 (0.2)(0.8) \doteq 4718.8$—use $n = 4719$. With $\hat{p} = 0.1$, $\text{SE}_{\hat{p}} \doteq 0.00437$, so the true margin of error is $(2.576)(0.00437) = 0.0112$.

8.25 **(a)** The margins of error are $1.96\sqrt{\hat{p}(1 - \hat{p})/100} = 0.196\sqrt{\hat{p}(1 - \hat{p})}$.

$\hat{p}$	0.1	0.2	0.3	0.4	0.5	0.6	0.7	0.8	0.9
m.e.	.0588	.0784	.0898	.0960	.0980	.0960	.0898	.0784	.0588

(b) No: $n\hat{p} = 100(0.04) = 4$ is less than 10.

8.26 The margins of error are $1.96\sqrt{\hat{p}(1 - \hat{p})/500} = 0.196\sqrt{\hat{p}(1 - \hat{p})/5}$.

$\hat{p}$	0.1	0.2	0.3	0.4	0.5	0.6	0.7	0.8	0.9
m.e.	.0263	.0351	.0402	.0429	.0438	.0429	.0402	.0351	.0263

With $n = 500$, we could use a normal approximation with $\hat{p} = 0.04$, since $n\hat{p} = 500(0.04) = 20$. The letter to the benefactor should mention the greatly reduced margins of error.

Section 2: Comparing Two Proportions

8.27 **(a)** $\hat{p}_f = \frac{48}{60} = 0.8$, so $\text{SE}_{\hat{p}} \doteq 0.05164$ for females. $\hat{p}_m = \frac{52}{132} = 0.\overline{39}$, so $\text{SE}_{\hat{p}} \doteq 0.04253$ for males. **(b)** $\text{SE}_D = \sqrt{0.05164^2 + 0.04253^2} \doteq 0.0669$, so the interval is $(\hat{p}_f - \hat{p}_m) \pm (1.96)(0.0669)$, or 0.2749 to 0.5372. There is (with high confidence) a considerably higher percentage of juvenile references to females than to males.

8.28 **(a)** We have $\hat{p}_f = \frac{27}{191} \doteq 0.1414$ and $\hat{p}_m = \frac{515}{1520} \doteq 0.3388$, which gives $\text{SE}_D = \sqrt{\hat{p}_f(1 - \hat{p}_f)/191 + \hat{p}_m(1 - \hat{p}_m)/1520} \doteq 0.02798$. The interval is $(\hat{p}_f - \hat{p}_m) \pm$

(1.645)(0.02798), or −0.2435 to −0.1514 (i.e., the female proportion is substantially lower). **(b)** The female $\text{SE}_{\hat{p}}$ contributes the greater amount, because there were considerably fewer women in the sample—dividing by 1520 makes the male $\text{SE}_{\hat{p}}$ very small by comparison.

8.29 (a) We have $\hat{p}_1 = \frac{15}{84} \doteq 0.1786$ and $\hat{p}_2 = \frac{21}{106} \doteq 0.1981$, which gives $\text{SE}_D = \sqrt{\hat{p}_1(1 - \hat{p}_1)/84 + \hat{p}_2(1 - \hat{p}_2)/106} \doteq 0.0570$, so the interval is $(\hat{p}_1 - \hat{p}_2) \pm (1.645)(0.0570)$, or −0.1132 to 0.0742. Since this interval includes 0, we have little evidence here to suggest that the two proportions are different.

8.30 Testing H_0: $p_f = p_m$ vs. H_a: $p_f \neq p_m$, we have $\hat{p}_f = 0.8$, $\hat{p}_m = 0.\overline{39}$, and $\hat{p} = \frac{48+52}{60+132} \doteq 0.5208$. This gives $s_p = \sqrt{\hat{p}(1 - \hat{p})(\frac{1}{60} + \frac{1}{132})} \doteq 0.0778$, so $z = (\hat{p}_f - \hat{p}_m)/s_p \doteq 5.22$. With $P < 0.0001$, we have strong evidence that the two proportions are different.

8.31 Test H_0: $p_f = p_m$ vs. H_a: $p_f \neq p_m$ (assuming we have no belief, before seeing the data, that the difference will lie in a particular direction—e.g., that $p_f < p_m$). The pooled estimate of p is $\hat{p} = \frac{27+515}{191+1520} \doteq 0.3168$, which gives $s_p \doteq 0.0357$, so $z = \frac{0.1414 - 0.3388}{0.0357} \doteq -5.53$. This gives $P < 0.0001$; it is significant at any α, so we conclude (with near certainty) that there is a difference between the proportions.

8.32 Testing H_0: $p_1 = p_2$ vs. H_a: $p_1 \neq p_2$, we have $\hat{p}_1 \doteq 0.1786$, $\hat{p}_2 \doteq 0.1981$, and $\hat{p} = \frac{15+21}{84+106} \doteq 0.1895$. This gives $s_p = \sqrt{\hat{p}(1 - \hat{p})(\frac{1}{84} + \frac{1}{106})} \doteq 0.0572$, so $z = (\hat{p}_1 - \hat{p}_2)/s_p \doteq -0.34$. With $P = 2(0.3669) = 0.7338$, we have no reason to believe that the two proportions are different.

8.33 (a) H_0: $p_1 = p_2$; H_a: $p_1 \neq p_2$. **(b)** $\hat{p}_1 = \frac{64}{160} = 0.4$, $\hat{p}_2 = \frac{89}{261} \doteq 0.3410$, and $\hat{p} = \frac{64+89}{160+261} \doteq 0.3634$, which gives $s_p \doteq 0.0483$, so $z = (\hat{p}_1 - \hat{p}_2)/s_p \doteq 1.22$. This gives $P \doteq 2(0.1112) = 0.2224$; there is little evidence to suggest a difference between rural and urban households. **(c)** $\text{SE}_D \doteq 0.04859$, so the interval is 0.0590 ± 0.0799, or −0.0209 to 0.1389.

8.34 (a) $\hat{p}_h = \frac{49}{80} = 0.6125$ and $\hat{p}_a = \frac{43}{82} \doteq 0.5244$. **(b)** $\text{SE}_D \doteq 0.0775$. **(c)** The interval is $(\hat{p}_h - \hat{p}_a) \pm (1.645)(0.0775) = -0.0394$ to 0.2156. Since this interval contains 0, we are not convinced that the true proportions are different.

8.35 (a) $\hat{p}_1 = \frac{263}{263+252} \doteq 0.5107$ and $\hat{p}_2 = \frac{260}{260+377} \doteq 0.4082$. **(b)** $\text{SE}_D \doteq 0.0294$. **(c)** $0.1025 \pm (2.576)(0.0294)$, or 0.0268 to 0.1783. Since 0 is not in this interval, there appears to be a real difference in the proportions (though it might be fairly small).

8.36 (a) $\hat{p} = \frac{49+43}{80+82} \doteq 0.5679$. (b) $s_p \doteq 0.0778$. (c) H_0: $p_h = p_a$ vs. H_a: $p_h > p_a$.
(d) $z = (\hat{p}_h - p_a)/s_p \doteq 1.13$, so $P = 0.1292$. There is not enough evidence to conclude that the Yankees were more likely to win at home.

8.37 (a) $\hat{p} = \frac{263+260}{263+252+260+377} \doteq 0.4540$. (b) $s_p \doteq 0.0295$. (c) H_0: $p_1 = p_2$ vs. H_a: $p_1 \neq p_2$ (assuming we have no prior information about which might be higher). (d) $z = (\hat{p}_1 - p_2)/s_p \doteq 3.47$, which gives $P \doteq 2(0.0003) = 0.0006$. We reject H_0 and conclude that there is a real difference in the proportions.

8.38 Note that the rules of thumb for the normal approximation are not satisfied here (the number of birth defects is less than 10). Additionally, one might call into question the assumption of independence, since there may have been multiple births to the same set of parents included in these counts (either twins/triplets/etc., or "ordinary" siblings).
  If we carry out the analysis in spite of these issues, we find $\hat{p}_1 = \frac{16}{414} \doteq 0.03865$ and $\hat{p}_2 = \frac{3}{228} \doteq 0.01316$. We might then find a 95% confidence interval: $\text{SE}_D \doteq 0.01211$, so the interval is $\hat{p}_1 - \hat{p}_2 \pm (1.96)(0.01211) = 0.00175$ to 0.04923. (Note that this does not take into account the presumed direction of the difference.) We could also perform a significance test of H_0: $p_1 = p_2$ vs. H_a: $p_1 > p_2$: $\hat{p} = \frac{19}{642} \doteq 0.02960$, $s_p \doteq 0.01398$, $z \doteq 1.82$, $P = 0.0344$.
  Both the interval and the significance test suggest that the two proportions are different, but we must recognize that the issues noted above make this conclusion questionable.

8.39 We have $\hat{p}_1 = \frac{381}{4096} \doteq 0.0930$ and $\hat{p}_2 = \frac{8}{28} \doteq 0.2857$; test H_0: $p_1 = p_2$ vs. H_a: $p_1 < p_2$. $\hat{p} = \frac{381+8}{4096+28} \doteq 0.0943$ and $s \doteq 0.0554$; so $z \doteq -3.48$, which gives $P \doteq 0.0002$. We reject H_0 and conclude that there is a real difference in the proportions; abnormal chromosomes are associated with increased criminality. (One could also construct, e.g., a 95% confidence interval, but this does not take into account the presumed direction of the difference.)
  Note that here, as in the previous exercise, one of our counts is less than 10, meaning that the normality assumption might not be valid for the abnormal-chromosome group.

8.40 We test H_0: $p_1 = p_2$ vs. H_a: $p_1 \neq p_2$. $\hat{p}_1 \doteq 0.6030$, $\hat{p}_2 \doteq 0.5913$, $\hat{p} \doteq 0.5976$; therefore, $s_p \doteq 0.0441$ and $z \doteq 0.27$, so $P \doteq 2(0.3936) = 0.7872$—$H_0$ is quite plausible given this sample.

8.41 $\hat{p}_1 = \frac{104}{267} \doteq 0.3895$ and $\hat{p}_2 = \frac{75}{230} \doteq 0.3261$; $\text{SE}_D \doteq 0.04297$, so the confidence interval is $0.0634 \pm (1.96)(0.04297)$, or -0.0208 to 0.1476.

8.42 (a) H_0: $p_m = p_f$ vs. H_a: $p_m \neq p_f$. $\hat{p}_m \doteq 0.9009$, $\hat{p}_f \doteq 0.8101$, and $\hat{p} \doteq 0.8574$. Then $s_p \doteq 0.01790$ and $z \doteq 5.07$, so $P < 0.0001$. There is strong evidence that the two proportions differ. (b) $\text{SE}_D \doteq 0.01795$, so the interval is $p_m - p_f \pm (2.576)(0.01785) = 0.0445$ to 0.1370. Whether this difference is "important" or not is a matter of opinion.

8.43 (a) For H_0: $p_1 = p_2$ vs. H_a: $p_1 \neq p_2$, we have $\hat{p}_1 = \frac{35}{83} \doteq 0.4217$, $\hat{p}_2 = \frac{15}{136} \doteq 0.1103$, $\hat{p} = \frac{35+15}{83+136} \doteq 0.2283$, and $s_p \doteq 0.0585$. Then $z \doteq 5.33$, so $P < 0.0001$. We reject H_0 and conclude that there is a real difference in the proportions for the two shield types. (b) $\text{SE}_D \doteq 0.0605$, so the interval is $0.3114 \pm (1.645)(0.0605)$, or 0.2119 to 0.4109. The flip-up shields are much more likely to remain on the tractor.

8.44 (a) $\hat{p}_1 \doteq 0.8077$, $\hat{p}_2 \doteq 0.5584$. (b) $\text{SE}_D \doteq 0.0721$; the interval is 0.1080 to 0.3905. (c) H_0: $p_1 = p_2$; H_a: $p_1 > p_2$. $\hat{p} \doteq 0.6839$, and $s_p \doteq 0.0747$, so $z \doteq 3.34$, so $P \doteq 0.0004$. There is strong evidence that aspirin was effective.

8.45 (a) $\hat{p}_1 = \frac{9}{18} = 0.5$ and $\hat{p}_2 = \frac{13}{18} = 0.7\overline{2}$. (b) $-0.2222 \pm (1.645)(0.1582)$, or -0.4825 to 0.0380. (c) H_0: $p_1 = p_2$; H_a: $p_1 < p_2$. $\hat{p} = \frac{9+13}{18+18} = 0.6\overline{1}$, $s_p \doteq 0.1625$, and $z \doteq -1.37$; the P-value is 0.0853. There is some evidence that the proportions are different, but it is not significant at the 5% level; if the two proportions were equal, we would observe such a difference between $\hat{p}_1$ and $\hat{p}_2$ about 8.5% of the time.

8.46 (a) Again testing H_0: $p_m = p_f$ vs. H_a: $p_m \neq p_f$, we have $\hat{p}_m = 0.9$, $\hat{p}_f \doteq 0.8082$, and $\hat{p} \doteq 0.8562$. Then $s_p \doteq 0.0568$ and $z \doteq 1.62$, so $P \doteq 0.1052$. We cannot conclude that the two proportions differ. (b) With the larger sample size, the difference was significant; a smaller sample size means more variability, so large differences are more likely to happen by chance.

8.47 (a) $\hat{p}_1 = 0.5$, $\hat{p}_2 = 0.7\overline{2}$, $\hat{p} = 0.6\overline{1}$, $s_p \doteq 0.1149$, and $z \doteq -1.93$; the P-value is 0.0268 (recall the alternative hypothesis is one-sided). This is significant evidence of a difference—specifically, that $p_1 < p_2$. (b) With the larger sample size, the difference $\hat{p}_1 - \hat{p}_2 = -0.\overline{2}$ is less likely to have happened by chance.

Exercises

8.48 We test H_0: $p_f = p_m$ vs. H_a: $p_f \neq p_m$ for each text, where, e.g., p_f is the proportion of juvenile female references. We can reject H_0 for texts 2, 3, 6, and 10. The last three texts do not stand out as different from the first seven. Texts 7 and 9 are notable as the only two with a majority of juvenile male references, while 6 of the 10 texts had juvenile female references a majority of the time.

Text	$\hat{p}_f$	$\hat{p}_m$	$\hat{p}$	z	P
1	.4000	.2059	.2308	0.96	.3370
2	.7143	.2857	.3286	2.29	.0220
3	.4464	.2154	.3223	2.71	.0068
4	.1447	.1210	.1288	0.51	.6100
5	.6667	.2791	.3043	1.41	.1586
6	.8000	.3939	.5208	5.22	.0000
7	.9500	.9722	.9643	−0.61	.5418
8	.2778	.1818	.2157	0.80	.4238
9	.6667	.7273	.7097	−0.95	.3422
10	.7222	.2520	.3103	4.04	.0000

8.49 The proportions, z-values, and P-values are

Text	1	2	3	4	5	6	7	8	9	10
$\hat{p}$	.872	.900	.537	.674	.935	.688	.643	.647	.710	.876
z	4.64	6.69	0.82	5.31	5.90	5.20	3.02	2.10	6.60	9.05
P	≈ 0	≈ 0	.413	≈ 0	≈ 0	≈ 0	.002	.036	≈ 0	≈ 0

We reject H_0: $p = 0.5$ for all texts but Text 3 and (perhaps) Text 8. (And maybe also for Text 7, if we are using, e.g., Bonferroni's procedure—see Chapter 6).

The last three texts do not seem to be any different from the first seven; the gender of the author does not seem to affect the proportion.

8.50 The null hypothesis is H_0: $p_1 = p_2$; the alternative might reasonably be $p_1 \neq p_2$ or $p_1 < p_2$—the latter since we might suspect that older children are more likely to sort correctly. $\hat{p}_1 = 0.2$, $\hat{p}_2 \doteq 0.5283$, $\hat{p} \doteq 0.3689$; therefore, $s_p \doteq 0.0951$ and $z \doteq -3.45$. Whichever alternative we use, the P-value is small (0.0003 or 0.0006), so we conclude that the older children are better at sorting.

The standard error for the confidence interval is $\text{SE}_D \doteq 0.0889$, so the interval is $\hat{p}_1 - \hat{p}_2 \pm (1.645)(0.0889) = -0.4745$ to -0.1821.

8.51 No: The percentage was based on a voluntary response sample, and so it cannot be assumed to be a fair representation of the population. Such a poll is likely to draw a higher-than-actual proportion of people with a strong opinion, especially a strong negative opinion. A confidence statement like the one given is not reliable under these circumstances.

8.52 Test H_0: $p = 0.11$ vs. H_a: $p < 0.11$. $\hat{p} = 0.05\overline{3}$ and $\sigma_{\hat{p}} \doteq 0.01806$, so $z \doteq -3.14$. This gives $P \doteq 0.0008$; we have strong evidence that the nonconformity rate is lower (i.e., that the modification is effective). Here we assume that each item in our sample is independent of the others.

8.53 $\hat{p} = \frac{16}{300} = 0.05\overline{3}$ and $\text{SE}_{\hat{p}} \doteq 0.0130$; the confidence interval for p is $0.05\overline{3} \pm (1.96)(0.0130)$, or 0.0279 to 0.0788.

Note that the confidence interval for $p - p_0$ is *not* constructed using the procedure for a difference of two proportions, since p_0 is not based on a sample, but is taken as a constant. This confidence interval is found by subtracting 0.11 from the previous interval: -0.0821 to -0.0312. In other words, we are 95% confident that the new process has a nonconformity rate that is 3.12% to 8.21% lower than the old process.

8.54 **(a)** $\hat{p} = \frac{444}{950} \doteq 0.4674$ and $\text{SE}_{\hat{p}} \doteq 0.0162$; the confidence interval for p is $0.4674 \pm (2.576)(0.0162) = 0.4257$ to 0.5091. **(b)** Between 42.6% and 50.9% of students change their majors. **(c)** We expect that between 14,900 and 17,800 students will change their majors.

8.55 **(a)** $p_0 = \frac{214}{851} \doteq 0.2515$. **(b)** $\hat{p} = \frac{15}{30} = 0.5$. **(c)** H_0: $p = p_0$; H_a: $p > p_0$. $\sigma_{\hat{p}} = \sqrt{p_0(1 - p_0)/30} \doteq 0.0792$ and $z = (0.5 - p_0)/\sigma_{\hat{p}} \doteq 3.14$, so $P = 0.0008$; we reject H_0 and conclude that women are more likely to be among the top students than their proportion in the class.

8.56 We test H_0: $p_1 = p_2$ vs. H_a: $p_1 \neq p_2$. $\hat{p}_1 \doteq 0.4719$, $\hat{p}_2 \doteq 0.6054$, $\hat{p} \doteq 0.5673$; therefore, $s_p \doteq 0.0621$, $z \doteq -2.15$, and $P = 0.0316$. We have fairly strong evidence that the proportions of vegetarians differ between black and white Seventh-Day Adventists. We should not assume that this extends to blacks and whites in general.

8.57 **(a)** $\hat{p}_1 = \frac{55}{3338} \doteq 0.0165$ and $\hat{p}_2 = \frac{21}{2676} \doteq 0.0078$; $SE_D \doteq 0.0028$, so the confidence interval is $0.0086 \pm (1.96)(0.0028)$, or 0.0032 to 0.0141. **(b)** H_0: $p_1 = p_2$; H_a: $p_1 > p_2$. $\hat{p} = \frac{55+21}{3338+2676} \doteq 0.0126$, and $s_p \doteq 0.0029$. Then $z \doteq 2.98$, so $P = 0.0014$. We reject H_0; this difference is unlikely to occur by chance, so we conclude that high blood pressure is associated with a higher death rate.

8.58 For the British study, $\hat{p}_1 = \frac{148}{3429} \doteq 0.0432$ and $\hat{p}_2 = \frac{79}{1710} \doteq 0.0462$. To test H_0: $p_1 = p_2$ vs. H_a: $p_1 \neq p_2$, we compute $\hat{p} \doteq 0.0442$, $s_p \doteq 0.0061$, and $z \doteq -0.50$, so $P = 2(0.3085) = 0.617$—there is very little evidence of a difference.

For the American study, $\hat{p}_1 = \frac{104}{11037} \doteq 0.0094$ and $\hat{p}_2 = \frac{189}{11034} \doteq 0.0171$. Testing the same hypotheses as above, we compute $\hat{p} \doteq 0.0133$, $s \doteq 0.0015$, and $z \doteq -5.00$, so P is essentially 0. This is strong evidence of a difference: aspirin reduced the risk of a fatal heart attack.

The difference in the conclusions can be attributed to the larger sample size for the American study (important for something as rare as a heart attack), as well as the shorter duration of the study and the lower dosage (taking the aspirin every other day rather than every day).

8.59 **(a)** H_0: $p_1 = p_2$; H_a: $p_1 \neq p_2$. $\hat{p}_1 = \frac{28}{82} \doteq 0.3415$, $\hat{p}_2 = \frac{30}{78} \doteq 0.3846$, and $\hat{p} = 0.3625$, so $s_p \doteq 0.0760$. Then $z \doteq -0.57$ and $P \doteq 0.5686$. **(b)** Gastric freezing is not significantly more (or less) effective than a placebo treatment.

8.60 The pooled estimate of p is $\hat{p} = (n\hat{p}_1 + n\hat{p}_2)/(n + n) = (\hat{p}_1 + \hat{p}_2)/2 = 0.5$, so $s_p = \sqrt{\hat{p}(1 - \hat{p})(1/n + 1/n)} = \sqrt{0.5/n}$, and $z = (0.6 - 0.4)/s_p = 0.2\sqrt{2n}$. The P-value is $2P(Z > z)$.

The difference $\hat{p}_1 - \hat{p}_2$ is not significant for small n, but it grows more and more significant as n increases.

n	z	P
15	1.095	0.2733
25	1.414	0.1573
50	2.000	0.0455
75	2.449	0.0143
100	2.828	0.0047
500	6.325	0.0000

8.61 $SE_D = \sqrt{\hat{p}_1(1 - \hat{p}_1)/n_1 + \hat{p}_2(1 - \hat{p}_2)/n_2} =$
$\sqrt{0.24/n + 0.24/n} = \sqrt{0.48/n}$. With $z^* = 1.96$, the
95% confidence interval is $0.2 \pm 1.96\sqrt{0.48/n}$, and
the margin of error is $1.96\sqrt{0.48/n}$.
   The interval narrows as n increases.

n	CI	m.e.
15	−0.151 to 0.551	0.351
25	−0.072 to 0.472	0.272
50	0.008 to 0.392	0.192
75	0.043 to 0.357	0.157
100	0.064 to 0.336	0.136
500	0.139 to 0.261	0.061

8.62 $SE_D = \sqrt{\hat{p}_1(1 - \hat{p}_1)/n_1 + \hat{p}_2(1 - \hat{p}_2)/n_2} =$
$\sqrt{0.25/n + 0.25/n} = \sqrt{0.5/n}$, and the margin of error is
$2.576\,SE_D$. [Note that when $n = 10$, the normal approximation
should not really be used: $n\hat{p} = n(1 - \hat{p}) = 5$.]
   The margin of error decreases as n increases (specifically, it is
inversely proportional to $\sqrt{n}$).

n	m.e.
10	0.5760
30	0.3326
50	0.2576
100	0.1822
200	0.1288
500	0.0815

8.63 **(a)** The margin of error is $z^*\sqrt{0.5(1 - 0.5)/n + 0.5(1 - 0.5)/n} = z^*\sqrt{0.5/n}$. With
$z^* = 1.96$, this means we need to choose n so that $1.96\sqrt{0.5/n} \leq 0.05$. The smallest
such n is 769. **(b)** Solving $z^*\sqrt{0.5/n} \leq m$ gives $n \geq 0.5(z^*/m)^2$.

8.64 The margin of error is $1.645\sqrt{\dfrac{0.5(1 - 0.5)}{20} + \dfrac{0.5(1 - 0.5)}{n_2}} = 1.645\sqrt{0.0125 + 0.25/n_2}$.
We therefore need to solve $1.645\sqrt{0.0125 + 0.25/n_2} = 0.1$—but there is no such value
of n_2 (except $n_2 \doteq -28.4$, which makes no sense here). No matter how big n_2 is, the
margin of error will always be greater than $1.645\sqrt{0.0125} \doteq 0.1840$.

8.65 It is likely that little or no useful information would come out of such an experiment;
the proportion of people dying of cardiovascular disease is so small that out of a group of
200, we would expect very few to die in a five- or six-year period. This experiment would
detect differences between treatment and control only if the treatment was *very* effective
(or dangerous)—i.e., if it almost completely eliminated (or drastically increased) the risk
of CV disease.

8.66 **(a)** $p_0 = \dfrac{143,611}{181,535} \doteq 0.7911$. **(b)** $\hat{p} = \dfrac{339}{870} \doteq 0.3897$, $\sigma_{\hat{p}} \doteq 0.0138$, and $z = (\hat{p} -$
$p_0)/\sigma_{\hat{p}} \doteq -29.1$, so $P \doteq 0$ (regardless of whether H_a is $p > p_0$ or $p \neq p_0$). This is very
strong evidence against H_0; we conclude that Mexican Americans are underrepresented
on juries. **(c)** $\hat{p}_1 = \dfrac{339}{870} \doteq 0.3897$, while $\hat{p}_2 = \dfrac{143,611-339}{181,535-870} \doteq 0.7930$. Then $\hat{p} \doteq 0.7911$
(the value of p_0 from part (a)), $s_p = 0.0138$, and $z \doteq -29.2$—and again, we have a tiny
P-value and reject H_0.

Chapter 9 Solutions

9.1 (a) At right.

(b) The expected counts are

$$\frac{(48)(511)}{1317} = 18.624,$$

$$\frac{(48)(806)}{1317} = 29.376,$$

$$\frac{(1269)(511)}{1317} = 492.376, \text{ and } \frac{(1269)(806)}{1317} = 776.624. \text{ Then}$$

Over 40?	Number of Employees	Proportion Terminated	Standard Error
No	511	0.0137	0.005142
Yes	806	0.0509	0.007740

$$X^2 = \frac{(7 - 18.624)^2}{18.624} + \frac{(41 - 29.376)^2}{29.376} + \frac{(504 - 492.376)^2}{492.376} + \frac{(765 - 776.624)^2}{776.624} = 12.303.$$

Comparing to a $\chi^2(1)$ distribution, we find $P < 0.0005$; we conclude that there is an association between age and whether or not the employee was terminated—specifically, older employees were more likely to be terminated.

9.2 The analysis might include, for example, expected counts and column percents (shown in the table). We note that older employees are almost twice as likely as under-40 employees to fall into the two lowest performance appraisal categories (partially/fully meets expectations), and are only about one-third as likely to have the highest appraisal. The differences in the percentages are significant:

	Under 40	Over 40	
Partially/ fully meets expectations	82 123.41 16.5%	230 188.59 30.3%	312 24.9%
Usually exceeds expectations	353 335.81 71.2%	496 513.19 65.4%	849 67.7%
Continually exceeds expectations	61 36.78 12.3%	32 56.22 4.2%	93 7.4%
	496	758	1254

$X^2 = 13.893 + 9.091 + 0.880 + 0.576 + 15.941 + 10.431 = 50.812$ (df = 2) has $P < 0.0005$.

9.3 (a) Use column percents, because we suspect that "source" is explanatory. See the table. **(b)** The expected counts are in the table. The test statistic is $X^2 = 1.305 + 0.666 + 2.483 + 0.632 + 0.323 + 1.202 = 6.611$; comparing to a $\chi^2(2)$ distribution, we find $0.025 < P < 0.05$ (software

	Private	Pet Store	Other	
Cases	124 111.92 36.2%	16 13.05 40%	76 91.03 27.2%	216 32.6%
Control	219 231.08 63.8%	24 26.95 60%	203 187.97 72.8%	446 67.4%
	343	40	279	662

gives 0.037). The conclusion depends on the chosen value of α. With $\alpha = 0.05$, e.g., so that $P < \alpha$, we conclude that there is an association between the source of a cat, and whether or not the pet ends up in the animal shelter.

9.4 Expected counts and column percents are given in the table. $X^2 = 0.569 + 9.423 + 9.369 + 0.223 + 3.689 + 3.668 = 26.939$ (df = 2); this has $P < 0.0005$. We conclude that there is an association between the source of a dog and whether or not the dog ends up in the animal shelter.

	Private	Pet Store	Other	
Cases	188	7	90	285
	198.63	21.10	65.27	
	26.6%	9.3%	38.8%	28.1%
Control	518	68	142	728
	507.37	53.90	166.73	
	73.4%	90.7%	61.2%	71.9%
	706	75	232	1013

9.5 This is a 2 × 3 table, with each household classified by pet (cat or dog) and by source. If we view "source" as explanatory for pet type, then we should look at the conditional distribution of pet type, given the source (i.e., column percents), as given in the table. It appears that cats are more likely to

	Private	Pet Store	Other	
Cats	219	24	203	446
	279.98	34.95	131.06	
	29.7%	26.1%	58.8%	38%
Dogs	518	68	142	728
	457.02	57.05	213.94	
	70.3%	73.9%	41.2%	62%
	737	92	345	1174

come from an "other" source. The test statistic bears this out: $X^2 = 13.283 + 8.138 + 3.431 + 2.102 + 39.482 + 24.188 = 90.624$ (df = 2), so that $P < 0.0005$. We conclude that there is a relationship between source and pet type.

9.6 (a) These are the percentages in the top row of the table. **(b)** H_0: There is no relationship between intervention and response rate; H_a: There is a relationship. **(c)** $X^2 = 4.906 + 56.765 + 41.398 + 2.872 + 33.234 + 24.237 = 163.413$, df = 2, $P < 0.0005$. The differences between the response rates are significant; specifically, letters and phone calls both increase the response rate, with the latter being more effective.

	Letter	Phone Call	None	
Yes	171	146	118	435
	144.38	79.02	211.59	
	43.7%	68.2%	20.6%	36.9%
No	220	68	455	743
	246.62	134.98	361.41	
	56.3%	31.8%	79.4%	63.1%
	391	214	573	1178

9.7 (a) With a letter, 51.2% responded; without, the response rate was 52.6%. **(b)** H_0: there is no relationship between whether or not a letter is sent and whether or not the subject responds; H_a: There is a relationship. The test statistic is $X^2 = 0.461 + 0.460 + 0.497 + 0.496 = 1.914$; comparing to a $\chi^2(1)$ distribution, we find $0.15 < P < 0.20$ (software gives 0.167). There is little reason to reject the null hypothesis.

	Letter	No Letter	
Yes	2570	2645	5215
	2604.65	2610.35	
	51.2%	52.6%	51.9%
No	2448	2384	4832
	2413.35	2418.65	
	48.8%	47.4%	48.1%
	5018	5029	10047

9.8 Responses may vary. Both surveys—especially the first one—may be somewhat dated. The questions asked of the college students was one that might have general interest to them, whereas the survey sent to the physicians was more important to them professionally (this might account for the higher response rate among physicians). Viewed from this perspective, we might expect our survey response to be more like the college student results, since Internet accessibility will likely (for most of our population) be of general, not professional, interest.

9.9 **(a)** No: No treatment was imposed. **(b)** See the column percents in the table. Pet owners seem to have better survival rates. **(c)** H_0 says that there is no relationship between patient status and pet ownership (i.e., that survival is independent of pet ownership). H_a says that there is a relationship between survival and pet ownership. **(d)** $X^2 =$

	No Pet	Pet	
Alive	28	50	78
	33.07	44.93	
	71.8%	94.3%	84.8%
Dead	11	3	14
	5.93	8.07	
	28.2%	5.7%	15.2%
	39	53	92

$0.776 + 0.571 + 4.323 + 3.181 = 8.851$ (df = 1), so $0.0025 < P < 0.005$ (in fact, $P = 0.003$). **(e)** Provided we believe that there are no confounding or lurking variables, we reject H_0 and conclude that owning a pet improves survival.

9.10 **(a)** In table. These percents show how January performance can predict rest-of-year performance: Among those years in which the S&P index was up in January, the index rose in the rest of the year 72.9% of the time, etc. **(b)** Since the table is symmetric, each pair of row percents is the same as the corresponding column pair (e.g., the first row is 72.9% and 27.1%—the same as the first column). These show, e.g., that if the index was up for the rest of the year, then there is a 72.9% chance that it was up in January,

	January		
	Up	Down	
Up	35	13	48
this	30.72	17.28	
year	72.9%	48.1%	64%
Down	13	14	27
this	17.28	9.72	
year	27.1%	51.9%	36%
	48	27	75

as well. **(c)** H_0 says that there is no relationship between January performance and rest-of-year performance. H_a says that there is a relationship. **(d)** The expected counts (in the table) are higher than observed in the Down/Up and Up/Down cells—suggesting that we are less likely than we might expect to see these combinations—and lower than observed in the Up/Up and Down/Down cells—suggesting that these are more likely than we expect. This is in line with the January indicator. **(e)** $X^2 = 0.596 + 1.060 + 1.060 + 1.885 = 4.601$, df = 1, $P = 0.032$. This is fairly strong evidence of a relationship. **(f)** The data support the January indicator, but mostly for the Up/Up case. That is, in years when the market was down in January, we have little indication of performance for the rest of the year; historically, it has been about 50% up, 50% down. If the market is up in January, however, history suggests it is more likely to be up for the whole year.

9.11 (a) At right. **(b)** Use column percents (here reported as proportions rather than percents): His batting average was .262 during the regular season, and .357—much higher—during the World Series. **(c)** H_0 says that the regular season and World Series distributions (batting averages) are the same; the alternative is that the two distributions are different. $X^2 = 0.033 + 3.311 + 0.012 + 1.181 = 4.536$, df $= 1$, $P = 0.033$. We have fairly strong (though not overwhelming) evidence that Jackson did better in the World Series.

Hit?	Regular Season	World Series	
Yes	2584	35	2619
No	7280	63	7343
	9864	98	9962

9.12 (a) & (b) See table. Percentage of children receiving tetracycline seems to rise as we move from urban to rural counties. **(c)** H_0: There is no relationship between county type and prescription practice; H_a: There is a relationship. **(d)** $X^2 = 7.370 + 0.372 + 7.242 + 5.440 + 0.275 + 5.345 = 26.044$, df $= 2$, $P < 0.0005$. The differences between the tetracycline prescription practices are significant; doctors in rural counties were most likely to prescribe tetracycline to young children, while urban doctors were least likely to do so.

	Urban	Intermed.	Rural	
Tetra.	65	90	172	327
	90.88	95.98	140.14	
	30.4%	39.8%	52.1%	42.5%
No tetra.	149	136	158	443
	123.12	130.02	189.86	
	69.6%	60.2%	47.9%	57.5%
	214	226	330	770

9.13 Expected counts and column percents in table. 69.7% of the second-year "winners" also had been winners in the first year, while only 29.7% of second-year losers had been winners in the first year. This suggests some persistence in performance. The test statistic supports this: $X^2 = 9.443 + 9.763 + 9.443 + 9.763 = 38.411$, df $= 1$, $P < 0.0005$. We have strong evidence to support persistence of fund performance.

	Next year Winner	Loser	
Winner this year	85	35	120
	61.00	59.00	
	69.7%	29.7%	50%
Loser this year	37	83	120
	61.00	59.00	
	30.3%	70.3%	50%
	122	118	240

9.14 $\hat{p}_1 = \frac{85}{122} \doteq 0.6967$, $\hat{p}_2 = \frac{35}{118} \doteq 0.2966$, and the "pooled" estimate of p is $\hat{p} = \frac{120}{240} = 0.5$. The test statistic for H_0: $p_1 = p_2$ vs. H_a: $p_1 \neq p_2$ is $z = (\hat{p}_1 - \hat{p}_2)/\sqrt{(0.5)(0.5)\left(\frac{1}{122} + \frac{1}{118}\right)} \doteq 6.197$. This agrees with the previous result: $z^2 = 38.411$ and the P-value is $2P(Z > 6.197) \doteq 0.000374$.

9.15 With the retrospective approach, we have $\hat{p}_1 = \frac{85}{120} = 0.708\overline{3}$, $\hat{p}_2 = \frac{37}{120} = 0.308\overline{3}$, and "pooled" estimate $\hat{p} = \frac{122}{240} = 0.508\overline{3}$. The test statistic is $z = (\hat{p}_1 - \hat{p}_2)/\sqrt{\hat{p}(1-\hat{p})\left(\frac{1}{120} + \frac{1}{120}\right)} \doteq 6.197$. This agrees with the previous result: $z^2 = 38.411$.

9.16 Expected counts and column percents in table. 39.8% of the second-year "winners" also had been winners in the first year, while 59.9% of second-year losers had been winners in the first year. This is evidence *against* persistence; note also that the expected counts are higher than observed in the Win/Win and Lose/Lose cells. The test statistic is $X^2 = 4.981 + 4.860 + 4.981 + 4.860 = 19.683$, df = 1, $P < 0.0005$. There is

	Next year		
	Winner	Loser	
Winner this year	96 120.50 39.8%	148 123.50 59.9%	244 50%
Loser this year	145 120.50 60.2%	99 123.50 40.1%	244 50%
	241	247	488

significant evidence against the null hypothesis (no relationship), but in this case, it is evidence of "antipersistence."

9.17 There is no reason to consider one of these as explanatory, but a conditional distribution is useful to determine the nature of the association. Each cell in the table contains a pair of percentages; the first is the column percent, and the second is the row percent. For example, among nonsmokers, 34.5% were nondrinkers; among nondrinkers, 85.4% were nonsmokers. The percentages in the right margin gives the distribution of alcohol consumption (the overall column percent), while the percentages in the bottom margin are the distribution of smoking behavior.

	0 mg	1–15 mg	16+ mg	
0 oz	105 82.73 34.5% 85.4%	7 17.69 10.8% 5.7%	11 22.59 13.3% 8.9%	123 27.2%
0.01– 0.10 oz	58 51.12 19.1% 76.3%	5 10.93 7.7% 6.6%	13 13.96 15.7% 17.1%	76 16.8%
0.11– 0.99 oz	84 109.63 27.6% 51.5%	37 23.44 56.9% 22.7%	42 29.93 50.6% 25.8%	163 36.1%
1.00+ oz	57 60.53 18.8% 63.3%	16 12.94 24.6% 17.8%	17 16.53 20.5% 18.9%	90 19.9%
	304 67.3%	65 14.4%	83 18.4%	452 100%

$X^2 = 42.252$ (df = 6) so $P < 0.0005$; we conclude that alcohol and nicotine consumption are not independent. The chief deviation from independence (based on comparison of expected and actual counts) is that nondrinkers are more likely to be nonsmokers than we might expect, while those drinking 0.11 to 0.99 oz/day are less likely to be nonsmokers than we might expect. One possible graph is below.

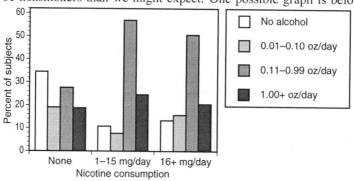

9.18 Based on the background information given in the problem, there is no reason to consider one of these as explanatory; each is linked to the other. Thus it may be useful to look at both conditional distributions (rows and columns). Comparing the column percents (the first percentage in each cell, along with those in the right margin), we note that children classified as "Normal" are more likely to be healthy than those whose nutrition is inadequate, but there is not much difference between the three inadequate nutrition groups.

Looking at row percents (the second percentage in the cells, and those in the bottom margin), we observe that those with no illness are considerably more likely to have normal nutrition. Comparing the three illness combinations, there is little variation for nutritional status I (31.6% to 31.8%) or for status III/IV (14.2% to 16.2%), and only small differences in the percentages classified as Normal (14.2% to 21.0%) or as status II (31.9% to 40.0%).

The differences in these percentages are statistically significant: $X^2 = 101.291$, df $= 9$, $P < 0.0005$.

	Normal	I	II	III & IV	
URI	95	143	144	70	452
	111.74	133.85	141.61	64.79	
	33.0%	41.4%	39.5%	41.9%	38.8%
	21.0%	31.6%	31.9%	15.5%	
Diarrhea	53	94	101	48	296
	73.17	87.66	92.74	42.43	
	18.4%	27.2%	27.7%	28.7%	25.4%
	17.9%	31.8%	34.1%	16.2%	
Both	27	60	76	27	190
	46.97	56.27	59.53	27.24	
	9.4%	17.4%	20.8%	16.2%	16.3%
	14.2%	31.6%	40.0%	14.2%	
None	113	48	44	22	227
	56.12	67.22	71.12	32.54	
	39.2%	13.9%	12.1%	13.2%	19.5%
	49.8%	21.1%	19.4%	9.7%	
	288	345	365	167	1165
	24.7%	29.6%	31.3%	14.3%	100%

9.19 (a) Blood pressure is explanatory. Of the low blood pressure group, 0.785% died from cardiovascular disease, compared to 1.648% of the high BP group, suggesting that high

Died?	Low BP	High BP	
Yes	21	55	76
No	2655	3283	5938
	2676	3338	6014

BP increases the risk of cardiovascular disease. **(b)** H_0: $p_1 = p_2$; H_a: $p_1 < p_2$. $\hat{p}_1 = 21/2676$, $\hat{p}_2 = 55/3338$, and the "pooled" estimate of p is $\hat{p} = 76/6014$. The test statistic is $z = (\hat{p}_1 - \hat{p}_2)/\sqrt{\hat{p}(1 - \hat{p})\left(\frac{1}{2676} + \frac{1}{3338}\right)} \doteq -2.98$, so that $P = 0.0014$; we conclude that the high blood pressure group has a greater risk. **(c)** Shown at right. The χ^2 test is not appropriate since the alternative is one-sided. **(d)** $SE_{\hat{p}_1 - \hat{p}_2} = \sqrt{\hat{p}_1(1 - \hat{p}_1)/2676 + \hat{p}_2(1 - \hat{p}_2)/3338} \doteq 0.002786$. The 95% confidence interval is $\hat{p}_1 - \hat{p}_2 \pm 1.960\,SE_{\hat{p}_1 - \hat{p}_2} = -0.0141$ to -0.0032.

9.20 **(a)** $H_0: p_1 = p_2; H_a: p_1 < p_2$.
$\hat{p}_1 = 457/1003$, $\hat{p}_2 = 437/620$, and the "pooled"
estimate of p is $\hat{p} = 894/1623$. The test statistic
is $z = (\hat{p}_1 - \hat{p}_2)/\sqrt{\hat{p}(1-\hat{p})\left(\frac{1}{1003} + \frac{1}{620}\right)} \doteq -9.81$,

Fed?	First Survey	Second Survey	
Yes	457	437	894
No	546	183	729
	1003	620	1623

so that $P < 0.0001$; we conclude that the second proportion is lower (the program
is effective). **(c)** Shown at right. The χ^2 test is not appropriate since the alternative
is one-sided. **(d)** $SE_{\hat{p}_1 - \hat{p}_2} = \sqrt{\hat{p}_1(1-\hat{p}_1)/1003 + \hat{p}_2(1-\hat{p}_2)/620} \doteq 0.002414$. The
95% confidence interval is $\hat{p}_1 - \hat{p}_2 \pm 1.960\, SE_{\hat{p}_1 - \hat{p}_2} = -0.2965$ to -0.2019.

9.21 25% of those with low
antacid use, 62.5% of the
medium-use group, and 80%
of the high-use group had
Alzheimer's, suggesting a connection. $X^2 = 7.118$ (df $= 3$),
so $P = 0.069$—there is some
evidence for the connection, but
it is not statistically significant.

	None	Low	Med	High	
Alzheimer's patient	112	3	5	8	128
	113.00	6.00	4.00	5.00	
	49.6%	25%	62.5%	80%	50%
Control group	114	9	3	2	128
	113.00	6.00	4.00	5.00	
	50.4%	75%	37.5%	20%	50%
	226	12	8	10	256

9.22 Use column percents, since we view
gender as explanatory. Women appear to be
more likely to have dropped out.
    H_0: There is no relationship between
gender and student status; H_a: There
is a relationship. $X^2 = 13.398$, df $=$
2, $P = 0.001$—there is strong evidence of
a relationship.
    Other factors to consider would be
anything that might account for someone
leaving a degree program—e.g., age of students entering program.

	Men	Women	
Completed	423	98	521
	404.49	116.51	
	53.2%	42.8%	50.9%
Still enrolled	134	33	167
	129.65	37.35	
	16.9%	14.4%	16.3%
Dropped out	238	98	336
	260.86	75.14	
	29.9%	42.8%	32.8%
	795	229	1024

9.23 71.3% of Irish, 76.0%
of Portuguese, 69.5% of
Norwegians, and 75.0% of
Italians can taste PTC; there
seems to be some variation
in the percentages among
the countries. $X^2 = 5.957$
(df $= 3$), so $P = 0.114$—the

	Ireland	Portugal	Norway	Italy	
Tasters	558	345	185	402	1490
	572.18	331.76	194.38	391.68	
	71.3%	76%	69.5%	75%	73.1%
Non-tasters	225	109	81	134	549
	210.82	122.24	71.62	144.32	
	28.7%	24%	30.5%	25%	26.9%
	783	454	266	536	2039

observed differences between the percentages are not significant (for typical choices
of α).

9.24 The differences between ethnic groups (as described by column percents, and represented in the graph) are significant: $X^2 = 1078.6$, df = 9, $P < 0.0005$. (With such large samples, even small differences would almost certainly be found significant.)

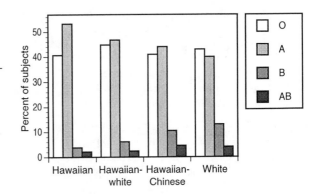

	Hawaiian	Hawaiian-White	Hawaiian-Chinese	White	
Type O	1903	4469	2206	53759	62337
	2006.89	4289.68	2314.16	53726.27	
	40.7%	44.8%	41.0%	43%	43.0%
Type A	2490	4671	2368	50008	59537
	1916.75	4097.00	2210.21	51313.04	
	53.3%	46.8%	44.0%	40%	41.0%
Type B	178	606	568	16252	17604
	566.75	1211.41	653.52	15172.33	
	3.8%	6.1%	10.5%	13%	12.1%
Type AB	99	236	243	5001	5579
	179.61	383.92	207.11	4808.36	
	2.1%	2.4%	4.5%	4%	3.8%
	4670	9982	5385	125020	145057

9.25 For the British study, $X^2 = 0.249$ (df = 1), which gives $P = 0.618$—there is very little evidence of an association. For the American study, $X^2 = 25.014$ (df = 1), which gives $P < 0.0005$. This is strong evidence of an association: aspirin reduced the risk of a fatal heart attack.

The difference in the conclusions can be attributed to the larger sample size for the American study (important for something as rare as a heart attack), as well as the shorter duration of the study and the lower dosage (taking the aspirin every other day rather than every day).

British study

	Aspirin	No aspirin	
Heart attack	148	79	227
	151.47	75.53	
	4.3%	4.6%	4.4%
No heart attack	3281	1631	4912
	3277.53	1634.47	
	95.7%	95.4%	95.6%
	3429	1710	5139

Physician's Health Study

	Aspirin	No aspirin	
Heart attack	104	189	293
	146.52	146.48	
	0.9%	1.7%	1.3%
No heart attack	10933	10845	21778
	10890.48	10887.52	
	99.1%	98.3%	98.7%
	11037	11034	22071

9.26 (a) H_0: $p_1 = p_2$; H_a: $p_1 \neq p_2$. $\hat{p}_1 =$ 28/82, $\hat{p}_2 = 30/78$, and the "pooled" estimate of p is $\hat{p} = 58/160$. The test statistic is $z = (\hat{p}_1 - \hat{p}_2)/\sqrt{\hat{p}(1-\hat{p})\left(\frac{1}{82} + \frac{1}{78}\right)} \doteq -0.5675$, so that $P > 0.5686 = 2(0.2843)$ (software gives $P = 0.57$); there is no reason to believe that the proportions are different. **(b)** Table at right (with expected

	Gastric Freezing	Control	
Relief	28	30	58
	29.73	28.27	
	34.1%	38.5%	36.3%
No relief	54	48	102
	52.28	49.72	
	65.9%	61.5%	63.8%
	82	78	160

counts and column percents). H_0: There is no relationship between treatment and relief; H_a: There is a relationship. $X^2 = 0.322$ (which does equal z^2, up to rounding error), df $= 1$, $P = 0.570$. **(c)** Gastric freezing is not effective (or "is no more effective than a placebo").

9.27 (a) $X^2 = 2.186$ (df $= 1$), which gives $0.10 < P < 0.15$ (in fact, $P = 0.140$); we do not have enough evidence to conclude that the observed difference in death rates is due to something other than chance. **(b)** Good condition: $X^2 = 0.289$ (df $= 1$), which gives $P > 0.25$ (in fact, $P = 0.591$). Poor condition: $X^2 = 0.019$ (df $= 1$), which gives $P > 0.25$ (in fact, $P = 0.890$). In both cases, we cannot reject the hypothesis that there is no difference between the hospitals. **(c)** No.

9.28 The study needs samples of *thousands*, not *hundreds*. Since cardiovascular disease is relatively rare, sample sizes must be quite large—otherwise, it is quite possible that we would observe *no* heart attacks in one or both of our groups, even if we track them for several years. See also the answer to Exercise 8.65.

9.29 For the sex/SC table (top): $X^2 = 23.450$, df $= 1$, $P < 0.0005$. This is strong evidence of a link between gender and social comparison.

For the sex/mastery table (bottom): $X^2 = 0.030$, df $= 1$, $P > 0.25$ (in fact, $P = 0.863$). There is no evidence of a link between gender and mastery.

It appears that the difference between male and female athletes observed in Example 9.4 is in social comparison, not in mastery.

	Female	Male	
HSC	21	49	70
	35.00	35.00	
	31.3%	73.1%	52.2%
LSC	46	18	64
	32.00	32.00	
	68.7%	26.9%	47.8%
	67	67	134
HM	35	36	71
	35.50	35.50	
	52.2%	53.7%	53%
LM	32	31	63
	31.50	31.50	
	47.8%	46.3%	47%
	67	67	134

9.30 Since we suspect that student loans may explain career choice, we examine column percents (in the table below, left). We observe that those with loans are *slightly* more likely to be in Agriculture, Science, and Technology fields, and less likely to be in Management. However, the differences in the table are not significant: $X^2 = 6.525$, df $= 6$, $P = 0.368$.

For 9.30.

	Loan	No Loan	
Agric.	32	35	67
	8.7%	7.0%	7.7%
CDFS	37	50	87
	10.1%	10.1%	10.1%
Eng.	98	137	235
	26.6%	27.6%	27.2%
LA/Educ.	89	124	213
	24.2%	24.9%	24.6%
Mgmt.	24	51	75
	6.5%	10.3%	8.7%
Science	31	29	60
	8.4%	5.8%	6.9%
Tech.	57	71	128
	15.5%	14.3%	14.8%
	368	497	865

For 9.31.

	Low	Medium	High	
Agric.	5	27	35	67
	13.5%	6.8%	8.2%	7.7%
CDFS	1	32	54	87
	2.7%	8.0%	12.6%	10.1%
Eng.	12	129	94	235
	32.4%	32.3%	22.0%	27.2%
LA/Educ.	7	77	129	213
	18.9%	19.3%	30.1%	24.6%
Mgmt.	3	44	28	75
	8.1%	11.0%	6.5%	8.7%
Science	7	29	24	60
	18.9%	7.3%	5.6%	6.9%
Tech.	2	62	64	128
	5.4%	15.5%	15.0%	14.8%
	37	400	428	865

9.31 For the table (above, right), $X^2 = 43.487$ (df $= 12$), so $P < 0.0005$, indicating that there is a relationship between PEOPLE score and field of study.

Among other observations we could make: Science has a large proportion of low-scoring students, while liberal arts/education has a large percentage of high-scoring students. (These two table entries make the largest contributions to the value of X^2.)

9.32 Death rates (deaths/1000 cases) are given in the table and illustrated in the graph. The statistic for testing the association is $X^2 = 19.715$ (df $= 7$, $P = 0.007$). The differences in death rates are significant; specifically, the risk of complications is greatest for children under 5, and adults over 25.

We cannot study the association between catching measles and age because we do not know the total number of people who were alive in each age group.

Age	Death Rate
< 1 year	4.44677
1–4	5.17483
5–9	1.35685
10–14	1.58646
15–19	2.93794
20–24	2.70880
25–29	5.99600
30+	8.48485

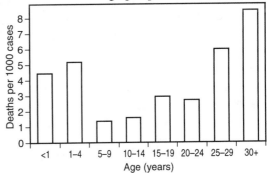

9.33 For example, there were $966 \doteq (0.883)(1094)$ hypertensive hypokalemic patients, and therefore there were 128 non-hypertensive hypokalemic patients.

The respective X^2 values are 83.147, 48.761, 12.042, and 13.639, all with df = 2, which are all significant (the largest P-value is 0.003). If we drop the hyperkalemic group, the X^2 values are 57.764, 33.125, 11.678, and 8.288, all with df = 2, which are also all significant (the largest P-value is 0.004).

Thus it appears that there is an association between potassium

	Hypo.	Normal	Hyper.	
Hypertension (yes)	966 873.51	3662 3743.94	11 21.56	4639
(no)	128 220.49	1027 945.06	16 5.44	1171
Heart failure (yes)	181 254.95	1158 1092.75	15 6.29	1354
(no)	913 839.05	3531 3596.25	12 20.71	4456
Diabetes (yes)	225 269.08	1196 1153.28	8 6.64	1429
(no)	869 824.92	3493 3535.72	19 20.36	4381
Female	793 752.24	3189 3224.19	13 18.57	3995
Male	301 341.76	1500 1464.81	14 8.43	1815
Totals	1094	4689	27	5810

level and each of the four risk factors. Looking at the percentages in the table, the hyperkalemic group is generally (for all but diabetes) quite different from the other two groups; the large sample sizes for hypokalemic and normal groups make even small differences (like the difference for gender) statistically significant.

9.34 The variation in the percentage of woman pharmacy students is so great that it is not surprising that the differences are significant: $X^2 = 359.677$, df = 8, $P < 0.0005$.

The plot (below, left) is roughly linear; the regression line is $\hat{y} = -4448 + 2.27x$.

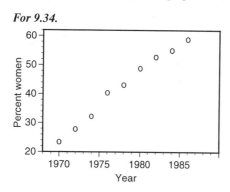

For 9.34.

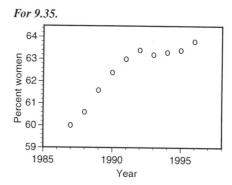

For 9.35.

9.35 Plot above, right. The percentage of women pharmacy students has gradually increased since 1987, from 60% to nearly 64%; by the end it seems to have nearly leveled out. The rate of increase is considerably less than that shown from 1970 to 1986 (note the very different vertical scales on the two graphs above).

To summarize, women were a minority of pharmacy students in the early 1970s, but the proportion of women steadily increased until the mid-1980s, and has increased less rapidly since then. Women became the majority in the early 1980s.

Estimates for 2000 should probably be between 63% and 64%, assuming that there are no big changes between 1996 and 2000.

9.36 $X^2 = 852.433$, df $= 1$, $P < 0.0005$.
Using $z = -29.2$, computed in 8.66(c), this equals z^2 (up to rounding).

	Mexican-American	Other	
Juror	339	531	870
	688.25	181.75	
Not a juror	143 272	37 393	180 665
	142 922.75	37 742.25	
	143 611	37 924	181 535

9.37 For cats: $X^2 = 8.460$ (df $= 4$), which gives $P = 0.077$. We do not reject H_0 this time; with the 2×3 table, we had $P = 0.037$, so having more cells has "weakened" the evidence. For dogs: $X^2 = 33.208$ (df $= 4$), which gives $P < 0.0005$. The conclusion is the same as before: we reject H_0.

9.38 *Note to instructors:* The distinctions between the models can be quite difficult to make, since the difference between several populations might, in fact, involve classification by a categorical variable. In many ways, it comes down to how the data were collected. For example, to compare male and female athletes (as in Example 9.3 and following), we can either (a) select n_1 male and n_2 female athletes and classify them according to some characteristic (e.g., social comparison and mastery categories)—as was described in Example 9.3—**or** (b) select a sample of athletes, then classify each as male or female, and also according to that other characteristic. The former case would be a "comparison of populations" (a.k.a. "homogeneity") model, while the latter is a test of independence.

Of course, the difficulty is that the method of collecting data may not always be apparent, in which case we have to make an educated guess. One question we can ask to educate our guess is whether we have data that can be used to estimate the (population) marginal distributions. E.g., in Example 9.3 and following, the table gives us no information about the proportion of all athletes who are male or female (these would be the proportions along the bottom margin); we simply picked 67 of each gender. Furthermore, we would get a different marginal distribution for the sports goals if we had a different mix of men and women—say, twice as many men as women—so we do not know the true sports goals marginal distribution, either. In Example 9.8, on the other hand, we could get information about the percentages of current smokers, former smokers, and "never" smokers in our sample (the right margin), and also about the SES distribution in our sample (the bottom margin).

For some of these problems, either answer may be acceptable, provided a reasonable explanation is given.

In 9.1, we are testing for independence between age and termination. (We have data to compute the marginals for both.) In 9.3, we have two populations: cats brought into the humane society ("cases"), and those which were not (control). (We do not know, and are not interested in, what proportion of all cats are brought to the humane society.) In 9.6, we are comparing three populations—one for each intervention. In 9.12, we test for independence between county type and tetracycline prescriptions.

9.39 Before we had $X^2 = 7.118$; with the counts doubled, $X^2 = 14.235$ (df $= 3$), which gives $P = 0.003$. The proportions are the same, but the increased sample size makes the differences between the categories statistically significant.

Chapter 10 Solutions

10.1 (a) Ignoring the (circled) outlier, there is a weak positive association.
(b) The regression equation is $\hat{y} = 43.4 + 0.0733x$. The significance test for the slope yields $t = 2.85$ from a t distribution with df $= 59 - 2 = 57$. This is significant—using Table E, we can estimate $P < 2(0.005) = 0.01$; Minitab reports $P = 0.006$. We conclude that linear regression on LOS is useful

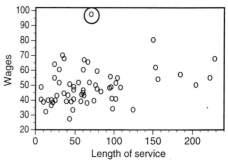

for predicting wages. **(c)** With $b_1 = 0.0733$, we can say that wages increase by 0.0733 per week of service. (Note: This is not \$0.0733, since we don't know the units of "Wages.") **(d)** From software, $SE_{b_1} = 0.02571$; we compute $b_1 \pm t^* SE_{b_1}$. Using $t^* = 2.009$ (df $= 50$, from the table), the interval is 0.0216 to 0.1250. With $t^* = 2.0025$ (df $= 57$, from software), the interval is 0.0218 to 0.1248.

Output from Minitab:

```
The regression equation is
Wages = 43.4 + 0.0733 LOS

Predictor       Coef      Stdev    t-ratio        p
Constant      43.383      2.248      19.30    0.000
LOS          0.07325    0.02571       2.85    0.006

s = 10.21      R-sq = 12.5%      R-sq(adj) = 10.9%
```

10.2 The new regression line is $\hat{y} = 44.2 + 0.0731x$. The intercept (b_0) is higher, since the outlier "pulls" the line up. The slope has not changed much; it now has $t = 2.42$ ($P = 0.018$)—still significant, though not as much as before. The estimated standard deviation is higher (11.98 vs. 10.21) since the outlier suggests a greater amount of variability in the data.

Output from Minitab:

```
The regression equation is
Wages = 44.2 + 0.0731 LOS

Predictor       Coef      Stdev    t-ratio        p
Constant      44.213      2.628      16.82    0.000
LOS          0.07310    0.03015       2.42    0.018

s = 11.98      R-sq = 9.2%      R-sq(adj) = 7.6%
```

10.3 **(a)** The plot shows a weak positive association. **(b)** Regression gives
$\hat{y} = 51,938 + 47.7x$. The slope is significantly different from 0 ($t = 6.94$, df $=$
$59 - 2 = 57$, $P < 0.0005$). We conclude
that linear regression on square footage
is useful for predicting selling price.

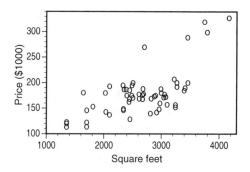

10.4 The new regression equation is $\hat{y} = 101,458 + 25.4x$. The slope is still significantly
different from 0 ($t = 5.30$, $P < 0.0005$), but the average increase in price for added
floor space (i.e., the slope) is considerably less with the five outliers removed. Those
five homes were more expensive than we would expect from the pattern of the rest of the
points, so they had the effect of increasing the slope.

10.5 **(a)** There is a fairly strong positive
relationship. There are no particular
outliers or unusual observations,
but one noteworthy feature is that
the spread seems to increase over
time. **(b)** The regression equation is
$\hat{y} = -3545 + 1.84x$. The slope is
significantly different from 0 ($t =$
13.06, with df $= 38$). Yield has
increased at an average rate of 1.84
bushels/acre each year.

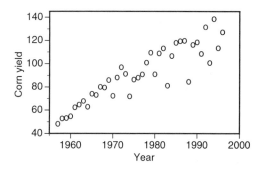

10.6 **(a)** $\hat{y} = 1.23 + 0.202x$. **(b)** $t = 17.66$ (df $= 7$), which has $P < 0.0005$. The slope
is significantly different from 0. **(c)** $t^* = 2.365$ and $SE_{b_1} = 0.01145$, so the interval is
0.175 to 0.229 (hundred ft^3 of gas/heating degree day per day). **(d)** $SE_{b_0} = 0.2860$, so
the interval is 0.554 to 1.906 hundred ft^3 of gas.

Output from Minitab:

```
The regression equation is
Gas = 1.23 + 0.202 HeatDeg

Predictor        Coef       Stdev      t-ratio         p
Constant       1.2324      0.2860         4.31     0.004
HeatDeg       0.20221     0.01145        17.66     0.000

s = 0.4345      R-sq = 97.8%     R-sq(adj) = 97.5%
```

10.7 **(a)** Powerboats registered is the explanatory variable, so it should be on the horizontal axis. The (positive) association appears to be a straight-line relationship. **(b)** $\hat{y} = -41.4 + 0.125x$. **(c)** $H_0: \beta_1 = 0$; $H_a: \beta_1 > 0$. The test statistic is $t = b_1/SE_{b_1} = 14.24$, which is significant (df $= 12$, $P < 0.0005$); this is good evidence that manatee deaths increase with powerboat

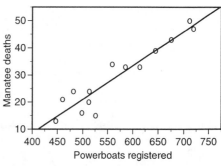

registrations. **(d)** Use $x = 716$: the equation gives $y = 48.1$, or about 48 manatee deaths. The mean number of manatee deaths for 1991–93 is 42—less than the 48 predicted. Evidence of "success" is perhaps in the eye of the beholder: the nature of the relationship between the two variables does not seem to have changed (not that we would have any reason to expect this), but the increase in the number of powerboat registrations evident in previous years seems to have been curtailed.

10.8 **(a)** The trend appears linear. **(b)** $\hat{y} = -61.1 + 9.32x$. The regression explains $r^2 = 98.8\%$ of the variation in lean. **(c)** The rate we seek is the slope. For df $= 11$, $t^* = 2.201$, so the interval is $9.32 \pm (2.201)(0.3099) = 8.64$ to 10.00 tenths of a millimeter/year.

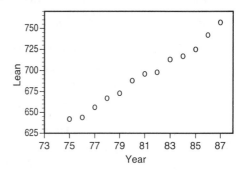

Output from Minitab:
```
The regression equation is
Lean = - 61.1 + 9.32 Year

Predictor      Coef      Stdev    t-ratio        p
Constant     -61.12      25.13      -2.43    0.033
Year         9.3187     0.3099      30.07    0.000

s = 4.181        R-sq = 98.8%      R-sq(adj) = 98.7%
```

10.9 **(a)** $\hat{y} = -61.1 + 9.32(18) \doteq 107$, for a prediction of 2.9107 m. **(b)** This is an example of extrapolation—trying to make a prediction outside the range of given x values. Minitab reports $SE_{\hat{y}} = 19.56$, so a 95% prediction interval for $\hat{y}$ when $x^* = 18$ is about 62.6 to 150.7. The width of the interval is an indication of how unreliable the prediction is.

10.10 **(a)** $\hat{y} = -61.1 + 9.32(97) \doteq 843$, for a prediction of 2.9843 m. **(b)** A prediction interval is appropriate, since we are interested in one future observation, not the mean of all future observations; in this situation, it does not make sense to talk of more than one future observation.

10.11 (a) β_1 represents the increase in gas consumption (in hundreds of cubic feet) for each additional degree day per day. With df $= 16$, $t^* = 2.120$, so the interval is $0.26896 \pm (2.120)(0.00815)$, or 0.2517 to 0.2862. **(b)** The margin of error would be smaller here, since for a fixed confidence level, the critical value t^* decreases as df increases. (Additionally, the standard error is slightly smaller here.) The margin of error for 10.6 was $t^*\,\mathrm{SE}_{b_1} = (2.365)(0.01145) = 0.027$, while it is 0.017 here.

10.12 (a) As stated in Exercise 10.6(d), β_0 is the natural gas consumed for nonheating uses—cooking, hot water, etc. $t^* = 2.120$ (as in 10.11), so the interval is $2.405 \pm (2.120)(0.20351) = 1.974$ to 2.836 hundred ft^3 of gas. **(b)** This interval is 0.862 units wide, while the interval of 10.6 was 1.352 units wide. This interval is shorter since for a fixed confidence level, the critical value t^* decreases as df increases. Also, the standard error is slightly less than in 10.6.

10.13 (a) $t = b_1/\mathrm{SE}_{b_1} = 0.20221/0.01145 = 17.66$. **(b)** With df $= 7$, we have $t^* = 1.895$. We reject H_0 at this level (or any reasonable level). **(c)** From the table, we report $P < 0.0005$. This is probably more readily understandable than the software value: $P \doteq 2.3 \times 10^{-7} = 0.00000023$.

10.14 $t = b_1/\mathrm{SE}_{b_1} = 0.82/0.38 = 2.158$. Table E gives a P-value between 0.02 and 0.04; software gives $P \doteq 0.035$. There is fairly good evidence that $\beta_1 \neq 0$ (significant at $\alpha = 0.05$, but not at $\alpha = 0.01$).

10.15 (a) $\bar{x} = 13.07$ and $\sum(x_i - \bar{x})^2 = 443.201$. **(b)** H_0: $\beta_1 = 0$; H_a: $\beta_1 > 0$. $\mathrm{SE}_{b_1} = s/\sqrt{\sum(x_i - \bar{x})^2} = 0.0835$, so $t = 0.902/0.0835 = 10.80$. For any reasonable α, this is significant; we conclude that the two variables are positively associated. **(c)** With df $= 8$, we have $t^* = 3.355$: $0.902 \pm (3.355)(0.0835) = 0.622$ to 1.182. **(d)** $\hat{y} = 1.031 + 0.902(15) = 14.56$. $\mathrm{SE}_{\hat{y}} = 1.757\sqrt{1 + \frac{1}{10} + \frac{(15.0-13.07)^2}{443.201}} = 1.850$ and $t^* = 1.860$, so the prediction interval is $14.56 \pm (1.860)(1.850)$, or 11.12 to 18.00.

Output from Minitab:
```
    Fit  Stdev.Fit      90.0% C.I.         90.0% P.I.
 14.561      0.578   ( 13.485,  15.637)  ( 11.121,  18.001)
```

10.16 (a) $\bar{x} = 1327/26 \doteq 51.038$ and $\sum(x_i - \bar{x})^2 \doteq 7836.96$. (Be sure to use only the 26 rural readings for which there is also a city reading.) **(b)** H_0: $\beta_1 = 0$; H_a: $\beta_1 \neq 0$. $\mathrm{SE}_{b_1} = s/\sqrt{\sum(x_i - \bar{x})^2} = 0.05060$, so $t = 1.0935/0.05060 = 21.61$. Then $P < 0.001$, which is significant for any reasonable α; we conclude that the slope is different from 0. **(c)** Use a prediction interval: $\hat{y} = -2.580 + 1.0935(43) \doteq 44.44$, $\mathrm{SE}_{\hat{y}} = 4.4792\sqrt{1 + \frac{1}{26} + \frac{(43-51.038)^2}{7836.96}} = 4.5826$ and $t^* = 2.064$, so the interval is $44.44 \pm (2.064)(4.5826) = 34.98$ to 53.90.

Output from Minitab:
```
    Fit  Stdev.Fit      95.0% C.I.         95.0% P.I.
 44.441      0.968   ( 42.442,  46.439)  ( 34.980,  53.901)
```

10.17 **(a)** The plot reveals no outliers or unusual points. **(b)** The regression equation is $\hat{y} = -0.06485 + 1.184x$, so we estimate $1/R = b_1 = 1.184$. $SE_{b_1} = 0.07790$ and $t^* = 3.182$, so the confidence interval is 0.936 to 1.432. **(c)** $R \doteq 1/b_1 = 0.8446$; the confidence interval is 0.698 to 1.068. **(d)** $SE_{b_0} = 0.1142$, so $t = -0.6485/0.1142 = -0.5679$. From the table, we can estimate that $P > 2(0.25) = 0.50$; Minitab gives $P = 0.61$. We have little reason to doubt that $\beta_0 = 0$.

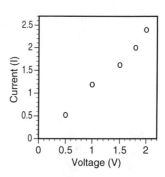

10.18 The new line is $\hat{y} = 1.1434x$; the slope has standard error 0.02646, and $t^* = 2.776$, so the 95% confidence interval for $1/R$ is 1.0699 to 1.2169. Taking reciprocals gives the interval for R: 0.8218 to 0.9346.

Output from Minitab:
```
The regression equation is
Current = 1.14 Voltage

Predictor      Coef      Stdev     t-ratio        p
Noconstant
Voltage      1.14339   0.02646     43.21      0.000
```

10.19 **(a)** The plot reveals no outliers or unusual points. **(b)** The regression equation is $\hat{y} = -2.80 + 0.0387x$. **(c)** $t = 16.10$ (df = 17); since $P < 0.0005$, we reject H_0 and conclude that linear regression on HR is useful for predicting VO2. **(d)** When $x = 95$, we have $\hat{y} = 0.8676$ and $SE_{\hat{y}} = 0.1205\sqrt{1 + \frac{1}{19} + \frac{(95-107)^2}{2518}} = 0.1269$, so the 95% prediction interval is $0.8676 \pm (2.110)(0.1269)$, or 0.5998 to 1.1354. When

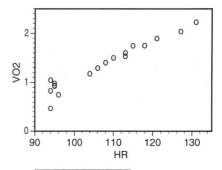

$x = 110$, we have $\hat{y} = 1.4474$ and $SE_{\hat{y}} = 0.1205\sqrt{1 + \frac{1}{19} + \frac{(110-107)^2}{2518}} = 0.1238$, so the interval is $1.4474 \pm (2.110)(0.1238) = 1.1861$ to 1.7086. A portion of the Minitab output that shows these intervals is reproduced below. **(e)** It depends on how accurately they need to know VO2; the regression equation predicts only the subject's *mean* VO2 for a given heart rate, and the intervals in (d) reveal that a particular *observation* may vary quite a bit from that mean.

Output from Minitab:
```
   Fit   Stdev.Fit      95.0% C.I.           95.0% P.I.
0.8676    0.0399    ( 0.7834,  0.9518)  ( 0.5998,  1.1354)
1.4474    0.0286    ( 1.3871,  1.5076)  ( 1.1861,  1.7086)
```

10.20 $t = 0.83/0.065 \doteq 12.77$. The alternative could reasonably be either $\beta_1 \neq 0$ or $\beta_1 > 0$; the latter makes the reasonable assumption that the association between the two measurements should be positive. In either case, the P-value (for df $= 79$) is very small: $P < 0.001$ for the two-sided alternative, $P < 0.0005$ for the one-sided alternative. In words, this study gives strong evidence that oscillometric measurements are useful for estimating intra-arterial measurements (though, as indicated by the parenthetic comments, these estimates are not clinically useful).

10.21 **(a)** H_0: $\beta_1 = 0$; H_a: $\beta_1 > 0$. $t = 0.00665/0.00182 = 3.654$; with df $= 16$, we have $0.001 < P < 0.0025$ (software gives 0.0011). We reject H_0 and conclude that greater airflow increases evaporation. **(b)** A 95% confidence interval for β_1 is $0.00665 \pm (2.120)(0.00182)$, or 0.00279 to 0.01051.

10.22 The plot shows a fairly strong positive relationship, with a hint of an upward curve at the high end. There are six unusually low observations in the middle of the plot. As with the corn yield plot, the spread seems to increase over time.

 Regression gives $\hat{y} = -659 + 0.348x$; this line is shown on the plot. The slope is significantly different from 0 ($t = 11.03$, df $= 38$, $P < 0.0005$). Yield has increased at an average rate of 0.348 bushels/acre each year.

 A normal quantile plot of the residuals (below) suggests deviation from normality. A plot of residuals vs. year (not shown) again suggests that variability is higher in later years. Linear regression may not be appropriate for this data set.

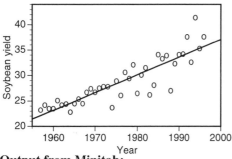 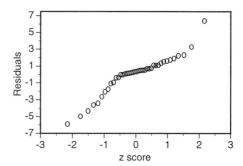

Output from Minitab:

```
The regression equation is
Soybeans = - 659 + 0.348 Year

Predictor      Coef      Stdev    t-ratio        p
Constant    -659.47      62.39     -10.57    0.000
Year         0.34827    0.03156     11.03    0.000

s = 2.304       R-sq = 76.2%     R-sq(adj) = 75.6%
```

10.23 **(a)** The prediction interval is about 123 to 168 bushels/acre: $\hat{y} = 145.60$, and $SE_{\hat{y}} = 10.28\sqrt{1 + \frac{1}{40} + \frac{(2006-1976.5)^2}{5330}} = 11.21$, so the 95% prediction interval is $145.60 \pm (2.042)(11.21) = 122.71$ to 168.49 (using the table value for df $= 30$), or $145.60 \pm (2.024)(11.21) = 122.91$ to 168.29 (using the software critical value for df $= 38$). **(b)** The centers are similar (150.25 vs. 145.60), but this interval is narrower. **(c)** The margin of error in Example 10.14 was 47 bushels/acre, compared to 23 here. It is smaller here because the sample size is larger, which decreases t^* (since df is larger), and decreases $SE_{\hat{y}}$ (since $1/n$ and $1/\sum(x_i - \bar{x})^2$ are smaller). [The latter effect is *slightly* offset because $\bar{x} = 1976.5$ rather than 1981, so $(x^* - \bar{x})^2 = (2006 - \bar{x})^2$ is larger than before, but this change is overcome by the greater change in $\sum(x_i - \bar{x})^2$: It was 500 in Example 10.14, and it is 5330 here.]

Output from Minitab:

```
      Fit  Stdev.Fit       95.0% C.I.          95.0% P.I.
   145.60       4.46   ( 136.57,  154.64)  ( 122.91,  168.30) X
```

10.24 (a) There is a fairly strong positive close-to-linear relationship. **(b)** $r = 0.9334$— this should be fairly good measure of the relationship, except to the extent that it is not linear. **(c)** Regression gives $\hat{y} = 12.2 + 0.183x$. For the slope, we have $t = 16.04$, df $= 38$, $P < 0.0005$; we conclude that the slope (and correlation) is not 0. **(d)** The residuals show a curved relationship with time: Generally, the residuals are positive in the earlier and later years, and mostly negative from about 1960 to 1990.

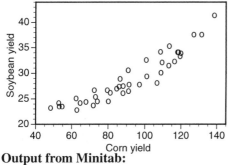 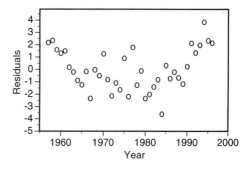

Output from Minitab:

```
The regression equation is
Soybeans = 12.2 + 0.183 Corn
```

Predictor	Coef	Stdev	t-ratio	p
Constant	12.175	1.077	11.31	0.000
Corn	0.18306	0.01142	16.04	0.000

```
s = 1.695      R-sq = 87.1%     R-sq(adj) = 86.8%
```

10.25 The log yield model (using common [base 10] logs) is $\hat{y} = -16.3 + 0.00925x$; if natural logs are used instead, the equation is $\hat{y} = -37.6 + 0.0213x$. For either regression, $r^2 = 81.7\%$ and $t = 13.02$. By comparison, for the original model we had $t = 13.06$ and $r^2 = 81.8\%$. The log model is not particularly better than the original; the plot still suggests that the spread increases as

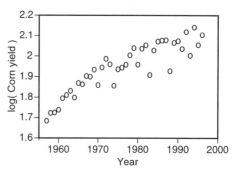

"year" increases—though a plot of residuals vs. year shows some improvement in this respect—and the numerical measures are actually slightly smaller than those in the original.

10.26 **(a)** Below (from Minitab). **(b)** H_0: $\beta_1 = 0$; this says that current is not linearly related to voltage. **(c)** If H_0 is true, F has an $F(1, 3)$ distribution; $F = 231.21$ has $P < 0.001$.

Output from Minitab:
Analysis of Variance

SOURCE	DF	SS	MS	F	p
Regression	1	2.0932	2.0932	231.21	0.001
Error	3	0.0272	0.0091		
Total	4	2.1203			

10.27 **(a)** Below (from Minitab). **(b)** H_0: $\beta_1 = 0$; this says that VO2 is not linearly related to HR. **(c)** If H_0 is true, F has an $F(1, 17)$ distribution; $F = 259.27$ has $P < 0.001$. **(d)** We found $t = 16.10$, and $t^2 = 259.21$. **(e)** $r^2 = \text{SSM/SST} = 3.7619/4.0085 = 93.8\%$.

Output from Minitab:
Analysis of Variance

SOURCE	DF	SS	MS	F	p
Regression	1	3.7619	3.7619	259.27	0.000
Error	17	0.2467	0.0145		
Total	18	4.0085			

10.28 **(a)** $t = 0.39\sqrt{38}/\sqrt{1 - 0.39^2} \doteq 2.611$ **(b)** This is a positive association; use H_a: $\rho > 0$. **(c)** $P = 0.0064$ (or $0.005 < P < 0.01$). We conclude that $\rho > 0$.

10.29 **(a)** $t = -0.19\sqrt{711}/\sqrt{1 - (-0.19)^2} = -5.160$. **(b)** We have df $= 711$, with $t = -5.16$, $P < 0.001$; this is significant (for any reasonable α), so we conclude that $\rho \neq 0$.

10.30 **(a)** The plot shows a strong positive linear pattern. **(b)** $\hat{y} = -0.0333 + 1.02x$, $s = 0.01472$.
(c) $r = 0.99645$; $r^2 = 99.3\%$ of T2's variability is explained by T1. **(d)** $t = 81.96$. The alternative H_a could reasonably be either $\beta_1 \neq 0$ or $\beta_1 > 0$; the latter makes the reasonable assumption that the association between the two measurements should be positive. Either way, P is tiny. In plain language: We can predict T2 to a very high degree of accuracy by multiplying the T1 measurement by 1.02 and subtracting 0.0333. The regression gives very strong evidence that the slope is not 0.

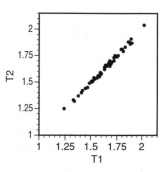

(e) They agree (up to rounding error): $t^2 = 6717.44$, while $F = 6717.94$.

Output from Minitab:
```
The regression equation is
T2 = - 0.0333 + 1.02 T1

Predictor       Coef       Stdev      t-ratio       p
Constant     -0.03328     0.02034      -1.64     0.108
T1            1.01760     0.01242      81.96     0.000

s = 0.01472      R-sq = 99.3%      R-sq(adj) = 99.3%

Analysis of Variance

SOURCE       DF        SS         MS         F          p
Regression    1     1.4564     1.4564    6717.94     0.000
Error        48     0.0104     0.0002
Total        49     1.4668
```

10.31 **(a)** Table below. b_0 and s_{b_1} have changed the most. **(b)** The full-set ANOVA table is above, the odd-set table below. The most important difference is that F_{odds} is about half as big as F_{full} (though both are quite significant). MSE is similar in both tables, reflecting the similarity in s in the full and reduced regressions. **(c)** See table. **(d)** The relationship is still strong even with half as many data points; most values are similar in both regressions. **(e)** Since these values did not change markedly for $n = 25$ vs. $n = 50$, it seems likely that they will be similar when $n = 100$.

	b_0	b_1	s	s_{b_1}	r
Full	−0.03328	1.01760	0.01472	0.01242	0.99645
Odds	−0.05814	1.03111	0.01527	0.01701	0.99688

Output from Minitab:
```
Analysis of Variance

SOURCE       DF        SS         MS         F          p
Regression    1     0.85681    0.85681   3673.71     0.000
Error        23     0.00536    0.00023
Total        24     0.86218
```

10.32 **(a)** $\hat{y} = 110 - 1.13x$. **(b)** $t = -3.63$; $P \doteq 0.001$ (or $0.0005 < P < 0.001$). **(c)** $t^* = 2.093$ and $SE_{b_1} = 0.3102$; the interval is -1.116 to -0.478. **(d)** $r^2 = 41.0\%$. **(e)** $s = 11.02$. **(f)** The new equation is only slightly changed: $\hat{y} = 108 - 1.05x$. The slope is still significantly different from 0, though it is not *as* significant as before ($t = -2.51$, $0.01 < P < 0.02$). The confidence interval is $-1.0499 \pm (2.110)(0.4186) = -1.933$ to -0.167—considerably wider than before. r^2 has decreased (to 27.0%), as has s (to 8.831). Removing Case 18 (high age/low score) makes the association less linear (hence the drop in r^2 and the rise in P). The absence of Case 19 (typical age/high score) lowers s, the estimated variation about the line.

Output from Minitab:
```
The regression equation is
Gesell = 110 - 1.13 Age

Predictor      Coef      Stdev    t-ratio        p
Constant    109.874      5.068      21.68    0.000
Age          -1.1270     0.3102     -3.63    0.002

s = 11.02       R-sq = 41.0%     R-sq(adj) = 37.9%
```
--------------- **Without 18 and 19** -----------------
```
The regression equation is
Gesell = 108 - 1.05 Age

Predictor      Coef      Stdev    t-ratio        p
Constant    107.585      5.724      18.80    0.000
Age          -1.0499     0.4186     -2.51    0.023

s = 8.831       R-sq = 27.0%     R-sq(adj) = 22.7%
```

10.33 **(a)** $\hat{y} = -9.1 + 1.09x$. **(b)** $SE_{b_1} = 0.6529$. **(c)** $t = 1.66$, which gives P between 0.10 and 0.20 (software gives $P = 0.140$)—not significant. With the original data, $t = 17.66$, which is strong evidence against H_0.

Output from Minitab:
```
The regression equation is
Gas = - 9.1 + 1.09 HeatDeg

Predictor      Coef      Stdev    t-ratio        p
Constant      -9.10     16.31      -0.56    0.594
HeatDeg       1.0857     0.6529      1.66    0.140

s = 24.78       R-sq = 28.3%     R-sq(adj) = 18.1%
```

10.34 (a) The plot suggests a linear relationship, so it is appropriate to use a correlation. Note that in this case, since both measurements are in centimeters, it is best if both axes have the same scale. Also note that either variable may be on the horizontal axis. (b) $r = 0.99415$, which gives $t = 15.94$ (df $= 3$), so the two-sided P-value is $P = 0.00054$. This correlation is different from (greater than) 0.

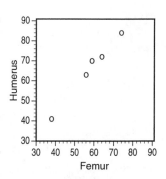

10.35 (a) There is a moderate positive relationship; player 8's point is an outlier. Note: Either variable may be plotted on the horizontal axis, although perhaps Round 1 scores are the most logical choice for the explanatory variable. Ideally, both scales should be equal. (b) $r = 0.687$, so $t = 0.687\sqrt{10}/\sqrt{1 - 0.687^2} = 2.99$ (df $= 10$); this gives two-sided P-value 0.0136 (or $0.01 < P < 0.02$)—fairly strong evidence that $\rho \neq 0$. (c) $r = 0.842$, so $t = 0.842\sqrt{9}/\sqrt{1 - 0.842^2} = 4.68$ (df $= 9$); this gives $P = 0.0012$ (or $0.001 < P < 0.002$)—stronger evidence that $\rho \neq 0$. The outlier makes the plot less linear, and so decreases the correlation.

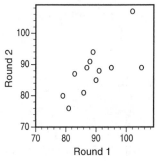

10.36 (a) $b_1 = r\, s_y/s_x = 0.68 \times 20.3/17.2 \doteq 0.80256$, and $b_0 = \bar{y} - b_1\bar{x} \doteq -21.43$. The equation is $\hat{y} = -21.42 + 0.80256x$. (b) $t = 0.68\sqrt{48}/\sqrt{1 - 0.68^2} = 6.42$ (df $= 48$); this gives $P < 0.0005$. We conclude that the slope is not 0.

10.37 With $n = 20$, $t = 2.45$ (df $= 18$, $0.02 < P < 0.04$), while with $n = 10$, $t = 1.63$ (df $= 8$, $0.1 < P < 0.2$). With the larger sample size, r should be a better estimate of ρ, so we are less likely to get $r = 0.5$ unless ρ is really not 0.

10.38 Most of the small banks have negative residuals, while the large ones have mostly positive residuals. This means that, generally, wages at large banks are higher, and small bank wages are lower, than we would predict from the regression.

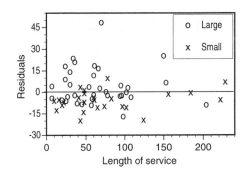

10.39 (a) There is a positive association between scores. The 47th pair of scores (circled) is an outlier—the ACT score (21) is higher than one would expect for the SAT score (420). Since this SAT score is so low, this point may be influential. No other points fall outside the pattern. (b) The regression equation is $\hat{y} = 1.63 + 0.0214x$; $t = 10.78$ which gives $P < 0.001$ (df = 58). (c) $r = 0.8167$.

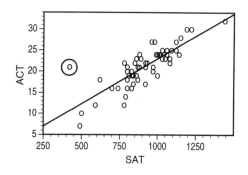

Output from Minitab:
```
The regression equation is
ACT = 1.63 + 0.0214 SAT

Predictor      Coef      Stdev    t-ratio        p
Constant      1.626      1.844       0.88    0.382
SAT        0.021374   0.001983      10.78    0.000

s = 2.744      R-sq = 66.7%    R-sq(adj) = 66.1%
```

10.40 (a) The means are identical (21.133). (b) For the observed ACT scores, $s_y = 4.714$; for the fitted values, $s_{\hat{y}} = 3.850$. (c) For $z = 1$, the SAT score is $\bar{x} + s_x = 912.7 + 180.1 = 1092.8$. The predicted ACT score is $\hat{y} \doteq 25$ (Minitab reports 24.983), which gives a standard score of about 1 (using the standard deviation of the *predicted* ACT scores. (d) For $z = -1$, the SAT score is $\bar{x} - s_x = 912.7 - 180.1 = 732.6$. The predicted ACT score is $\hat{y} \doteq 17.3$ (Minitab reports 17.285), which gives a standard score of about -1. (e) It appears that the standard score of the predicted value is the same as the standard score of the explanatory variable value. (See note below.)

Notes: (a) This will always be true, since $\sum_i \hat{y}_i = \sum_i (b_0 + b_1 x_i) = n b_0 + b_1 \sum_i x_i = n(\bar{y} - b_1 \bar{x}) + b_1 n \bar{x} = n \bar{y}$. (b) The standard deviation of the predicted values will be $s_{\hat{y}} = |r| s_y$; in this case, $s_{\hat{y}} = (0.8167)(4.714)$. To see this, note that the variance of the predicted values is $\frac{1}{n-1} \sum_i (\hat{y}_i - \bar{y})^2 = \frac{1}{n-1} \sum_i (b_1 x_i - b_1 \bar{x})^2 = b_1^2 s_x^2 = r^2 s_y^2$. (e) For a given standard score z, note that $\hat{y} = b_0 + b_1(\bar{x} + z s_x) = \bar{y} - b_1 \bar{x} + b_1 \bar{x} + b_1 z s_x = \bar{y} + z r s_y$. If $r > 0$, the standard score for $\hat{y}$ equals z; if $r < 0$, the standard score is $-z$.

10.41 **(a)** SAT: $\bar{x} = 912.\overline{6}$ and $s_x = 180.1$ points. ACT: $\bar{y} = 21.1\overline{3}$ and $s_y = 4.714$ points. So, $a_1 \doteq 0.02617$ and $a_0 \doteq -2.756$. (More accurate computation gives $a_0 \doteq -2.752$.) **(b)** The new line is dashed. **(c)** For example, the first prediction is $-2.756 + (0.02617)(1000) = 23.42$. Up to rounding error, the mean and standard deviation are the same.

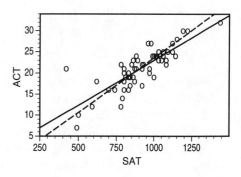

Chapter 11 Solutions

11.1 **(a)** H_0: $\beta_1 = \beta_2 = \cdots = \beta_{13} = 0$ vs. H_a: at least one $\beta_j \neq 0$. The degrees of freedom are 13 and 2215, and $P < 0.001$ (referring to an $F(12, 1000)$ distribution). We have strong evidence that at least one of the β_j is not 0. **(b)** The regression explains 29.7% of the variation. **(c)** Each t statistic tests H_0: $\beta_j = 0$ vs. H_a: $\beta_j \neq 0$, and has df = 2215. The critical value is $t^* = 1.961$. **(d)** The only three coefficients that are *not* significantly different from 0 are those for "total payments," "male borrower," and "married." **(e)** Interest rates are lower for larger loans, for longer terms, with larger down payments, when there is a cosigner, when the loan is secured, when the borrower has a higher income, when the credit report is not considered "bad," for older borrowers, when the borrower owns a home, and for borrowers who have lived for a long time at their present address.

11.2 **(a)** H_0: $\beta_1 = \beta_2 = \cdots = \beta_{13} = 0$ vs. H_a: at least one $\beta_j \neq 0$. The degrees of freedom are 13 and 5650, and $P < 0.001$ (referring to an $F(12, 1000)$ distribution). We have strong evidence that at least one of the β_j is not 0. **(b)** The regression explains 14.1% of the variation—much less than for the direct loans. **(c)** Each t statistic tests H_0: $\beta_j = 0$ vs. H_a: $\beta_j \neq 0$, and has df = 5650. The critical value is $t^* = 1.9604$. **(d)** Only the coefficients of "loan size," "length of loan," "percent down payment," and "unsecured loan" are significantly different from 0. **(e)** Interest rates are lower for larger loans, for longer terms, with larger down payments, and when the loan is secured.

11.3 In 11.1, we found that 10 factors have a significant effect on the interest rate for direct loans, while based on 11.2, only four of the factors examined have a significant impact on the interest rate for indirect loans. Furthermore, a greater proportion of the variation in interest rates is explained by the regression for direct loans than that for indirect.

11.4 **(a)** Between GPA and IQ, $r = 0.634$ (straight-line regression explains $r^2 = 40.2\%$ of the variation in GPA). Between GPA and self-concept, $r = 0.542$ (straight-line regression explains $r^2 = 29.4\%$ of the variation in GPA). Since gender is categorical, the correlation between GPA and gender is not meaningful. **(b)** Model: $\mu_{\text{GPA}} = \beta_0 + \beta_1 \text{ IQ} + \beta_2 \text{ Self-Concept}$. **(c)** Regression gives the equation $\widehat{\text{GPA}} = -3.88 + 0.0772 \text{ IQ} + 0.0513 \text{ Self-Concept}$. Based on the reported value of R^2, the regression explains 47.1% of the variation in GPA. (So the inclusion of self-concept only adds about 6.9% to the variation explained by the regression.) **(d)** We test H_0: $\beta_2 = 0$ vs. H_a: $\beta_2 \neq 0$. The test statistic $t = 3.14$ (df = 75) has $P = 0.002$; we conclude that the coefficient of Self-Concept is not 0.

Output from Minitab:

```
The regression equation is
GPA = - 3.88 + 0.0772 IQ + 0.0513 SelfCcpt

Predictor       Coef      Stdev    t-ratio       p
Constant      -3.882      1.472      -2.64   0.010
IQ           0.07720    0.01539       5.02   0.000
SelfCcpt     0.05125    0.01633       3.14   0.002

s = 1.547      R-sq = 47.1%    R-sq(adj) = 45.7%
```

11.5 **(a)** With the given values, $\mu_{\text{GPA}} = \beta_0 + 9\beta_1 + 8\beta_2 + 7\beta_3$. **(b)** We estimate $\widehat{\text{GPA}} = 2.697$. Among all computer science students with the given high school grades, we expect the mean college GPA after three semesters to be about 2.7.

11.6 **(a)** With the given values, $\mu_{\text{GPA}} = \beta_0 + 6\beta_1 + 7\beta_2 + 8\beta_3$. **(b)** We estimate $\widehat{\text{GPA}} = 2.202$. Among all computer science students with the given high school grades, we expect the mean college GPA after three semesters to be about 2.2.

11.7 The critical value for df $= 220$ is $t^* \doteq 1.9708$. If using the table, take $t^* = 1.984$. **(a)** $b_1 \pm t^* \text{SE}_{b_1} = 0.0986$ to 0.2385 (or 0.0982 to 0.2390). This coefficient gives the average increase in college GPA for each 1-point increase in high school math grade. **(b)** $b_3 \pm t^* \text{SE}_{b_3} = -0.0312$ to 0.1214 (or -0.0317 to 0.1219). This coefficient gives the average increase in college GPA for each 1-point increase in high school English grade.

11.8 The critical value for df $= 221$ is $t^* \doteq 1.9708$. If using the table, take $t^* = 1.984$. **(a)** $b_1 \pm t^* \text{SE}_{b_1} = 0.1197$ to 0.2456 (or 0.1193 to 0.2461). This coefficient gives the average increase in college GPA for each 1-point increase in high school math grade. **(b)** $b_2 \pm t^* \text{SE}_{b_2} = -0.0078$ to 0.1291 (or -0.0082 to 0.1296). This coefficient gives the average increase in college GPA for each 1-point increase in high school English grade. The coefficients (and standard errors) can change greatly when the model changes.

11.9 **(a)** $\widehat{\text{GPA}} = 0.590 + 0.169 \, \text{HSM} + 0.034 \, \text{HSS} + 0.045 \, \text{HSE}$. **(b)** $s = \sqrt{\text{MSE}} = 0.69984$. **(c)** H_0: $\beta_1 = \beta_2 = \beta_3 = 0$; H_a: at least one $\beta_j \neq 0$. In words, H_0 says that none of the high school grade variables are predictors of college GPA (in the form given in the model); H_a says that at least one of them is. **(d)** Under H_0, F has an $F(3, 220)$ distribution. Since $P = 0.0001$, we reject H_0. **(e)** The regression explains 20.46% of the variation in GPA.

11.10 **(a)** $\widehat{\text{GPA}} = 1.289 + 0.002283 \, \text{SATM} - 0.00002456 \, \text{SATV}$. **(b)** $s = \sqrt{\text{MSE}} = 0.75770$. **(c)** H_0: $\beta_1 = \beta_2 = 0$; H_a: at least one $\beta_j \neq 0$. In words, H_0 says that neither SAT score predicts college GPA (in the form given in the model); H_a says that at least one of them is a predictor. **(d)** Under H_0, F has an $F(2, 221)$ distribution. Since $P = 0.0007$, we reject H_0. **(e)** The regression explains 6.34% of the variation in GPA.

11.11 A 95% prediction interval is $\$2.136 \pm (1.984)(\$0.013)$, or $\$2.1102$ to $\$2.1618$. The actual price falls in this interval (in fact, it is less than one standard error below the predicted value), so there is not enough evidence to reject H_0, which in this situation would be "there was no manipulation."

11.12 There are no clear, strong patterns. The GPA/SATM plot suggests a slight positive association, but it is weakened by the two low SATM scores which do not follow the pattern.

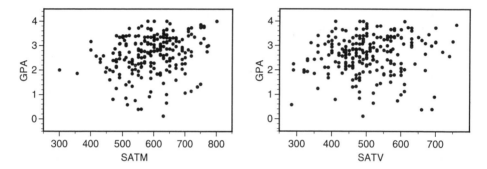

11.13 All of the plots display lots of scatter; high school grades seem to be poor predictors of college GPA. Of the three, the math plot seems to most strongly suggest a positive association, although the association appears to be quite weak, and almost nonexistent for HSM < 5. We also observe that scores below 5 are unusual for all three high school variables, and could be considered outliers and influential.

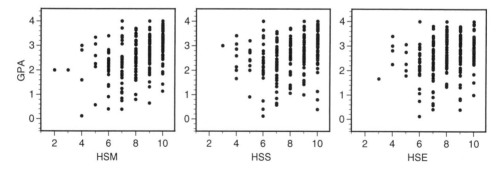

11.14 The regression equation (given in the answer to Exercise 11.9 and Figure 11.4) is $\widehat{\text{GPA}} = 0.590 + 0.169\text{HSM} + 0.034\text{HSS} + 0.045\text{ HSE}$. Among other things, we note that most of the residuals associated with low HS grades, and (not coincidentally) with low predicted GPAs, are "large" (positive, or just slightly negative). Also, using this model, the predicted GPAs are all between 1.33 and 3.07.

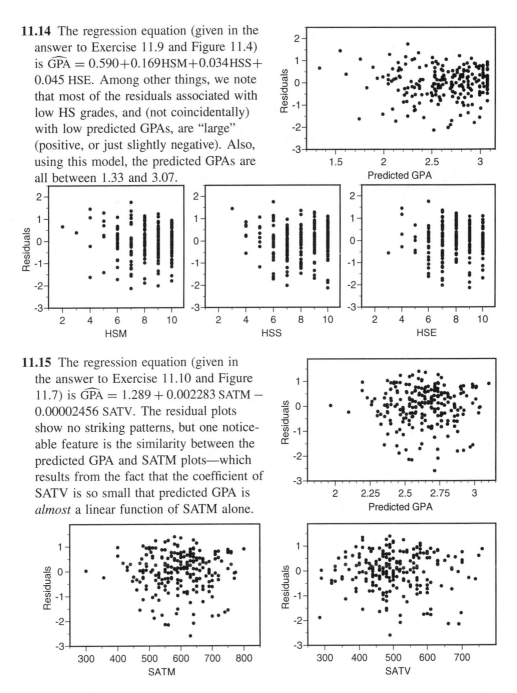

11.15 The regression equation (given in the answer to Exercise 11.10 and Figure 11.7) is $\widehat{\text{GPA}} = 1.289 + 0.002283\text{ SATM} - 0.00002456\text{ SATV}$. The residual plots show no striking patterns, but one noticeable feature is the similarity between the predicted GPA and SATM plots—which results from the fact that the coefficient of SATV is so small that predicted GPA is *almost* a linear function of SATM alone.

11.16 (a) $\widehat{\text{GPA}} = 0.666 + 0.193\text{ HSM} + 0.000610\text{ SATM}$. (b) $H_0: \beta_1 = \beta_2 = 0$; H_a: at least one $\beta_j \neq 0$. In words, H_0 says that neither mathematics variable is a predictor of college GPA (in the form given in the model); H_a says that at least one of them is. The F statistics

(with df 2 and 221) is 26.63; this has $P < 0.0005$, so we reject H_0. Minitab output follows.
(c) The critical value for df $= 221$ is $t^* \doteq 1.9708$. If using the table, take $t^* = 1.984$.
For the coefficient of HSM, $SE_{b_1} = 0.03222$, so the interval is 0.1295 to 0.2565 (or
0.1291 to 0.2569). For the coefficient of SATM, $SE_{b_2} = 0.0006112$, so the interval
is -0.000594 to 0.001815 (or -0.000602 to 0.001823)—which contains 0. **(d)** HSM:
$t = 5.99$, $P < 0.0005$. SATM: $t = 1.00$, $P = 0.319$. As the intervals indicated, the
coefficient of SATM is not significantly different from 0. **(e)** $s = \sqrt{\text{MSE}} = 0.7028$.
(f) The regression explains 19.4% of the variation in GPA.

Output from Minitab:
```
The regression equation is
GPA = 0.666 + 0.193 HSM +0.000610 SATM

Predictor        Coef       Stdev     t-ratio        p
Constant       0.6657      0.3435        1.94    0.054
HSM            0.19300     0.03222       5.99    0.000
SATM           0.0006105   0.0006112     1.00    0.319

s = 0.7028     R-sq = 19.4%     R-sq(adj) = 18.7%

Analysis of Variance

SOURCE         DF          SS         MS         F        p
Regression      2      26.303     13.151     26.63    0.000
Error         221     109.160      0.494
Total         223     135.463
```

11.17 The regression equation is $\widehat{\text{GPA}} = 1.28 + 0.143\,\text{HSE} + 0.000394\,\text{SATV}$, and $R^2 = 8.6\%$. The regression is significant ($F = 10.34$, with df 2 and 221); the t-tests reveal that
the coefficient of SATV is not significantly different from 0 ($t = 0.71$, $P = 0.481$). For
mathematics variables, we had $R^2 = 19.4\%$—not overwhelmingly large, but considerably
more than that for verbal variables.

Output from Minitab:
```
The regression equation is
GPA = 1.28 + 0.143 HSE +0.000394 SATV

Predictor        Coef       Stdev     t-ratio        p
Constant       1.2750      0.3474        3.67    0.000
HSE            0.14348     0.03428       4.19    0.000
SATV           0.0003942   0.0005582     0.71    0.481

s = 0.7487     R-sq = 8.6%     R-sq(adj) = 7.7%

Analysis of Variance

SOURCE         DF          SS         MS         F        p
Regression      2      11.5936     5.7968     10.34    0.000
Error         221     123.8692     0.5605
Total         223     135.4628
```

11.18 For males, regression gives $\widehat{\text{GPA}} = 0.582 + 0.155\,\text{HSM} + 0.0502\,\text{HSS} + 0.0445\,\text{HSE}$,
with $R^2 = 18.4\%$. The regression is significant ($F = 10.62$ with df 3 and 141; $P <$

0.0005), but only the coefficient of HSM is significantly different from 0 (even the constant 0.582 has $t = 1.54$ and $P = 0.125$). Regression with HSM and HSS (excluding HSE since it has the largest P-value) gives the equation $\widehat{GPA} = 0.705 + 0.159 \, HSM + 0.0738 \, HSS$, and $R^2 = 18.0\%$. The P-values for the constant and the coefficient of HSS are smaller (although the latter is still not significantly different from 0). One might also regress on HSM alone; this has $R^2 = 16.3\%$.

Minitab output for all three models follows. Residual plots (not shown) do not suggest problems with any of the models.

Comparing these results to Figures 11.4 and 11.6, note that with all students, we excluded HSS (rather than HSE) in the second model.

Output from Minitab:
```
The regression equation is
GPAm = 0.582 + 0.155 HSMm + 0.0502 HSSm + 0.0445 HSEm

Predictor       Coef       Stdev     t-ratio        p
Constant       0.5818      0.3767       1.54     0.125
HSMm           0.15502     0.04487      3.45     0.001
HSSm           0.05015     0.05070      0.99     0.324
HSEm           0.04446     0.05037      0.88     0.379

s = 0.7363     R-sq = 18.4%     R-sq(adj) = 16.7%
```

---------------- SECOND MODEL ------------------

```
The regression equation is
GPAm = 0.705 + 0.159 HSMm + 0.0738 HSSm

Predictor       Coef       Stdev     t-ratio        p
Constant       0.7053      0.3495       2.02     0.045
HSMm           0.15863     0.04465      3.55     0.001
HSSm           0.07383     0.04299      1.72     0.088

s = 0.7357     R-sq = 18.0%     R-sq(adj) = 16.8%
```

---------------- THIRD MODEL ------------------

```
The regression equation is
GPAm = 0.962 + 0.200 HSMm

Predictor       Coef       Stdev     t-ratio        p
Constant       0.9619      0.3181       3.02     0.003
HSMm           0.19987     0.03790      5.27     0.000

s = 0.7407     R-sq = 16.3%     R-sq(adj) = 15.7%
```

11.19 For females, regression gives $\widehat{GPA} = 0.648 + 0.205 \, HSM + 0.0018 \, HSS + 0.0324 \, HSE$, with $R^2 = 25.1\%$. In this equation, only the coefficient of HSM is significantly different from 0 (even the constant 0.648 has $t = 1.17$ and $P = 0.247$). Regression with HSM and HSE (excluding HSS since it has the largest P-value) gives the equation $\widehat{GPA} = 0.648 + 0.206 \, HSM + 0.0333 \, HSE$, and $R^2 = 25.1\%$—but the P-values for the constant and coefficient of HSE have changed very little. With HSM alone, the regression equation is $\widehat{\text{GPA}} = 0.821 + 0.220\,\text{HSM}$, R^2 decreases only slightly to 24.9%, and both the constant and coefficient are significantly different from 0.

Minitab output for all three models follows. Residual plots (not shown) do not suggest problems with any of the models.

Comparing the results to males, we see that both HSM and HSS were fairly useful for men, but HSM was sufficient for women—based on R^2, HSM alone does a better job for women than all three variables for men.

Output from Minitab:

```
The regression equation is
GPAf = 0.648 + 0.205 HSMf + 0.0018 HSSf + 0.0324 HSEf

Predictor       Coef      Stdev     t-ratio      p
Constant       0.6484    0.5551      1.17      0.247
HSMf           0.20512   0.06134     3.34      0.001
HSSf           0.00178   0.05873     0.03      0.976
HSEf           0.03243   0.08270     0.39      0.696

s = 0.6431     R-sq = 25.1%    R-sq(adj) = 22.1%
```

--------------- **SECOND MODEL** ------------------

```
The regression equation is
GPAf = 0.648 + 0.206 HSMf + 0.0333 HSEf

Predictor       Coef      Stdev     t-ratio      p
Constant       0.6483    0.5514      1.18      0.243
HSMf           0.20596   0.05430     3.79      0.000
HSEf           0.03328   0.07732     0.43      0.668

s = 0.6389     R-sq = 25.1%    R-sq(adj) = 23.1%
```

--------------- **THIRD MODEL** ------------------

```
The regression equation is
GPAf = 0.821 + 0.220 HSMf

Predictor       Coef      Stdev     t-ratio      p
Constant       0.8213    0.3755      2.19      0.032
HSMf           0.21984   0.04347     5.06      0.000

s = 0.6355     R-sq = 24.9%    R-sq(adj) = 24.0%
```

11.20 The correlations are on the right. Of these, the correlation between GPA and IQ is largest in absolute value, so the relationship between them is closest to a straight line. About 40.2% of the variation in GPA is explained by the relationship with IQ.

IQ	0.634	C2	0.601
AGE	-0.389	C3	0.495
SEX	-0.097	C4	0.267
SC	0.542	C5	0.472
C1	0.441	C6	0.401

11.21 **(a)** Regression gives $\widehat{\text{GPA}} = -2.83 + 0.0822\,\text{IQ} + 0.163\,\text{C3}$, and $R^2 = 45.9\%$. For the coefficient of C3, $t = 2.83$, which has $P = 0.006$—significantly different from 0. C3 increases R^2 by $5.7\% = 45.9\% - 40.2\%$. **(b)** Regression now gives $\widehat{\text{GPA}} = -3.49 + 0.0761\,\text{IQ} + 0.0670\,\text{C3} + 0.0369\,\text{SC}$, and $R^2 = 47.5\%$. For the coefficient of C3, $t = 0.78$, which has $P = 0.436$—*not* significantly different from 0. When self-concept (SC) is included in the model, C3 adds little. (If we regress on IQ and SC, $R^2 = 47.1\%$). **(c)** The values change because coefficients are quite sensitive to changes in the model, especially when the explanatory variables are highly correlated (the correlation between SC and C3 is about 0.80). In this case, the predictive information of SC and C3 overlap, so that the two of them together add little more than either one separately (with IQ).

Output from Minitab:
```
The regression equation is
GPA = - 2.83 + 0.0822 IQ + 0.163 C3

Predictor       Coef        Stdev     t-ratio        p
Constant       -2.829       1.507       -1.88     0.064
IQ            0.08220     0.01508        5.45     0.000
C3            0.16289     0.05752        2.83     0.006

s = 1.564       R-sq = 45.9%     R-sq(adj) = 44.5%

- - - - - - - - - - - - - - - - SECOND MODEL  - - - - - - - - - - - - - - - -


The regression equation is
GPA = - 3.49 + 0.0761 IQ + 0.0670 C3 + 0.0369 SC

Predictor       Coef        Stdev     t-ratio        p
Constant       -3.491       1.558       -2.24     0.028
IQ            0.07612     0.01549        4.91     0.000
C3            0.06701     0.08558        0.78     0.436
SC           0.03691     0.02456        1.50     0.137

s = 1.551       R-sq = 47.5%     R-sq(adj) = 45.4%
```

11.22 (a) Regression gives $\widehat{\text{GPA}} = -4.94 + 0.0815\,\text{IQ} + 0.183\,\text{C1} + 0.142\,\text{C5}$, $R^2 = 52.5\%$, and $s = 1.475$. With the given values of IQ, C1, and C5, $\widehat{\text{GPA}} = 7.457$. (b) GPA would increase by about 0.0815 per IQ point (the coefficient of IQ). $\text{SE}_{b_1} = 0.01367$; with df $= 74$, $t^* = 1.9926$ (or use $t^* = 2.000$ from the table). Interval: 0.0543 to 0.1087 (or 0.0542 to 0.1088). (c) The residual plots are below. The residual for OBS $= 55$ stands out as being extraordinarily low; this student had the lowest GPA and, at 15 years old, was the oldest. (d) Regression now gives $\widehat{\text{GPA}} = -4.68 + 0.0805\,\text{IQ} + 0.197\,\text{C1} + 0.109\,\text{C5}$, $R^2 = 57.4\%$, and $s = 1.303$. With the given values of IQ, C1, and C5, $\widehat{\text{GPA}} = 7.534$. Removing this observation did not greatly change the model or the prediction, although the coefficient of C5 is not quite significant under the new regression (see Minitab output).

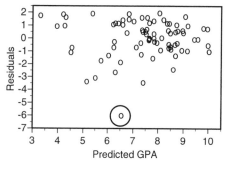
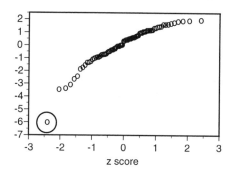

Output from Minitab:

```
The regression equation is
GPA = - 4.94 + 0.0815 IQ + 0.183 C1 + 0.142 C5

Predictor       Coef       Stdev     t-ratio         p
Constant      -4.937       1.491       -3.31     0.001
IQ           0.08145     0.01367        5.96     0.000
C1           0.18308     0.06475        2.83     0.006
C5           0.14205     0.06663        2.13     0.036

s = 1.475       R-sq = 52.5%    R-sq(adj) = 50.6%
```

--------------------   **Without OBS 55**   -------------------

```
The regression equation is
GPA = - 4.68 + 0.0805 IQ + 0.197 C1 + 0.109 C5

Predictor       Coef       Stdev     t-ratio         p
Constant      -4.678       1.318       -3.55     0.001
IQ           0.08050     0.01207        6.67     0.000
C1           0.19707     0.05724        3.44     0.001
C5           0.10950     0.05923        1.85     0.069

s = 1.303       R-sq = 57.4%    R-sq(adj) = 55.7%
```

11.23 In the table, two *IQRs* are given; those in parentheses are based on quartiles reported by Minitab, which computes quartiles in a slightly different way from this text's method.

	$\bar{x}$	M	s	IQR
Taste	24.53	20.95	16.26	23.9 (or 24.58)
Acetic	5.498	5.425	0.571	0.656 (or 0.713)
H2S	5.942	5.329	2.127	3.689 (or 3.766)
Lactic	1.442	1.450	0.3035	0.430 (or 0.4625)

None of the variables show striking deviations from normality in the quantile plots (not shown). Taste and H2S are slightly right-skewed, and Acetic has two peaks. There are no outliers.

Taste		*Acetic*		*H2S*		*Lactic*	
0	00	4	455	2	9	8	6
0	556	4	67	3	1268899	9	9
1	1234	4	8	4	17799	10	689
1	55688	5	1	5	024	11	56
2	011	5	2222333	6	11679	12	5599
2	556	5	444	7	4699	13	013
3	24	5	677	8	7	14	469
3	789	5	888	9	025	15	2378
4	0	6	0011	10	1	16	38
4	7	6	3			17	248
5	4	6	44			18	1
5	67					19	09
						20	1

11.24 The plots show positive associations between the variables. The correlations and *P*-values (in parentheses) are at the right; all are positive (as expected) and significantly different from 0. [Recall that the *P*-values are correct if the two variables are normally distributed, in which case $t = r\sqrt{n-2}/\sqrt{1-r^2}$ has a $t(n-2)$ distribution if $\rho = 0$.]

	Taste	Acetic	H2S
Acetic	0.5495 (0.0017)		
H2S	0.7558 (<0.0001)	0.6180 (0.0003)	
Lactic	0.7042 (<0.0001)	0.6038 (0.0004)	0.6448 (0.0001)

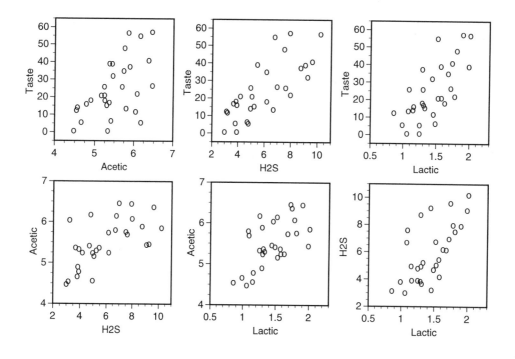

11.25 The regression equation is
$\widehat{\text{Taste}} = -61.5 + 15.6$ Acetic; the
coefficient of Acetic has $t = 3.48$,
which is significantly different from 0
($P = 0.002$). The regression explains
$r^2 = 30.2\%$ of the variation in Taste.

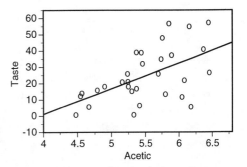

 Based on stem- and quantile plots (not
shown), the residuals seem to have a
normal distribution. Scatterplots (below)
reveal positive associations between
residuals and both H2S and Lactic. Further analysis of the residuals shows a stronger
positive association between residuals and Taste, while the plot of residuals vs.
Acetic suggests greater scatter in the residuals for large Acetic values.

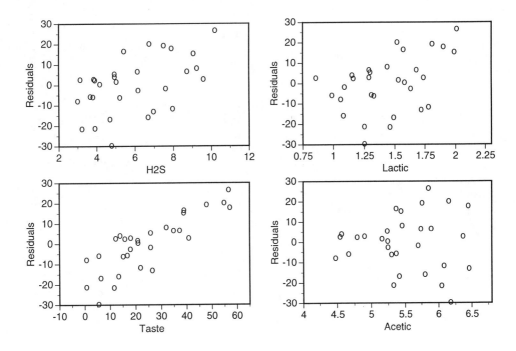

11.26 Regression gives $\widehat{\text{Taste}} = -9.79 +$
5.78 H2S. The coefficient of H2S has
$t = 6.11$ ($P < 0.0005$); it is significantly
different from 0. The regression explains
$r^2 = 57.1\%$ of the variation in Taste.

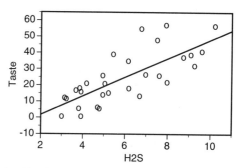

Based on stem- and quantile plots (not
shown), the residuals may be slightly
skewed, but do not differ greatly from
a normal distribution. Scatterplots
(below) reveal weak positive associations
between residuals and both Acetic and Lactic. Further analysis of the residuals
shows a moderate positive association between residuals and Taste, while the plot of
residuals vs. H2S suggests greater scatter in the residuals for large H2S values.

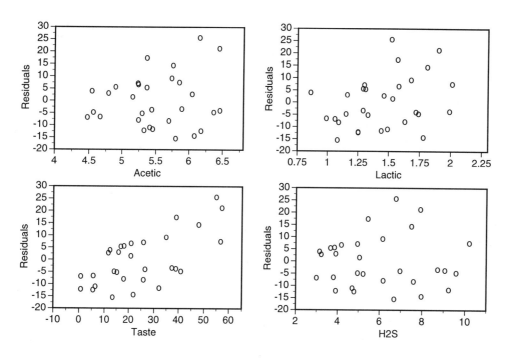

11.27 Regression gives $\widehat{\text{Taste}} = -29.9 + 37.7$ Lactic. The coefficient of Lactic has $t = 5.25$ ($P < 0.0005$); it is significantly different from 0. The regression explains $r^2 = 49.6\%$ of the variation in Taste.

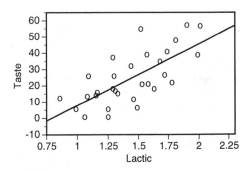

Based on stem- and quantile plots (not shown), the residuals seem to have a normal distribution. Scatterplots reveal a moderately strong positive association between residuals and Taste, but no striking patterns for residuals vs. the other variables.

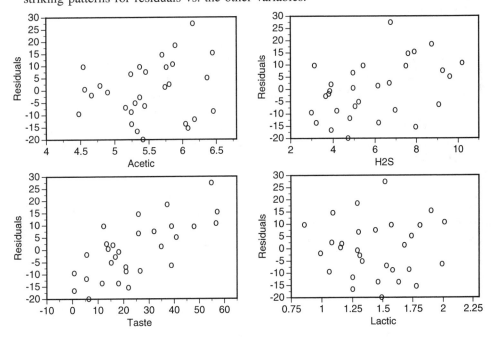

11.28 All information is in the table at the right. The intercepts differ from one model to the

x	$\widehat{\text{Taste}} =$	F	P	r^2	s
Acetic	$-61.5 + 15.6x$	12.11	0.002	30.2%	13.82
H2S	$-9.79 + 5.78x$	37.29	<0.0005	57.1%	10.83
Lactic	$-29.9 + 37.7x$	27.55	<0.0005	49.6%	11.75

next because they represent different things—e.g., in the first model, the intercept is the predicted value of Taste with Acetic $= 0$, etc.

11.29 The regression equation is $\widehat{\text{Taste}} = -26.9 + 3.80$ Acetic $+ 5.15$ H2S. The model explains 58.2% of the variation in Taste. The t-value for the coefficient of Acetic is 0.84 ($P = 0.406$), indicating that it does not add significantly to the model when H2S is used, because Acetic and H2S are correlated (in fact, $r = 0.618$ for these two variables). This model does a better job than any of the three simple linear regression models, but it is not much better than the model with H2S alone (which explained 57.1% of the variation in Taste)—as we might expect from the t-test result.

11.30 The regression equation is $\widehat{\text{Taste}} = -27.6 + 3.95$ H2S $+ 19.9$ Lactic. The model explains 65.2% of the variation in Taste, which is higher than for the two simple linear regressions. Both coefficients are significantly different from 0 ($P = 0.002$ for H2S, and $P = 0.019$ for Lactic).

11.31 The regression equation is $\widehat{\text{Taste}} = -28.9 + 0.33$ Acetic $+ 3.91$ H2S $+ 19.7$ Lactic. The model explains 65.2% of the variation in Taste (the same as for the model with only H2S and Lactic). Residuals of this regression are positively associated with Taste, but they appear to be normally distributed and show no patterns in scatterplots with other variables.

The coefficient of Acetic is not significantly different from 0 ($P = 0.942$); there is no gain in adding Acetic to the model with H2S and Lactic. It appears that the best model is the H2S/Lactic model of Exercise 11.30.

11.32 **(a)** Equation: $\widehat{\text{Corn}} = -3545 + 1.84$ Year. The slope is significantly different from 0 ($t = 13.06$, $P < 0.0005$). $r^2 = 81.8\%$. **(b)** Plot below, left. The residuals look reasonably close to normal (perhaps slightly left-skewed). **(c)** Plot below, right. The residuals show a weak positive association with soybean yield.

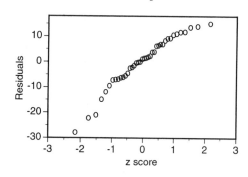
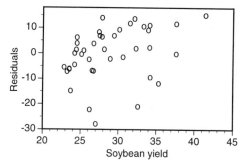

11.33 **(a)** Equation: $\widehat{\text{Corn}} = -46.2 + 4.76$ Soybeans. The slope is significantly different from 0 ($t = 16.04$, $P < 0.0005$). $r^2 = 87.1\%$. **(b)** Plot below, left. The quantile plot is fairly close to linear; there is one high residual, but it is not so high that we would call it an outlier. **(c)** The plot (below, right) reveals a curved pattern: Generally, the residuals are negative in the earlier and later years, and mostly positive from 1964 to 1990.

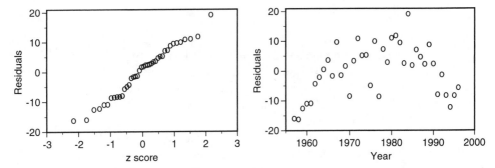

11.34 **(a)** H_0: $\beta_1 = \beta_2 = 0$; H_a: Not all $\beta_j = 0$. $F = 176.05$ (df 2 and 37) has $P < 0.0005$; we reject H_0. **(b)** $R^2 = 90.5\%$—slightly better than the Soybeans model (with $r^2 = 87.1\%$) and considerably better than the Year model ($r^2 = 81.8\%$). **(c)** $\widehat{\text{Corn}} = -1510 + 0.765$ Year $+ 3.08$ Soybeans. The coefficients can change greatly when the model changes. **(d)** Year: $t = 3.62$, $P = 0.001$. Soybeans: $t = 5.82$, $P < 0.0005$. Both are significantly different from 0. **(e)** With df $= 37$, use $t^* = 2.0262$ (or 2.042 from the table). For the coefficient of Year, $SE_{b_1} = 0.2114$, so the interval is 0.3369 to 1.1935 (or 0.3335 to 1.1969). For the coefficient of Soybeans, $SE_{b_2} = 0.5300$, so the interval is 2.0109 to 4.1587 (or 2.0025 to 4.1671). **(f)** The plot of residuals vs. soybean yield looks fine, but the plot of residuals vs. year still shows a curved relationship.

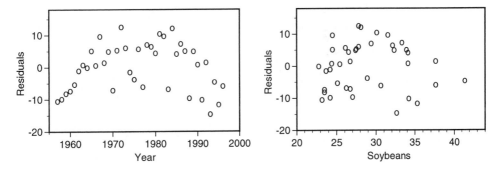

Output from Minitab:

```
The regression equation is
Corn = - 1510 + 0.765 Year + 3.08 Soybeans
```

Predictor	Coef	Stdev	t-ratio	p
Constant	-1510.3	404.6	-3.73	0.001
Year	0.7652	0.2114	3.62	0.001
Soybeans	3.0848	0.5300	5.82	0.000

(Output continues)
```
    s = 7.529          R-sq = 90.5%      R-sq(adj) = 90.0%

    Analysis of Variance

    SOURCE        DF        SS         MS        F         p
    Regression    2      19957.9     9978.9    176.05    0.000
    Error        37       2097.3       56.7
    Total        39      22055.2
```

11.35 **(a)** The regression equation is $\widehat{\text{Corn}} = -964 + 0.480\,\text{Year} - 0.0451\,\text{Year2} + 3.90\,\text{Soybeans}$. **(b)** H_0: $\beta_1 = \beta_2 = \beta_3 = 0$ vs. H_a: Not all $\beta_j = 0$. $F = 233.05$ (df 3 and 36) has $P < 0.0005$, so we conclude that the regression is significant (at least one coefficient is not 0). **(c)** $R^2 = 95.1\%$ (compared with 90.5% for the model without Year2). **(d)** All three coefficients are significantly different from 0—the t values are 2.97, -5.82, and 9.51, all with df $= 36$; the largest P-value (for the first of these) is 0.005, while the other two are less than 0.0005. **(e)** The residuals seem to be (close to) normal, and they have no apparent relationship with the explanatory or response variables.

Output from Minitab:
```
    The regression equation is
    Corn = - 964 + 0.480 Year - 0.0451 Year2 + 3.90 Soybeans

    Predictor      Coef      Stdev     t-ratio      p
    Constant     -964.1      308.9      -3.12     0.004
    Year          0.4800     0.1614      2.97     0.005
    Year2        -0.045083   0.007742   -5.82     0.000
    Soybeans      3.9039     0.4104      9.51     0.000

    s = 5.477      R-sq = 95.1%      R-sq(adj) = 94.7%

    Analysis of Variance

    SOURCE        DF        SS         MS        F         p
    Regression    3      20975.2     6991.7    233.05    0.000
    Error        36       1080.0       30.0
    Total        39      22055.2
```

11.36 **(a)** The regression is significant ($F = 89.03$ with df 2 and 37, $P < 0.0005$). The t-statistics for Year and Year2 are 13.26 ($P < 0.0005$) and -1.48 ($P = 0.148$), respectively. **(b)** Coefficients can change greatly when the model changes; the Year2 term does not make a significant contribution to the model in the absence of Soybeans. **(c)** The regression func-

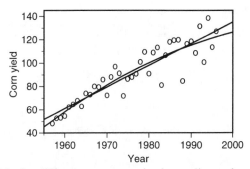

tions are similar from about 1960 to 1990; the differences emerge in the earlier and later years from the data set.

Output from Minitab:
```
The regression equation is
Corn = - 3542 + 1.84 Year - 0.0198 Year2

Predictor       Coef      Stdev    t-ratio        p
Constant     -3542.0      274.2     -12.92    0.000
Year          1.8396     0.1387      13.26    0.000
Year2        -0.01985    0.01345     -1.48    0.148

s = 10.13      R-sq = 82.8%    R-sq(adj) = 81.9%
```

11.37 Portions of the Minitab output follow; see also the graph in Exercise 11.36. For the simple linear regression, the predicted yield is 145.6; the 95% prediction interval is 122.91 to 168.30. For the multiple regression, the predicted yield is 130.98; the 95% prediction interval is 100.91 to 161.04. The second prediction is lower because the quadratic (curved) model allows for the rate of change to decrease—with the multiple regression model, corn yield grows less rapidly in later years than it did in the earlier years.

Output from Minitab:
```
   - - - - - - - - - - - - - - - -   Linear model   - - - - - - - - - - - - - - - - -
MTB > Regress 'Corn' 1 'Year';
SUBC>    predict 2006.

The regression equation is
Corn = - 3545 + 1.84 Year
 . . .
    Fit  Stdev.Fit      95.0% C.I.            95.0% P.I.
  145.60       4.46   ( 136.57, 154.64)  ( 122.91, 168.30) X
```

(Output continues)
```
– – – – – – – – – – – – – – – –   Quadratic model   – – – – – – – – – – – – – – – –
MTB > Regress 'Corn' 2 'Year' 'Year2';
SUBC>    predict 2006 870.25.

The regression equation is
Corn = - 3542 + 1.84 Year - 0.0198 Year2
...
      Fit   Stdev.Fit       95.0% C.I.            95.0% P.I.
   130.98       10.84  (  109.01,  152.95) (  100.91,  161.04) XX
X  denotes a row with X values away from the center
```

11.38 Portions of the Minitab output are below; see also the graph in Exercise 11.36. For the simple linear regression, the predicted yield is 129.05; the 95% prediction interval is 107.17 to 150.92. For the multiple regression, the predicted yield is 123.35; the 95% prediction interval is 100.41 to 146.29. The second prediction is again lower, but not as much as before: Since 1997 is not so far from the years in the data set, the two models have not separated too much. This also accounts for the prediction intervals being smaller.

Output from Minitab:
```
– – – – – – – – – – – – – – – –   Linear model   – – – – – – – – – – – – – – – –
MTB > Regress 'Corn' 1 'Year';
SUBC>    predict 1997.

The regression equation is
Corn = - 3545 + 1.84 Year
...
      Fit   Stdev.Fit       95.0% C.I.            95.0% P.I.
   129.05        3.31  (  122.34,  135.76) (  107.17,  150.92)

– – – – – – – – – – – – – – – –   Quadratic model   – – – – – – – – – – – – – – – –
MTB > Regress 'Corn' 2 'Year' 'year2';
SUBC>    predict 1997 420.25.

The regression equation is
Corn = - 3542 + 1.84 Year - 0.0198 year2
...
      Fit   Stdev.Fit       95.0% C.I.            95.0% P.I.
   123.35        5.05  (  113.11,  133.59) (  100.41,  146.29) X
X  denotes a row with X values away from the center
```

11.39 The outlier is observation 15 (Wages = 97.6801). Without it, the regression equation is $\widehat{\text{Wages}} = 43.4 + 0.0733\,\text{LOS}$. For the coefficient of LOS, $t = 2.85$ ($P = 0.006$). While this is significant, the predictions are not too good: Only $r^2 = 12.5\%$ of the variation in Wages is explained by the regression.

Output from Minitab:
```
The regression equation is
Wages = 43.4 + 0.0733 LOS

Predictor       Coef      Stdev    t-ratio        p
Constant      43.383      2.248      19.30    0.000
LOS          0.07325    0.02571       2.85    0.006

s = 10.21      R-sq = 12.5%      R-sq(adj) = 10.9%
```

11.40 **(a)** The regression equation is $\widehat{\text{Wages}} = 44.0 + 7.93\,\text{Size}$. For testing H_0: $\beta_1 = 0$ vs. H_a: $\beta_1 \neq 0$, $t = 2.96$ with df $= 57$; $P = 0.004$, so the coefficient of Size is significantly different from 0. **(b)** Large banks: $n_1 = 34$, $\bar{x}_1 = 51.91$, $s_1 = 10.67$. Small banks: $n_2 = 25$, $\bar{x}_2 = 43.97$, $s_2 = 9.41$. The pooled standard deviation is $s_p = 10.16$ (the same as $\sqrt{\text{MSE}}$); the t-statistic is

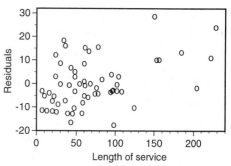

the same (up to rounding), and df $= n_1 + n_2 - 2 = 57$. The slope β_1 represents the change in Wages per unit change in bank size, so it estimates the difference in the means between small (size 0) and large (size 1) banks. Testing $\beta_1 = 0$ is therefore equivalent to testing $\mu_0 = \mu_1$. **(c)** The residuals are positively associated with LOS.

11.41 The regression equation is $\widehat{\text{Wages}} = 37.6 + 0.0829\,\text{LOS} + 8.92\,\text{Size}$. Both coefficients are significantly different from 0 ($t = 3.53$ and $t = 3.63$, respectively); the regression explains 29.1% of the variation in Wages (compared to 12.5% for LOS alone, and 13.4% for Size alone). The residuals look normal, and do not seem to be associated with LOS. There may be a relationship between the residuals and the size; specifically, the residuals for small banks have less scatter than do those for large banks ($s_0 = 7.0$ vs. $s_1 = 10.5$).

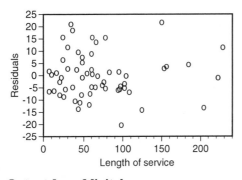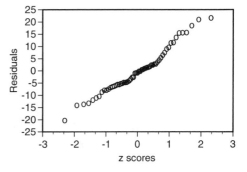

Output from Minitab:

```
The regression equation is
Wages = 37.6 + 0.0829 LOS + 8.92 SizeCode
```

Predictor	Coef	Stdev	t-ratio	p
Constant	37.565	2.596	14.47	0.000
LOS	0.08289	0.02349	3.53	0.001
SizeCode	8.916	2.459	3.63	0.001

```
s = 9.273      R-sq = 29.1%      R-sq(adj) = 26.6%
```

Chapter 12 Solutions

12.1 **(a)** Below ($\bar{x}$, s, $s_{\bar{x}}$ in mg/100g). **(b)** H_0: $\mu_1 = \mu_2 = \mu_3 = \mu_4 = \mu_5$ vs. H_a: not all μ_i are equal. $F = 367.74$ with 4 and 5 degrees of freedom; $P < 0.0005$, so we reject the null hypothesis. Minitab output below. **(c)** Plot below. We conclude that vitamin C content decreases over time.

Condition	n	$\bar{x}$	s	$s_{\bar{x}}$
Immediate	2	48.705	1.534	1.085
One day	2	41.955	2.128	1.505
Three days	2	21.795	0.771	0.545
Five days	2	12.415	1.082	0.765
Seven days	2	8.320	0.269	0.190

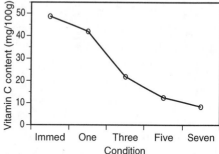

Output from Minitab:
```
Analysis of Variance on VitC
Source    DF       SS       MS       F       p
Days       4  2565.72   641.43  367.74   0.000
Error      5     8.72     1.74
Total      9  2574.44
```

12.2 Means, etc., at right ($\bar{x}$, s, $s_{\bar{x}}$ in mg/100g). Plots of means below. The hypotheses are H_0: $\mu_1 = \cdots = \mu_5$ vs. H_a: not all μ_i are equal. For vitamin A, $F = 12.09$ (df 4 and 5), so $P = 0.009$— we reject H_0 and conclude that vitamin A content changes over time (it appears to decrease, except for the rise at "Five days"). For vitamin E, $F = 0.69$ (df 4 and 5), so $P = 0.630$—we cannot reject the null hypothesis. Minitab output on page 244.

Vitamin A	n	$\bar{x}$	s	$s_{\bar{x}}$
Immediate	2	3.350	0.01414	0.010
One day	2	3.240	0.05657	0.040
Three days	2	3.210	0.07071	0.050
Five days	2	3.305	0.07778	0.055
Seven days	2	2.965	0.06364	0.045
Vitamin E				
Immediate	2	95.30	0.98995	0.700
One day	2	94.45	1.76777	1.250
Three days	2	95.85	2.19203	1.550
Five days	2	96.35	1.90919	1.350
Seven days	2	93.70	1.97990	1.400

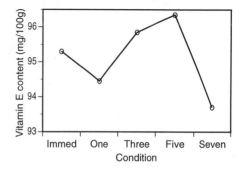

Output from Minitab:
```
Analysis of Variance on VitA
Source     DF        SS        MS       F        p
Days        4   0.17894   0.04473   12.09    0.009
Error       5   0.01850   0.00370
Total       9   0.19744
-------------------------------------------------
Analysis of Variance on VitE
Source     DF        SS        MS       F        p
Days        4      9.09      2.27    0.69    0.630
Error       5     16.47      3.29
Total       9     25.56
```

12.3 **(a)** All four data sets appear to be reasonably close to normal, although "3 promotions" seems to have a low outlier. Plots below. **(b)** At right ($\bar{x}$, s, $s_{\bar{x}}$ in dollars). **(c)** The ratio

Promotions	n	$\bar{x}$	s	$s_{\bar{x}}$
One	40	4.2240	0.2734	0.0432
Three	40	4.0627	0.1742	0.0275
Five	40	3.7590	0.2526	0.0399
Seven	40	3.5487	0.2750	0.0435

of largest to smallest standard deviations is about 1.58, so the assumption of equal standard deviations is reasonable. **(d)** H_0: $\mu_1 = \cdots = \mu_4$; H_a: not all μ_i are equal. Minitab output (page 245) gives $F = 59.90$ with df 3 and 156, and $P < 0.0005$, so we reject the null hypothesis. With more promotions, expected price decreases.

One Promotion.

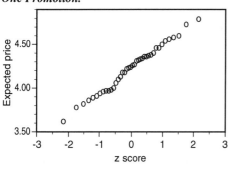

Three Promotions.

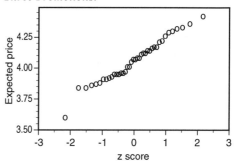

Five Promotions.

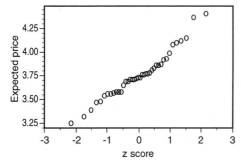

Seven Promotions.

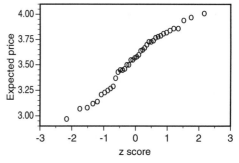

Output from Minitab:

```
Analysis of Variance on ExpPrice
Source    DF      SS       MS       F       p
NumPromo   3   10.9885   3.6628   59.90   0.000
Error    156    9.5388   0.0611
Total    159   20.5273
```

12.4 We have six comparisons to make, and df = 156, so the Bonferroni critical value with $\alpha = 0.05$ is $t^{**} = 2.67$. The pooled standard deviation is $s_p \doteq 0.2473$, so the standard deviation of each difference is $s_p\sqrt{1/40 + 1/40} \doteq 0.05529$. All six differences are significant. [Note that because the means decrease, we could consider only the differences in consecutive means, i.e., $\bar{x}_1 - \bar{x}_3$, $\bar{x}_3 - \bar{x}_5$, and $\bar{x}_5 - \bar{x}_7$. Since these three differences are significant, it follows that the others must be, too. (These are the three smallest t-values.)]

$\bar{x}_1 - \bar{x}_3 = 0.16125$	$t_{13} = 2.916$
$\bar{x}_1 - \bar{x}_5 = 0.46500$	$t_{15} = 8.410$
$\bar{x}_1 - \bar{x}_7 = 0.67525$	$t_{17} = 12.212$
$\bar{x}_3 - \bar{x}_5 = 0.30375$	$t_{35} = 5.493$
$\bar{x}_3 - \bar{x}_7 = 0.51400$	$t_{37} = 9.296$
$\bar{x}_5 - \bar{x}_7 = 0.21025$	$t_{57} = 3.802$

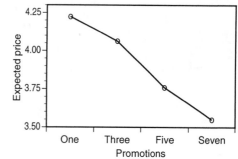

12.5 (a) At right. **(b)** H_0: $\mu_1 = \cdots = \mu_4$; H_a: not all μ_i are equal. $F = 9.24$ with df 3 and 74; $P < 0.0005$, so we reject the null hypothesis. The type of lesson does affect the mean score change;

Lesson	n	$\bar{x}$	s	$s_{\bar{x}}$
Piano	34	3.618	3.055	0.524
Singing	10	−0.300	1.494	0.473
Computer	20	0.450	2.212	0.495
None	14	0.786	3.191	0.853

in particular, it appears that students who take piano lessons had significantly higher scores than the other students.

Output from Minitab:

```
Analysis of Variance on Scores
Source     DF      SS       MS      F       p
LssnCode    3   207.28   69.09   9.24   0.000
Error      74   553.44    7.48
Total      77   760.72
```

12.6 We have six comparisons to make, and df $= 74$, so the Bonferroni critical value with $\alpha = 0.05$ is $t^{**} = 2.71$. The pooled standard deviation is $s_p \doteq 2.7348$.

The Piano mean is significantly higher than the other three, but the other three means are not significantly different.

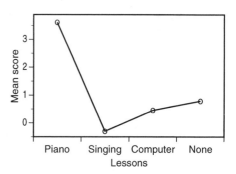

$D_{PS} =$	3.91765	$D_{PC} =$	3.16765	$D_{PN} =$	2.83193
$SE_{PS} =$	0.98380	$SE_{PC} =$	0.77066	$SE_{PN} =$	0.86843
$t_{PS} =$	3.982	$t_{PC} =$	4.110	$t_{PN} =$	3.261
		$D_{SC} =$	-0.75000	$D_{SN} =$	-1.08571
		$SE_{SC} =$	1.05917	$SE_{SN} =$	1.13230
		$t_{SC} =$	-0.708	$t_{SN} =$	-0.959
				$D_{CN} =$	-0.33571
				$SE_{CN} =$	0.95297
				$t_{CN} =$	-0.352

12.7 We test the hypothesis H_0: $\psi = \mu_1 - \frac{1}{3}(\mu_2 + \mu_3 + \mu_4) = 0$; the sample contrast is $c = 3.618 - \frac{1}{3}(-0.300 + 0.450 + 0.786) = 3.306$. The pooled standard deviation estimate is $s_p = 2.735$, so $SE_c = 2.735\sqrt{1/34 + \frac{1}{9}/10 + \frac{1}{9}/20 + \frac{1}{9}/14} \doteq 0.6356$. Then $t = 3.306/0.6356 \doteq 5.20$, with df $= 74$. This is enough evidence ($P < 0.001$) to reject H_0 in favor of H_a: $\psi > 0$, so we conclude that mean score changes for piano students are greater than the average of the means for the other three groups.

12.8 (a) Response: Yield (in pounds). Populations: Varieties A, B, C, and D. $I = 4$, $n_i = 12$ ($i = 1, 2, 3, 4$), $N = 48$. **(b)** Response: Attractiveness rating. Populations: Packaging type. $I = 5$, $n_i = 40$ ($i = 1, 2, 3, 4, 5$), $N = 200$. **(c)** Response: Weight loss. Populations: Dieters using the various weight-loss programs. $I = 3$, $n_i = 20$ ($i = 1, 2, 3$), $N = 60$.

12.9 (a) Response: Typical number of hours of sleep. Populations: Nonsmokers, moderate smokers, heavy smokers. $I = 3$, $n_i = 100$ ($i = 1, 2, 3$), $N = 300$. **(b)** Response: Strength of the concrete. Populations: Mixtures A, B, C, and D. $I = 4$, $n_i = 5$ ($i = 1, 2, 3, 4$), $N = 20$. **(c)** Response: Scores on final exam. Populations: Students using Methods A, B, and C. $I = 3$, $n_i = 20$ ($i = 1, 2, 3$), $N = 60$.

12.10 **(a)** The data suggest that the presence of too many nematodes reduces growth. Table at right; two versions of the plot below. (The second shows accurately the scale for the number of nematodes.)

Nematodes	$\bar{x}$	s
0	10.650	2.053
1000	10.425	1.486
5000	5.600	1.244
10000	5.450	1.771

(b) $H_0: \mu_1 = \cdots = \mu_4$ vs. H_a: not all μ_i are equal. This ANOVA tests whether nematodes affect mean plant growth. **(c)** Minitab output below. $F = 12.08$ with df 3 and 12; $P = 0.001$, so we reject H_0; it appears that somewhere between 1000 and 5000 nematodes, the worms hurt seedling growth. $s_p = \sqrt{2.78} = 1.667$ and $R^2 = 100.65/133.97 = 75.1\%$.

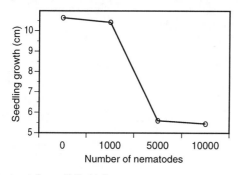 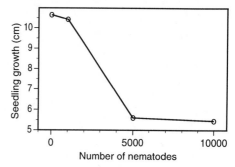

Output from Minitab:

```
Analysis of Variance on Growth
Source     DF      SS      MS      F       p
Nematode    3   100.65   33.55   12.08   0.001
Error      12    33.33    2.78
Total      15   133.97
                                    Individual 95% CIs For Mean
                                    Based on Pooled StDev
Level      N     Mean    StDev   ------+---------+---------+---------+
    0      4   10.650    2.053                        (-------*------)
 1000      4   10.425    1.486                        (-------*------)
 5000      4    5.600    1.244   (------*-------)
10000      4    5.450    1.771   (------*------)
                                 ------+---------+---------+---------+
Pooled StDev =     1.667           5.0       7.5      10.0      12.5
```

12.11 **(a)** Below. **(b)** $H_0: \mu_1 = \cdots = \mu_4$; H_a: not all μ_i are equal. ANOVA tests if there are differences in the mean number of insects attracted to each color. **(c)** $F = 30.55$ with df 3 and 20; $P < 0.0005$, so we reject H_0. The color of the board does affect the number of insects attracted; in particular, it appears that yellow draws the most, green is second, and white and blue draw the least. The pooled standard deviation is $s_p = 6.784$, and $R^2 = 4218.5/5139.0 = 82.1\%$. [Note that the largest-to-smallest SD ratio is almost 3, so the use of ANOVA is questionable here.]

Color	$\bar{x}$	s
Lemon yellow	47.17	6.79
White	15.67	3.33
Green	31.50	9.91
Blue	14.83	5.34

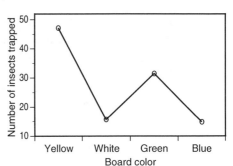

Output from Minitab:

```
Analysis of Variance on Insects
Source     DF      SS       MS       F       p
ColCode     3    4218.5   1406.2   30.55   0.000
Error      20     920.5     46.0
Total      23    5139.0
```

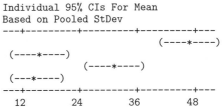

```
                                 Individual 95% CIs For Mean
                                 Based on Pooled StDev
Level    N     Mean    StDev    ---+---------+---------+---------+---
  1      6    47.167   6.795                              (----*----)
  2      6    15.667   3.327    (----*----)
  3      6    31.500   9.915                  (----*----)
  4      6    14.833   5.345    (---*----)
                                ---+---------+---------+---------+---
Pooled StDev =    6.784          12        24        36        48
```

12.12 **(a)** $\psi = \mu_1 - \frac{1}{3}(\mu_2 + \mu_3 + \mu_4)$. **(b)** H_0: $\psi = 0$; H_a: $\psi > 0$. **(c)** The sample contrast is $c = 3.49$. $SE_c = 1.6665\sqrt{1/4 + \frac{1}{9}/4 + \frac{1}{9}/4 + \frac{1}{9}/4} \doteq 0.9622$, so $t = 3.49/0.9622 \doteq 3.63$, with df $= 12$. This is enough evidence ($P = 0.002$) to reject H_0, so we conclude that mean seedling growth with no nematodes is greater than the average of the means for the other three groups. **(d)** $\psi_2 = \mu_1 - \mu_4$. The estimated contrast is $c_2 = 5.2$, with $SE_{c_2} = 1.178$; the 95% confidence interval is 2.632 to 7.768.

12.13 If doing computations by hand, note that $s_p\sqrt{1/n_i + 1/n_j} \doteq 3.916$. The t statistics for the multiple comparisons are $t_{12} \doteq 8.04$, $t_{13} \doteq 4.00$, $t_{14} \doteq 8.26$, $t_{23} \doteq -4.04$, $t_{24} \doteq 0.21$, $t_{34} \doteq 4.26$. These indicate that the only *non*significant difference is between white and blue boards; lemon yellow is the best.

12.14 **(a)** Plot below, left. Form 2 scores are typically about one point higher than form 1 scores; form 3 scores are about two points higher than form 2 scores. **(b)** $F = 7.61$ (df 2 and 238) with $P = 0.0006$, so we conclude that the means are different. The comparisons reveal that the form 3 minus form 1 difference is the significant one.

For 12.14.

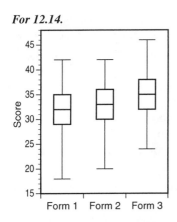

For 12.15.

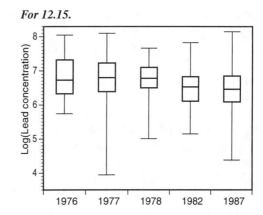

12.15 (**a**) Plot above, right. The low observation for 1977 is an outlier, as are the maximum and minimum in 1987 (using the $1.5 \times IQR$ criterion). There is no strong suggestion of a trend in the medians. Note that "side-by-side" boxplots are somewhat misleading since the elapsed times between observations differ. (**b**) $F = 5.75$ is significant ($P = 0.0002$), indicating that the mean log-concentration does vary over the years. The t-tests for individual differences suggest that the mean in 1987 is significantly lower than the others.

12.16 Yes: The ratio of largest to smallest standard deviations is $10.1/5.2 \doteq 1.94 < 2$. The pooled variance is $s_p^2 = \dfrac{(19)(5.2^2) + (19)(8.9^2) + (19)(10.1^2)}{19 + 19 + 19} = 69.42$, so $s_p \doteq 8.33$.

12.17 Yes: The ratio of largest to smallest standard deviations is $12.2/9.2 \doteq 1.33 < 2$. The pooled variance is $s_p^2 = \dfrac{(91)(12.2^2) + (33)(10.4^2) + (34)(9.2^2) + (23)(11.7^2)}{91 + 33 + 34 + 23} \doteq 127.845$, so $s_p \doteq 11.3$.

12.18 The degrees of freedom are in the table at the right. "Groups" refers to variation between (**a**) the mean yields for the tomato varieties, (**b**) the mean attractiveness ratings for each of the five packaging types, and (**c**) the mean weight-losses for each of the three diet methods.

Source	df (a)	(b)	(c)
Groups	3	4	2
Error	44	195	57
Total	47	199	59

12.19 The degrees of freedom are in the table at the right. "Groups" refers to variation between (**a**) the mean hours of sleep for nonsmokers, moderate smokers, and heavy smokers, (**b**) the mean strengths for each of the four concrete mixtures, and (**c**) the mean scores for each of the three teaching methods.

Source	df (a)	(b)	(c)
Groups	2	3	2
Error	297	16	57
Total	299	19	59

12.20 (a) H_0: $\mu_1 = \mu_2 = \mu_3$; H_a: not all μ_i are equal. **(b)** The sources of variation are "among groups" (that is, among the mean SATM scores for each of the three groups), with df $= 2$, and "within groups," with df $= 253$. The total variation has df $= 255$. **(c)** If H_0 is true, F has an $F(2, 253)$ distribution. **(d)** Referring to the $F(2, 200)$ distribution, the critical value is 3.04.

12.21 (a) H_0: $\mu_1 = \cdots = \mu_4$; H_a: not all μ_i are equal. **(b)** The sources of variation are "among groups" (that is, among the mean amounts spent on books for each of the four classes), with df $= 3$, and "within groups," with df $= 196$. The total variation has df $= 199$. **(c)** If H_0 is true, F has an $F(3, 196)$ distribution. **(d)** Referring to the $F(3, 100)$ distribution, the critical value is 2.70.

12.22 (a) At right. **(b)** H_0: $\mu_1 = \mu_2 = \mu_3$; H_a: not all μ_i are equal. **(c)** If H_0 is true, F has an $F(3, 32)$ distribution. Referring to the $F(3, 30)$

Source	df	SS	MS	F
Groups	3	104 855.87	34 951.96	15.86
Error	32	70 500.59	2 203.14	
Total	35	175 356.46		

distribution, $P < 0.001$—strong evidence of a difference. **(d)** $s_p^2 = \text{MSE} = 2203.14$, so $s_p \doteq 46.94$.

12.23 (a) At right. **(b)** H_0: $\mu_1 = \cdots = \mu_4$; H_a: not all μ_i are equal. **(c)** If H_0 is true, F has an $F(3, 32)$ distribution. Referring to the $F(3, 30)$ distribution, P

Source	df	SS	MS	F
Groups	3	476.88	158.96	2.531
Error	32	2009.92	62.81	
Total	35	2486.80		

is between 0.05 and 0.10 (there is *some* evidence of a difference, but not what we would usually call significant). **(d)** $s_p^2 = \text{MSE} = 62.81$, so $s_p \doteq 7.925$.

12.24 (a) $s_p^2 = \text{MSE} \doteq 3.898 \doteq$
$$\frac{(45)(2.5^2) + (110)(1.8^2) + (51)(1.8^2)}{45 + 110 + 51}.$$
(b) At right. **(c)** H_0: $\mu_1 = \mu_2 = \mu_3$; H_a: not all μ_i are equal. **(d)** If H_0 is true, F has an

Source	df	SS	MS	F
Groups	2	17.22	8.61	2.21
Error	206	802.89	3.90	
Total	208	820.11		

$F(2, 206)$ distribution. Referring to the $F(2, 200)$ distribution, $P > 0.10$; we have no reason to reject H_0. **(e)** $R^2 = 17.22/802.89 \doteq 0.021 = 2.1\%$.

12.25 (a) $s_p^2 = \text{MSE} \doteq 72 412 \doteq$
$$\frac{(87)(327^2) + (90)(184^2) + (53)(285^2)}{87 + 90 + 53}.$$
(b) At right. **(c)** H_0: $\mu_1 = \mu_2 = \mu_3$; H_a: not all μ_i are equal.

Source	df	SS	MS	F
Groups	2	6 572 551	3 286 275.5	45.38
Error	230	16 654 788	72 412	
Total	232	23 227 339		

(d) If H_0 is true, F has an $F(2, 230)$ distribution. Referring to the $F(2, 200)$ distribution, $P < 0.001$; we conclude that the means are not all the same. **(e)** $R^2 = 6 572 551/23 227 339 \doteq 0.283 = 28.3\%$.

12.26 (a) $\psi_1 = \frac{1}{2}(\mu_1 + \mu_2) - \mu_3 = 0.5\mu_1 + 0.5\mu_2 - \mu_3$ (or, $\psi_1 = \mu_3 - 0.5\mu_1 - 0.5\mu_2$.) **(b)** $\psi_2 = \mu_1 - \mu_2$ (or, $\psi_2 = \mu_2 - \mu_1$).

12.27 (a) $\psi_1 = \frac{1}{2}(\mu_1 + \mu_2) - \frac{1}{2}(\mu_3 + \mu_4) = 0.5\mu_1 + 0.5\mu_2 - 0.5\mu_3 - 0.5\mu_4$ (or, $\psi_1 = 0.5\mu_3 + 0.5\mu_4 - 0.5\mu_1 - 0.5\mu_2$.) (b) $\psi_2 = \mu_1 - \mu_2$ (or, $\psi_2 = \mu_2 - \mu_1$). (c) $\psi_3 = \mu_3 - \mu_4$ (or, $\psi_3 = \mu_4 - \mu_3$).

12.28 (a) For $\psi_1 = \frac{1}{2}(\mu_1 + \mu_2) - \mu_3$, H_0: $\psi_1 = 0$ vs. H_a: $\psi_1 > 0$ (since we might expect that the science majors would have higher SATM scores). For $\psi_2 = \mu_1 - \mu_2$, H_0: $\psi_2 = 0$ vs. H_a: $\psi_2 \neq 0$ (since we have no prior expectation of the direction of the difference). (b) $c_1 = \frac{1}{2}(619 + 629) - 575 = 49$ and $c_2 = 619 - 629 = -10$. (c) $SE_{c_1} = 82.5\sqrt{\frac{1}{4}/103 + \frac{1}{4}/31 + 1/122} \doteq 11.28$ and $SE_{c_2} = 82.5\sqrt{1/103 + 1/31 + 0/122} \doteq 16.90$. (d) $t_1 = 49/11.28 \doteq 4.344$ (df $= 253$, $P < 0.0005$)—we conclude that science majors have higher mean SATM scores than other majors. $t_2 = -10/16.90 \doteq -0.5916$ (df $= 253$, $P > 0.25$)—the difference in mean SATM scores for computer science vs. other science students is not significant. (e) Use $t^* = 1.984$ (for df $= 100$, from the table), or $t^* = 1.9694$ (for df $= 253$). For ψ_1, this gives 26.6 to 71.4, or 26.8 to 71.2. For ψ_2, -43.5 to 23.5, or -43.3 to 23.3.

12.29 (a) For $\psi_1 = \frac{1}{2}(\mu_1 + \mu_2) - \mu_3$, H_0: $\psi_1 = 0$ vs. H_a: $\psi_1 > 0$ (since we might expect that the science majors would have higher math scores). For $\psi_2 = \mu_1 - \mu_2$, H_0: $\psi_2 = 0$ vs. H_a: $\psi_2 \neq 0$ (since we have no prior expectation of the direction of the difference). (b) $c_1 = \frac{1}{2}(8.77 + 8.75) - 7.83 = 0.93$ and $c_2 = 8.77 - 8.75 = 0.02$. (c) $SE_{c_1} = 1.581\sqrt{\frac{1}{4}/90 + \frac{1}{4}/28 + 1/106} \doteq 0.2299$ and $SE_{c_2} = 1.581\sqrt{1/90 + 1/28 + 0/106} \doteq 0.3421$. (d) $t_1 = 0.93/0.2299 \doteq 4.045$ (df $= 221$, $P < 0.0005$)—we conclude that science majors have higher mean HS math grades than other majors. $t_2 = 0.02/0.3421 \doteq 0.0585$ (df $= 221$, $P > 0.25$)—the difference in mean HS math grades for computer science vs. other science students is not significant. (e) Use $t^* = 1.984$ (for df $= 100$, from the table), or $t^* = 1.9708$ (for df $= 221$). For ψ_1, this gives 0.474 to 1.386, or 0.477 to 1.383. For ψ_2, -0.659 to 0.699, or -0.654 to 0.694.

12.30 (a) $\psi_1 = \mu_T - \mu_C$; H_0: $\psi_1 = 0$ vs. H_a: $\psi_1 > 0$. $\psi_2 = \mu_T - \frac{1}{2}(\mu_C + \mu_S)$; H_0: $\psi_2 = 0$ vs. H_a: $\psi_2 > 0$. $\psi_3 = \mu_J - \frac{1}{3}(\mu_T + \mu_C + \mu_S)$; H_0: $\psi_3 = 0$ vs. H_a: $\psi_3 > 0$.
(b) First note $s_p \doteq 46.9432$ and df $= 32$. $c_1 = -17.06$, $SE_{c_1} \doteq 25.71$, and $t_1 \doteq -0.66$, which has $P > 0.25$—not significant. $c_2 = 24.39$, $SE_{c_2} \doteq 19.64$, and $t_2 \doteq 1.24$, which has $0.10 < P < 0.15$—not significant. $c_3 = 91.22$, $SE_{c_3} \doteq 17.27$, and $t_3 \doteq 5.28$, which has $P < 0.0005$—strong evidence of a difference.
The contrasts allow us to determine which differences between sample means represent "true" differences in population means: T is not significantly better than C, nor is it better than the average of C and S. Joggers have higher fitness scores than the average of the other three groups.
(c) No: Although this seems like a logical connection, we cannot draw this conclusion, since the treatment imposed by the study (the T group) did not produce a significantly lower result than the control group. The only significant contrast involved all four groups, including the joggers and sedentary persons who did not have treatments imposed on them. In these cases, causation cannot be determined because of confounding or "common

response" issues; e.g., perhaps some people choose not to jog because they are less fit to begin with.

12.31 (a) $\psi_1 = \mu_T - \mu_C$; H_0: $\psi_1 = 0$ vs. H_a: $\psi_1 < 0$. $\psi_2 = \mu_T - \frac{1}{2}(\mu_C + \mu_S)$; H_0: $\psi_2 = 0$ vs. H_a: $\psi_2 < 0$. $\psi_3 = \mu_J - \frac{1}{3}(\mu_T + \mu_C + \mu_S)$; H_0: $\psi_3 = 0$ vs. H_a: $\psi_3 < 0$.

(b) First note $s_p = \sqrt{\text{MSE}} \doteq 7.93$ and df $= 32$. $c_1 = -5.5$, $\text{SE}_{c_1} \doteq 4.343$, and $t_1 \doteq -1.27$, which has $0.10 < P < 0.15$—not significant. $c_2 = -5.9$, $\text{SE}_{c_2} \doteq 3.317$, and $t_2 \doteq -1.78$, which has $0.025 < P < 0.05$—fairly strong evidence of a difference. $c_3 = -6.10\overline{3}$, $\text{SE}_{c_3} \doteq 2.917$, and $t_3 \doteq -2.09$, which has $0.02 < P < 0.025$—fairly strong evidence of a difference.

The contrasts allow us to determine which differences between sample means represent "true" differences in population means: T is not significantly better than C, but it is better than the average of C and S. Joggers have lower mean depression scores than the average of the other three groups.

(c) No: The treatment imposed by the study (the T group) did not produce a significantly lower result than the control group. The contrasts that *were* significant involved joggers and sedentary persons—the two groups that did not have treatments imposed on them. In these cases, causation cannot be determined because of confounding or "common response" issues; e.g., there may be personality factors that dispose a person to be depressed and also to be sedentary.

12.32 In this context, $\alpha = 0.05$ means that for all three comparisons, there is a probability no more than 0.05 that we will falsely conclude that means are unequal.

$t_{12} \doteq 1.73$	$t_{13} \doteq 2.00$
$\text{SE}_{12} \doteq 0.3462$	$\text{SE}_{13} \doteq 0.3996$
	$t_{23} \doteq 0.603$
	$\text{SE}_{23} \doteq 0.3318$

$s_p = \sqrt{\text{MSE}} \doteq \sqrt{3.898} \doteq 1.974$; the t statistics (and standard errors) for the three differences are at the right. According to the Bonferroni criterion, none of the differences are significant.

12.33 In this context, $\alpha = 0.05$ means that for all three comparisons, there is a probability no more than 0.05 that we will falsely conclude that means are unequal.

$t_{12} \doteq 9.27^*$	$t_{13} \doteq 2.11$
$\text{SE}_{12} \doteq 40.232$	$\text{SE}_{13} \doteq 46.517$
	$t_{23} \doteq -5.95^*$
	$\text{SE}_{23} \doteq 46.224$

$s_p = \sqrt{\text{MSE}} \doteq \sqrt{72412} \doteq 269.095$; the t statistics (and standard errors) for the three differences are at the right. The mean toddler food intake for Kenya is significantly different from (less than) the means for the other two countries.

12.34 $s_p = \sqrt{MSE} \doteq 46.94$; the t statistics (and standard errors) for the six differences are at the right. Those marked with an asterisk (*) are significantly different. The T group is significantly lower (worse) than the jogging group; the first three groups (T, C, J) are all significantly higher (better) than the sedentary group.

$t_{TC} \doteq -0.66$	$t_{TJ} \doteq -3.65^*$	$t_{TS} \doteq 3.14^*$
$SE_{TC} \doteq 25.71$	$SE_{TJ} \doteq 20.51$	$SE_{TS} \doteq 20.99$
	$t_{CJ} \doteq -2.29$	$t_{CS} \doteq 3.22^*$
	$SE_{CJ} \doteq 25.32$	$SE_{CS} \doteq 25.71$
		$t_{JS} \doteq 6.86^*$
		$SE_{JS} \doteq 20.51$

12.35 $s_p = \sqrt{MSE} \doteq 7.925$; the t statistics (and standard errors) for the six differences are at the right. None of the differences are significant.

$t_{TC} \doteq -1.27$	$t_{TJ} \doteq 0.63$	$t_{TS} \doteq -1.78$
$SE_{TC} \doteq 4.343$	$SE_{TJ} \doteq 3.465$	$SE_{TS} \doteq 3.546$
	$t_{CJ} \doteq 1.79$	$t_{CS} \doteq -0.18$
	$SE_{CJ} \doteq 4.277$	$SE_{CS} \doteq 4.343$
		$t_{JS} \doteq -2.44$
		$SE_{JS} \doteq 3.465$

12.36 Results may vary slightly based on software used. $\bar{\mu} = 3.0$ and
$$\lambda = \frac{n(0.5^2 + 0^2 + 0.5^2)}{2.3^2} = \frac{n}{10.58}$$
With a total sample size of $3n$, the degrees of freedom are 2 and $3n-3$.

n	DFG	DFE	F^*	λ	Power
50	2	147	3.0576	4.7259	0.4719
100	2	297	3.0262	9.4518	0.7876
150	2	447	3.0159	14.1777	0.9295
175	2	522	3.0130	16.5406	0.9614
200	2	597	3.0108	18.9036	0.9795

Choices of sample size might vary. As n gets bigger, the return (increased power) for larger sample size is smaller and smaller; n between 150 and 200 is probably a reasonable choice.

12.37 Results may vary slightly based on software used. $\bar{\mu} = 3.0$ and
$$\lambda = \frac{n(0.3^2 + 0^2 + 0.3^2)}{2.3^2} = \frac{18n}{529}$$
With a total sample size of $3n$, the degrees of freedom are 2 and $3n - 3$.

n	DFG	DFE	F^*	λ	Power
50	2	147	3.0576	1.7013	0.1940
100	2	297	3.0262	3.4026	0.3566
150	2	447	3.0159	5.1040	0.5096
175	2	522	3.0130	5.9546	0.5780
200	2	597	3.0108	6.8053	0.6399

Choices of sample size might vary. "At least 150" is a reasonable response; one might wish to go higher than $n = 200$ (to get more power). [In fact, we need $n \doteq 325$ in order to get power $\doteq 0.90$.]

12.38 (a) Below. (b) $H_0: \mu_1 = \cdots = \mu_4$; H_a: not all μ_i are equal. The F statistic, with df 3 and 351, is 967.82, which has $P < 0.0005$. Minitab output below. We conclude that the means are different; specifically, the 'Placebo' mean is much higher than the other three means.

Shampoo	n	$\bar{x}$	s	$s_{\bar{x}}$
PyrI	112	17.393	1.142	0.108
PyrII	109	17.202	1.352	0.130
Keto	106	16.028	0.931	0.090
Placebo	28	29.393	1.595	0.301

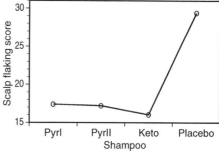

Output from Minitab:

```
Analysis of Variance on Flaking
Source     DF        SS        MS        F        p
Code        3    4151.43   1383.81   967.82   0.000
Error     351     501.87      1.43
Total     354    4653.30
```

12.39 **(a)** The plot (below) shows granularity (which varies between groups), but that should not make us question independence; it is due to the fact that the scores are all integers. **(b)** The ratio of the largest to the smallest standard deviations is $1.595/0.931 \doteq 1.714$— less than 2. **(c)** Apart from the granularity, the quantile plots (below) are reasonably straight. **(d)** Again, apart from the granularity, the quantile plot looks pretty good.

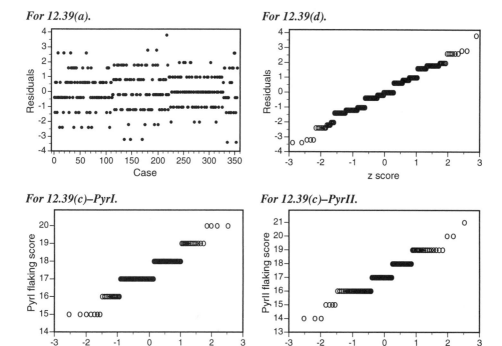

For 12.39(a).

For 12.39(d).

For 12.39(c)–PyrI.

For 12.39(c)–PyrII.

For 12.39(c)–Keto.

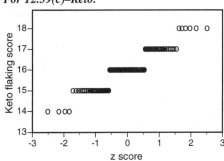

For 12.39(c)–Placebo.

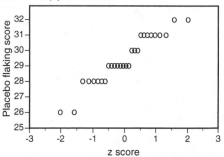

12.40 We have six comparisons to make, and df $= 351$, so the Bonferroni critical value with $\alpha = 0.05$ is $t^{**} = 2.65$. The pooled standard deviation is $s_p = \sqrt{\text{MSE}} \doteq 1.1958$; the differences, standard errors, and t statistics are below. The only *non*significant difference is between the two Pyr treatments (meaning the second application of the shampoo is of little benefit). The Keto shampoo mean is the lowest; the placebo mean is by far the highest.

$D_{12} = 0.19102$	$D_{13} = 1.36456$	$D_{14} = -12.0000$
$SE_{12} = 0.16088$	$SE_{13} = 0.16203$	$SE_{14} = 0.25265$
$t_{12} = 1.187$	$t_{13} = 8.421$	$t_{14} = -47.497$
	$D_{23} = 1.17353$	$D_{24} = -12.1910$
	$SE_{23} = 0.16312$	$SE_{24} = 0.25334$
	$t_{23} = 7.195$	$t_{24} = -48.121$
		$D_{34} = -13.3646$
		$SE_{34} = 0.25407$
		$t_{34} = -52.601$

12.41 **(a)** $\psi_1 = \frac{1}{3}\mu_1 + \frac{1}{3}\mu_2 + \frac{1}{3}\mu_3 - \mu_4$, $\psi_2 = \frac{1}{2}\mu_1 + \frac{1}{2}\mu_2 - \mu_3$, $\psi_3 = \mu_1 - \mu_2$. **(b)** The pooled standard deviation is $s_p = \sqrt{\text{MSE}} \doteq 1.1958$. The

$c_1 = -12.51$	$c_2 = 1.269$	$c_3 = 0.191$
$SE_{c_1} \doteq 0.2355$	$SE_{c_2} \doteq 0.1413$	$SE_{c_3} \doteq 0.1609$
$t_1 = -53.17$	$t_2 = 8.98$	$t_3 = 1.19$
$P_1 < 0.0005$	$P_2 < 0.0005$	$P_3 \doteq 0.2359$

estimated contrasts and their standard errors are in the table. For example, $SE_{c_1} = s_p\sqrt{\frac{1}{9}/112 + \frac{1}{9}/109 + \frac{1}{9}/106 + 1/28} \doteq 0.2355$. **(c)** We test H_0: $\psi_i = 0$ vs. H_a: $\psi_i \neq 0$ for each contrast. The t and P values are given in the table.

The Placebo mean is significantly higher than the average of the other three, while the Keto mean is significantly lower than the average of the two Pyr means. The difference between the Pyr means is not significant (meaning the second application of the shampoo is of little benefit)—this agrees with our conclusion from 12.40.

12.42 (a) At right. **(b)** Each new value (except for n) is simply

$$\text{(old value)}/64 \times 100\%$$

(c) The SS and MS entries differ from those of Exercise 12.1—by a factor of $(100/64)^2$. However,

Condition	n	$\bar{x}$	s	$s_{\bar{x}}$
Immediate	2	76.10%	2.40%	1.70%
One day	2	65.55%	3.33%	2.35%
Three days	2	34.055%	1.204%	0.852%
Five days	2	19.40%	1.69%	1.20%
Seven days	2	13%	0.420%	0.297%

everything else is the same: $F = 367.74$ with df 4 and 5; $P < 0.0005$, so we (again) reject H_0 and conclude that vitamin C content decreases over time.

Output from Minitab:
```
Analysis of Variance on VitCPct
Source    DF       SS        MS       F         p
Days       4   6263.97   1565.99   367.74    0.000
Error      5     21.29      4.26
Total      9   6285.26
```

12.43 Transformed values for vitamin A are at right; each value is

$$\text{(old value)}/5 \times 100\%$$

The transformation has no effect on vitamin E, since the number of mil-ligrams remaining is also the percent-age of the original 100 mg.

Condition	n	$\bar{x}$	s	$s_{\bar{x}}$
Immediate	2	67.0%	0.28284%	0.2%
One day	2	64.8%	1.13137%	0.8%
Three days	2	64.2%	1.41421%	1.0%
Five days	2	66.1%	1.55563%	1.1%
Seven days	2	59.3%	1.27279%	0.9%

   For vitamin A, the SS and MS entries differ from those of Exercise 12.2—by a factor of $(100/5)^2 = 400$. Everything else is the same: $F = 12.09$ with df 4 and 5; $P = 0.009$, so we (again) reject H_0 and conclude that vitamin A content decreases over time.

   Since the vitamin E numbers are unchanged, the ANOVA table is unchanged, and we again fail to reject H_0 ($F = 0.69$ with df 4 and 5; $P = 0.630$).

   In summary, transforming to percents (or doing any linear transformation) has no effect on the results of the ANOVA.

Output from Minitab:
```
Analysis of Variance on VitAPct
Source    DF       SS       MS       F        p
Days       4    71.58    17.89    12.09    0.009
Error      5     7.40     1.48
Total      9    78.98
```

12.44 There is no effect on the test statistic, df, P-value, and conclusion. The degrees of freedom are not affected, since the number of groups and sample sizes are unchanged; meanwhile, the SS and MS values change (by a factor of b^2), but this change does not affect F, since the factors of b^2 cancel out in the ratio $F = \text{MSG}/\text{MSE}$. With the same F and df values, the P-value and conclusion are necessarily unchanged.

   Proof of these statements is not too difficult, but it requires knowledge of the SS formulas. For most students, a demonstration with several choices of a and b would probably be more convincing than a proof. However, here is the basic idea: Using results of Chapter 1, we know that the means undergo the same transformation as the data $(\bar{x}_i^* = a + b\bar{x}_i)$, while the standard deviations are changed by a factor of $|b|$. Let $\bar{x}_T$ be the average of *all* the data; note that $\bar{x}_T^* = a + b\bar{x}_T$.

Now $\text{SSG} = \sum_{i=1}^{I} n_i (\bar{x}_i - \bar{x}_T)^2$, so $\text{SSG}^* = \sum_i n_i (\bar{x}_i^* - \bar{x}_T^*)^2 = \sum_i n_i (b\bar{x}_i - b\bar{x}_T)^2 = \sum_i n_i b^2 (\bar{x}_i - \bar{x}_T)^2 = b^2\text{SSG}$. Similarly, we can establish that $\text{SSE}^* = b^2\text{SSE}$ and $\text{SST}^* = b^2\text{SST}$; for these formulas, consult a more advanced text. Since the MS values are merely SS values divided by the (unchanged) degrees of freedom, these also change by a factor of b^2.

12.45 **(a)** Below. **(b)** Below. There are no marked deviations from normality, apart from the granularity of the scores. **(c)** $2.7634/1.8639 = 1.4826 < 2$; ANOVA is reasonable. **(d)** H_0: $\mu_B = \mu_D = \mu_S$; H_a: at least one mean is different. $F = 0.11$ with df 2 and 63, so $P = 0.895$; there is no evidence against H_0. **(e)** There is no reason to believe that the mean PRE2 scores differ between methods.

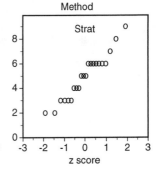

Method	n	$\bar{x}$	s
Basal	22	$5.\overline{27}$	2.7634
DRTA	22	$5.\overline{09}$	1.9978
Strat	22	$4.9\overline{54}$	1.8639

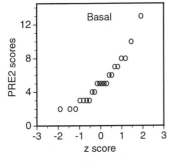
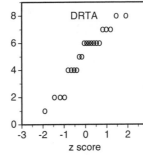
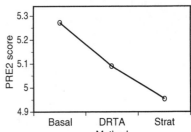

Output from Minitab:

```
Analysis of Variance on Pre2
Source      DF        SS       MS       F        p
GrpCode      2      1.12     0.56     0.11    0.895
Error       63    317.14     5.03
Total       65    318.26
```

12.46 **(a)** The mean for Basal increases by 1; the mean for Strat decreases by 1. **(b)** Minitab output below; $F = 5.87$ with df 2 and 63; $P = 0.005$. **(c)** SSG increases by 58 (from 1.12 to 59.12), so MSG increases by 29 (half as much as SSG). The resulting F statistic is *much* larger. **(d)** The altered data changes the formerly small differences between means into large, statistically significant differences

Method	n	$\bar{x}$	s
Basal	22	$6.\overline{27}$	2.7634
DRTA	22	$5.\overline{09}$	1.9978
Strat	22	$3.9\overline{54}$	1.8639

Output from Minitab:
```
Analysis of Variance on Pre2X
Source     DF       SS       MS       F         p
GrpCode     2    59.12    29.56    5.87     0.005
Error      63   317.14     5.03
Total      65   376.26
```

12.47 **(a)** Below. **(b)** Below. There are no marked deviations from normality, apart from the granularity of the scores. **(c)** $3.9271/2.7244 = 1.4415 < 2$; ANOVA is reasonable. **(d)** $H_0: \mu_B = \mu_D = \mu_S$; H_a: at least one mean is different. $F = 5.32$ with df 2 and 63, so $P = 0.007$; this is strong evidence that the means differ. **(e)** $s_p = \sqrt{\text{MSE}} = 3.18852$. For the contrast $\psi = \mu_B - \frac{1}{2}\mu_D - \frac{1}{2}\mu_S$, we have $c = -2.09$, $\text{SE}_c = 0.8326$, and $t = -2.51$ with df $= 63$. The one-sided P-value (for the alternative $\psi < 0$) is 0.0073; this is strong evidence that the Basal mean is less than the average of the other two means. The 95% confidence interval is -3.755 to -0.427. **(f)** For the contrast $\psi = \mu_D - \mu_S$, we have $c = 2$, $\text{SE}_c = 0.9614$, and $t = 2.0504$ with df $= 63$. The two-sided P-value is 0.0415; this is fairly strong evidence that the DRTA and Strat means differ. The 95% confidence interval is 0.079 to 3.921. **(g)** Among POST1 scores, the order of means is Basal (lowest), Strat, DRTA. The differences are big enough that they are not likely to occur by chance.

Method	n	$\bar{x}$	s
Basal	22	$6.6\overline{81}$	2.7669
DRTA	22	$9.\overline{772}$	2.7244
Strat	22	$7.\overline{772}$	3.9271

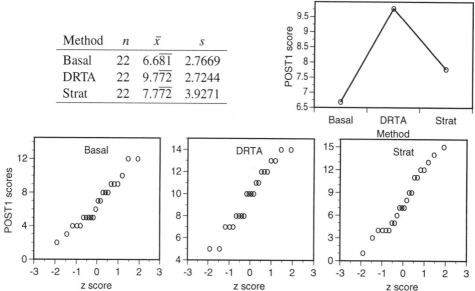

Output from Minitab:
```
Analysis of Variance on Post1
Source      DF       SS        MS        F         p
GrpCode      2     108.1      54.1      5.32     0.007
Error       63     640.5      10.2
Total       65     748.6
```

12.48 **(a)** Below. **(b)** Below. Basal and Strat look fine, apart from the granularity of the scores; the DRTA scores show some nonnormality (specifically, there were many 6's). **(c)** $3.9040/2.0407 = 1.913 < 2$; ANOVA is reasonable. **(d)** H_0: $\mu_B = \mu_D = \mu_S$; H_a: at least one mean is different. $F = 8.41$ with df 2 and 63, so $P = 0.001$; this is strong evidence that the means differ. **(e)** $s_p = \sqrt{\text{MSE}} \doteq 2.3785$. For the contrast $\psi = \mu_B - \frac{1}{2}\mu_D - \frac{1}{2}\mu_S$, we have $c = -1.75$, $\text{SE}_c = 0.6211$, and $t = -2.82$ with df $= 63$. The one-sided P-value (for the alternative $\psi < 0$) is 0.0032; this is strong evidence that the Basal mean is less than the average of the other two means. The 95% confidence interval is -2.991 to -0.509. **(f)** For the contrast $\psi = \mu_D - \mu_S$, we have $c = -2.1\overline{36}$, $\text{SE}_c = 0.7172$, and $t = -2.98$ with df $= 63$. The two-sided P-value is 0.0041; this is fairly strong evidence that the DRTA and Strat means differ. The 95% confidence interval is -3.569 to -0.703. **(g)** Among POST2 scores, the order of means is Basal (lowest), DRTA, Strat. The differences are big enough that they are not likely to occur by chance.

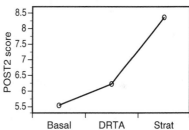

Method	n	$\bar{x}$	s
Basal	22	$5.\overline{54}$	2.0407
DRTA	22	$6.2\overline{27}$	2.0915
Strat	22	$8.\overline{36}$	3.9040

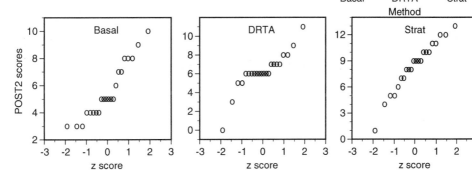

Output from Minitab:
```
Analysis of Variance on Post2
Source      DF       SS        MS        F         p
GrpCode      2      95.12     47.56     8.41     0.001
Error       63     356.41      5.66
Total       65     451.53
```

12.49 (a) $F = 1.33$ with df 3 and 12, giving $P = 0.310$; not enough evidence to stop believing that all four means are equal. **(b)** With the correct data, $F = 12.08$ with df 3 and 12, giving $P = 0.001$. This is fairly strong evidence that the means are not all the same. Though the outlier made the means more different, it also increased the variability ($s_p = 24.41$, compared to 1.667 with the correct data), which makes the difference between the means less significant. **(c)** The table is in the Minitab output below ($\bar{x}$ and s in cm). The marked difference in the values for 0 nematodes would have caught our attention, especially the relatively large standard deviation (which, had it been correct, would have made ANOVA unreasonable, since 48.74/1.24 is a lot bigger than 2).

Output from Minitab:

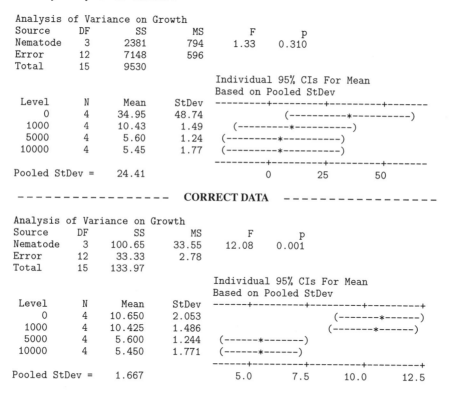

```
One-Way Analysis of Variance

Analysis of Variance on Growth
Source      DF        SS        MS        F         p
Nematode     3      2381       794      1.33     0.310
Error       12      7148       596
Total       15      9530
                                        Individual 95% CIs For Mean
                                        Based on Pooled StDev
  Level      N      Mean      StDev    ---------+---------+---------+-------
     0       4     34.95      48.74                    (----------*----------)
  1000       4     10.43       1.49        (---------*----------)
  5000       4      5.60       1.24    (---------*-----------)
 10000       4      5.45       1.77    (---------*----------)
                                        ---------+---------+---------+-------
Pooled StDev =     24.41                        0        25        50


- - - - - - - - - - - - - -   CORRECT DATA   - - - - - - - - - - - - - - -


Analysis of Variance on Growth
Source      DF        SS        MS        F         p
Nematode     3    100.65     33.55     12.08     0.001
Error       12     33.33      2.78
Total       15    133.97
                                        Individual 95% CIs For Mean
                                        Based on Pooled StDev
  Level      N      Mean      StDev    ------+---------+---------+---------+
     0       4    10.650     2.053                    (-------*------)
  1000       4    10.425     1.486                    (-------*------)
  5000       4     5.600     1.244    (------*-------)
 10000       4     5.450     1.771    (------*------)
                                        ------+---------+---------+---------+
Pooled StDev =      1.667               5.0       7.5      10.0      12.5
```

12.50 (a) $F = 2.00$ with df 3 and 20, giving $P = 0.146$; not enough evidence to stop believing that all four means are equal. (b) With the correct data, $F = 30.55$ with df 3 and 20, giving $P < 0.0005$. This is strong evidence that the means are not all the same. Though the outlier made the means more different, it also increased the variability ($s_p = 82.42$, compared to 6.784 with the correct data), which makes the difference between the means less significant. (c) The table is in the Minitab output below. The marked difference in the values for lemon yellow ("Level 1") would have caught our attention, especially the relatively large standard deviation (which, had it been correct, would have made ANOVA unreasonable, since $164.42/3.33$ is a lot bigger than 2).

Output from Minitab:

```
Analysis of Variance on Insects
Source     DF        SS        MS        F        p
ColCode     3     40820     13607     2.00    0.146
Error      20    135853      6793
Total      23    176673
                                  Individual 95% CIs For Mean
                                  Based on Pooled StDev
 Level      N      Mean     StDev   --------+---------+---------+--------
     1      6    114.67    164.42                    (---------*---------)
     2      6     15.67      3.33   (---------*---------)
     3      6     31.50      9.91      (----------*----------)
     4      6     14.83      5.34   (---------*---------)
                                  --------+---------+---------+--------
Pooled StDev =     82.42             0        70       140
```

```
---------------  CORRECT DATA  -----------------
```

```
Analysis of Variance on Insects
Source     DF        SS        MS        F        p
ColCode     3    4218.5    1406.2    30.55    0.000
Error      20     920.5      46.0
Total      23    5139.0
                                  Individual 95% CIs For Mean
                                  Based on Pooled StDev
 Level      N      Mean     StDev   ---+---------+---------+---------+---
     1      6    47.167     6.795                           (----*----)
     2      6    15.667     3.327   (----*----)
     3      6    31.500     9.915                 (----*----)
     4      6    14.833     5.345   (---*----)
                                  ---+---------+---------+---------+---
Pooled StDev =     6.784            12        24        36        48
```

12.51 (a) Table at right; plot not shown (it is similar to that from Exercise 12.10). [Note that this transformation actually makes the largest-to-smallest standard deviation ratio larger than it had been— 1.94 vs. 1.65.] (b) The hypotheses are the same as before (H_0: $\mu_0 = \mu_{1000} = \mu_{5000} = \mu_{10000}$ vs. H_a: at least one mean is different), except that now μ_i represents the mean *logarithm* of the growth for each group. (c) The new F is 10.39 (using either natural or common logs), with df 3 and 12; the P-value is 0.001. The conclusion is the same as with the

Natural (base e) logarithms:		
Nematodes	$\bar{x}$	s
0	2.3524	0.1843
1000	2.3357	0.1546
5000	1.7058	0.2077
10000	1.6509	0.3569
Common (base 10) logarithms:		
0	1.0217	0.0800
1000	1.0144	0.0671
5000	0.7408	0.0902
10000	0.7170	0.1550

original data (although the new F is slightly smaller than the old F, meaning P is slightly greater): It appears that somewhere between 1000 and 5000 nematodes, the worms hurt seedling growth.

For the original data, $s_p = 1.667$ and $R^2 = 75.1\%$. For the transformed data, $s_p = 0.2389$ (natural logs) or $s_p = 0.1038$ (common logs), and $R^2 = 1.7792/2.4643 = 0.3356/0.4648 = 72.2\%$.

12.52 (a) Table at right; plot not shown (it is similar to that from Exercise 12.11). [Note that the largest-to-smallest SD ratio is slightly better— 2.32 vs. 2.98—but ANOVA is still questionable.] (b) H_0: $\mu_1 = \cdots = \mu_4$; H_a: not all μ_i are

Color	$\bar{x}$	s
Lemon yellow	6.8533	0.4882
White	3.9400	0.4142
Green	5.5435	0.9613
Blue	3.7931	0.7312

equal. ANOVA tests if there are differences in the mean square root of the number of insects attracted to each color. (c) The new F is 27.00, with df 3 and 20; this has $P < 0.0005$. The conclusion is the same as before (although the new F is slightly smaller than the old F, meaning P is slightly greater): Board color does affect the (square root of the) number of insects attracted; in particular, it appears that yellow draws the most, green is second, and white and blue draw the least.

For the original data, $s_p = 6.784$ and $R^2 = 4218.5/5139.0 = 82.1\%$. For the transformed data, $s_p = 0.6835$ and $R^2 = 37.836/47.180 = 80.2\%$.

Output from Minitab:
```
Analysis of Variance on SqrtIns
Source      DF        SS        MS        F        p
ColCode      3    37.836    12.612    27.00    0.000
Error       20     9.343     0.467
Total       23    47.180
                                  Individual 95% CIs For Mean
                                  Based on Pooled StDev
Level    N       Mean     StDev    ----+---------+---------+---------+--
    1    6     6.8533    0.4882                          (----*----)
    2    6     3.9400    0.4142    (----*----)
    3    6     5.5435    0.9613             (----*----)
    4    6     3.7931    0.7312    (----*---)
                                  ----+---------+---------+---------+--
Pooled StDev =    0.6835           3.6       4.8       6.0       7.2
```

12.53 Results may vary slightly based on software used. **(a)** $\bar{\mu} = (620 + 600 + 580 + 560)/4 = 590$ and

$$\lambda = \frac{n(30^2 + 10^2 + 10^2 + 30^2)}{90^2} = \frac{20n}{81}$$

n	DFG	DFE	F^*	λ	Power
25	3	96	2.6994	6.1728	0.5128
50	3	196	2.6507	12.3457	0.8437
75	3	296	2.6351	18.5185	0.9618
100	3	396	2.6274	24.6914	0.9922

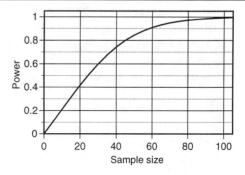

With a total sample size of $4n$, the degrees of freedom are 3 and $4n - 4$.

Answers will vary with the choices of α and n. The table and plot show values for $\alpha = 0.05$. **(b)** The power rises to about 0.90 for $n = 60$; it continues rising (getting closer to 1) after that, but much more slowly. **(c)** Choice of sample size will vary; be sure to consider the balance between increased power and the additional expense of a larger sample.

12.54 Results may vary slightly based on software used. **(a)** $\bar{\mu} = (610 + 600 + 590 + 580)/4 = 595$ and

$$\lambda = \frac{n(15^2 + 5^2 + 5^2 + 15^2)}{90^2} = \frac{5n}{81}$$

n	DFG	DFE	F^*	λ	Power
50	3	196	2.6507	3.0864	0.2767
100	3	396	2.6274	6.1728	0.5262
150	3	596	2.6199	9.2593	0.7215
200	3	796	2.6161	12.3457	0.8493

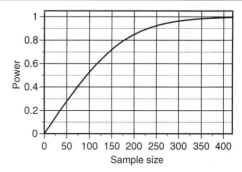

With a total sample size of $4n$, the degrees of freedom are 3 and $4n - 4$.

Answers will vary with the choices of α and n. The table and plot show values for $\alpha = 0.05$. **(b)** The power rises to about 0.80 for $n = 180$, and 0.90 for $n = 225$; it continues rising (getting closer to 1) after that, but much more slowly. Since the alternative we want to detect is less extreme (closer to the null) than in 12.53, it is harder to detect, so the power increases much more slowly than in the previous exercise. **(c)** Choice of sample size will vary; be sure to consider the balance between increased power and the additional expense of a larger sample.

12.55 The regression equation is $\hat{y} = 4.36 - 0.116x$ ($\hat{y}$ is the expected price, and x is the number of promotions). The regression is significant (i.e., the slope is significantly different from 0): $t = -13.31$ with df $= 158$, giving $P < 0.0005$. The regression on number of promotions explains $r^2 = 52.9\%$ of the variation in expected price. (This is similar to the ANOVA value: $R^2 = 53.5\%$.)

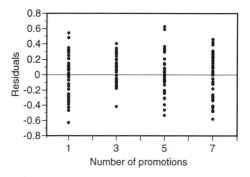

The granularity of the "Number of promotions" observations makes interpreting the plot a bit tricky. For 5 promotions, the residuals seem to be more likely to be negative (in fact, 26 of the 40 residuals are negative), while for 3 promotions, the residuals are weighted toward the positive side. (We also observe that in the plot of mean expected price vs. number of promotions [see 12.4], the mean for 3 promotions is not as small as one would predict from a line near the other three points.) This suggests that a linear model may not be appropriate.

Output from Minitab:

```
The regression equation is
ExpPrice = 4.36 - 0.116 NumPromo

Predictor       Coef       Stdev     t-ratio         p
Constant     4.36452     0.04009      108.87     0.000
NumPromo    -0.116475    0.008748      -13.31     0.000

s = 0.2474      R-sq = 52.9%      R-sq(adj) = 52.6%
```

Chapter 13 Solutions

13.1 (a) Response variable: Yield (pounds of tomatoes/plant). Factors: Variety ($I = 5$) and fertilizer type ($J = 2$). $N = 5 \times 2 \times 4 = 40$. (b) Response variable: Attractiveness rating. Factors: Packaging type ($I = 6$) and city ($J = 6$). $N = 6 \times 6 \times 50 = 1800$. (c) Response variable: Weight loss. Factors: Weight-loss program ($I = 4$) and gender ($J = 2$). $N = 4 \times 2 \times 10 = 80$.

13.2 (a) Response variable: Typical number of hours of sleep. Factors: Smoking level ($I = 3$) and gender ($J = 2$). $N = 3 \times 2 \times 120 = 720$. (b) Response variable: Strength of the concrete. Factors: Mixture ($I = 4$) and number of freezing/thawing cycles ($J = 3$). $N = 4 \times 3 \times 2 = 24$. (c) Response variable: Scores on final exam. Factors: Teaching method ($I = 3$) and student's area ($J = 2$). $N = 3 \times 2 \times 7 = 42$.

13.3 (a) Variety (df $= 4$), Fertilizer type (df $= 1$), Variety/Fertilizer interaction (df $= 4$), and Error (df $= 30$). Total df $= 39$. (b) Packaging type (df $= 5$), City (df $= 5$), Packaging/City interaction (df $= 25$), and Error (df $= 1765$). Total df $= 1799$. (c) Weight-loss program (df $= 3$), Gender (df $= 1$), Program/Gender interaction (df $= 3$), and Error (df $= 72$). Total df $= 79$.

13.4 (a) Smoking level (df $= 2$), Gender (df $= 1$), Smoking/Gender interaction (df $= 2$), and Error (df $= 714$). Total df $= 719$. (b) Mixture (df $= 3$), Cycles (df $= 2$), Mixture/Cycles interaction (df $= 6$), and Error (df $= 12$). Total df $= 23$. (c) Teaching method (df $= 2$), Area (df $= 1$), Method/Area interaction (df $= 2$), and Error (df $= 36$). Total df $= 41$.

13.5 (a) Plot below, left. (b) Nonwhite means are all slightly higher than white means. Mean systolic BP rises with age. There does not seem to be any interaction; both plots rise in a similar fashion. (c) By race, the marginal means are 135.98 (White) and 137.82 (Nonwhite). By age, they are 131.65, 133.25, 136.2, 140.35, 143.05. The Nonwhite minus White means are 1.3, 1.9, 2, 1.9, and 2.1. The mean systolic BP rises about 2 to 4 points from one age group to the next; the Nonwhite means are generally about 2 points higher.

For 13.5.

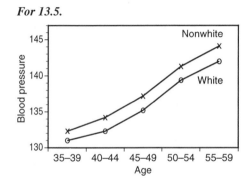

For 13.6.

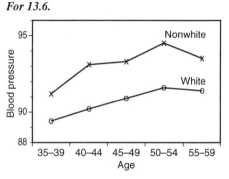

13.6 **(a)** Plot above, right. **(b)** Nonwhite means are all slightly higher than white means. Generally, mean diastolic BP rises with age, except for the last age group, where it seems to drop. There may be an interaction—the two plots have different appearance (the means for nonwhites "jump around" more than those of whites). **(c)** By race, the marginal means are 90.7 (White) and 93.12 (Nonwhite). By age, they are 90.3, 91.65, 92.1, 93.05, and 92.45. The Nonwhite minus White means are 1.8, 2.9, 2.4, 2.9, and 2.1. The mean diastolic BP rises about 0.5 to 1.5 points from one age group to the next, except in the end when it drops 0.6 points. The Nonwhite means are generally 2 to 3 points higher.

13.7 **(a)** Plot below, left. **(b)** There seems to be a fairly large difference between the means based on how much the rats were allowed to eat, but not very much difference based on the chromium level. There may be an interaction: the NM mean is lower than the LM mean, while the NR mean is higher than the LR mean. **(c)** L mean: 4.86. N mean: 4.871. M mean: 4.485. R mean: 5.246. LR minus LM: 0.63. NR minus NM: 0.892. Mean GITH levels are lower for M than for R; there is not much difference for L vs. N. The difference between M and R is greater among rats who had normal chromium levels in their diets (N).

For 13.7.   *For 13.8.*

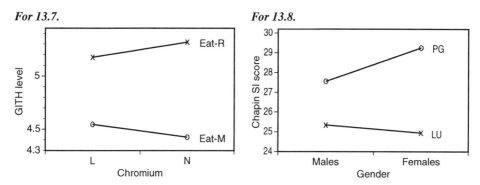

13.8 Plot above, right. PG students generally scored higher than LU students. PG females outscored PG males, while LU males had a higher mean than LU females (an interaction). Male mean: 26.45. Female mean: 27.095. PG mean: 28.405. LU mean: 25.14.

13.9 The "Other" category had the lowest mean SATM score for both genders; this is apparent from the graph (below, left) as well as from the marginal means (CS: 605, EO: 624.5, O: 566.) Males had higher mean scores in CS and O, while females are slightly higher in EO; this seems to be an interaction. Overall, the marginal means are 611.7 (males) and 585.3 (females).

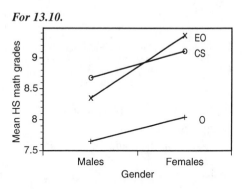

For 13.9.

For 13.10.

13.10 The "Other" category had the lowest mean HS math grades for both genders; this is apparent from the graph (above, right) as well as from the marginal means (CS: 8.895, EO: 8.855, O: 7.845.) Females had higher mean grades; the female marginal mean is $8.83\overline{6}$ compared to $8.22\overline{6}$ for males. The female − male difference is similar for CS and O (about 0.5), but is about twice as big for EO (an interaction).

13.11 **(a)** At right. **(b)** Plot on page 268, left. Elasticity appears to differ between species, with a smaller effect by flake size. There also seems to be an interaction (birch has the smallest mean for S1, but the largest mean for S2). **(c)** Minitab output is below. With A = Species and B = Flake size, $F_A = 0.59$ with df 2 and 12; this has

	Size of flakes		
Species	S1	S2	
Aspen	$\bar{x} = 387.333$	$\bar{x} = 335.667$	362
	$s = 68.712$	$s = 60.136$	
Birch	$\bar{x} = 292.667$	$\bar{x} = 455.333$	374
	$s = 121.829$	$s = 117.717$	
Maple	$\bar{x} = 323.333$	$\bar{x} = 293.667$	308
	$s = 52.013$	$s = 183.919$	
	334	362	

$P = 0.569$. $F_B = 0.27$ with df 1 and 12; this has $P = 0.613$. $F_{AB} = 1.70$ with df 2 and 12; this has $P = 0.224$. None of these statistics are significant; the differences we observed could easily be attributable to chance.

Output from Minitab:
```
Analysis of Variance for Elast

Source          DF       SS       MS       F      P
Species          2    14511     7256    0.59  0.569
Flake            1     3308     3308    0.27  0.613
Species*Flake    2    41707    20854    1.70  0.224
Error           12   147138    12262
Total           17   206664
```

For 13.11.   *For 13.12.*

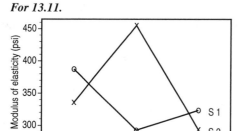

13.12 **(a)** At right. **(b)** Plot above, right. Strength appears to differ between species, and between flake sizes. There also seems to be an interaction (birch has the smallest mean for S1, but the largest mean for S2). **(c)** Minitab output is below. With A = Species and B = Flake size, $F_A = 1.10$ with df 2 and 12;

Species	Size of flakes		
	S1	S2	
Aspen	$\bar{x} = 1659.67$	$\bar{x} = 1321.33$	1491
	$s = 351.241$	$s = 234.628$	
Birch	$\bar{x} = 1168.00$	$\bar{x} = 1345.33$	1257
	$s = 235.879$	$s = 95.757$	
Maple	$\bar{x} = 1526.33$	$\bar{x} = 1142.00$	1334
	$s = 308.262$	$s = 355.848$	
	1451	1270	

this has $P = 0.365$. $F_B = 1.92$ with df 1 and 12; this has $P = 0.191$. $F_{AB} = 1.88$ with df 2 and 12; this has $P = 0.194$. None of these statistics are significant; the differences we observed could easily be attributable to chance.

Output from Minitab:

```
Analysis of Variance for Strength

Source          DF        SS        MS       F      P
Species          2    170249     85124    1.10  0.365
Flake            1    148694    148694    1.92  0.191
Species*Flake    2    291749    145874    1.88  0.194
Error           12    929765     77480
Total           17   1540456
```

13.13 **(a)** At right. **(b)** Plot below. Except for tool 1, mean diameter is highest at time 2. Tool 1 had the highest mean diameters, followed by tool 2, tool 4, tool 3, and tool 5.

Tool	Time	$\bar{x}$	s
1	1	25.0307	0.0011541
	2	25.0280	0
	3	25.0260	0
2	1	25.0167	0.0011541
	2	25.0200	0.0019999
	3	25.0160	0
3	1	25.0063	0.0015275
	2	25.0127	0.0011552
	3	25.0093	0.0011552
4	1	25.0120	0
	2	25.0193	0.0011552
	3	25.0140	0.0039997
5	1	24.9973	0.0011541
	2	25.0060	0
	3	25.0003	0.0015277

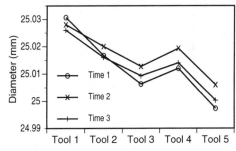

(c) Minitab output below. With A = Tool and B = Time, $F_A = 412.98$ with df 4 and 30; this has $P < 0.0005$. $F_B = 43.61$ with df 2 and 30; this has $P < 0.0005$. $F_{AB} = 7.65$ with df 8 and 30; this has $P < 0.0005$. **(d)** There is strong evidence of a difference in mean diameter among the tools (A) and among the times (B). There is also an interaction (specifically, tool 1's mean diameters changed differently over time compared to the other tools).

Output from Minitab:
```
Analysis of Variance for Diameter

Source      DF        SS          MS        F       P
Tool         4  0.00359714  0.00089928  412.98  0.000
Time         2  0.00018992  0.00009496   43.61  0.000
Tool*Time    8  0.00013324  0.00001665    7.65  0.000
Error       30  0.00006533  0.00000218
Total       44  0.00398562
```

13.14 All means and standard deviations will change by a factor of 0.04; the plot is identical to that in Exercise 13.13, except that the vertical scale is different. All SS and MS values change by a factor of $0.04^2 = 0.0016$, but the F (and P) values are the same. (Or at least they should be; Minitab [see output below] does not carry out the computation because the MS values are too small.)

Output from Minitab:
```
Analysis of Variance for Diameter

Source      DF        SS          MS        F    P
Tool         4  5.7556E-06  1.4389E-06   **
Time         2  3.0385E-07  1.5193E-07   **
Tool*Time    8  2.1312E-07  2.6640E-08   **
Error       30  1.0453E-07  3.4844E-09
Total       44  6.3771E-06

** Denominator of F-test is zero.
```

13.15 (a) Table at right; plot below. The mean expected price decreases as percent discount increases, and also as the number of promotions increases.

(b) Minitab output below. With A = Number of promotions and B = Percent discount, $F_A = 47.73$ with df 3 and 144; this has

Promos	Discount	$\bar{x}$	s
1	10%	4.423	0.1848
	20%	4.225	0.3856
	30%	4.689	0.2331
	40%	4.920	0.1520
3	10%	4.284	0.2040
	20%	4.097	0.2346
	30%	4.524	0.2707
	40%	4.756	0.2429
5	10%	4.058	0.1760
	20%	3.890	0.1629
	30%	4.251	0.2648
	40%	4.393	0.2685
7	10%	3.780	0.2144
	20%	3.760	0.2618
	30%	4.094	0.2407
	40%	4.269	0.2699

$P < 0.0005$. $F_B = 47.42$ with df 3 and 144; this has $P < 0.0005$. $F_{AB} = 0.44$ with df 9 and 144; this has $P = 0.912$. (c) There is strong evidence of a difference in mean expected price based on the number of promotions and the percent discount. Specifically, the two effects noted in (a) are significant: more promotions and higher discounts decrease the expected price. There is no evidence of an interaction.

Output from Minitab:
```
Analysis of Variance for ExpPrice

Source           DF        SS        MS       F      P
Promos            3    8.3605    2.7868   47.73  0.000
Discount          3    8.3069    2.7690   47.42  0.000
Promos*Discount   9    0.2306    0.0256    0.44  0.912
Error           144    8.4087    0.0584
Total           159   25.3067
```

13.16 *Note:* If your software allows it, generate a new "subscript column" from the Promotions and Discount columns. For example, in Minitab, "let c6=c2+100*c3" (where c2=Promos and c3=Discount) places in c6 the numbers 110, 120, 130, ..., 740—the first digit is the number of promotions, and the last two are the percent discount. Then "Oneway c4 c6" will do the 16-treatment analysis.

The F statistic (with df 15 and 144) is 19.29, which has $P < 0.0005$—there is a significant difference between the 16 means. Full analysis of all possible differences between means is not given here. (There are 120 such differences!) For each difference, we (or a computer) must find $t_{ij} = (\bar{x}_i - \bar{x}_j)/0.1080$. (The divisor 0.1080 is the value of $s_p\sqrt{\frac{1}{10} + \frac{1}{10}}$, where $s_p = \sqrt{\text{MSE}} \doteq 0.2416$.) Compare this to the appropriate Bonferroni critical value t^{**}; answers will differ based on the chosen significance level α—e.g., for $\alpha = 0.05$, $t^{**} = 3.61$.

In the Minitab output below, we can see the individual 95% confidence intervals, which give some indication of which pairs of means may be different. Specifically, the confidence interval for level 110 (one promotion, 10% discount) overlaps those for 120 and 130, but not the 140 interval, meaning that for some choice of α, the 110 and 140 means are different. The t statistic for this comparison is $t \doteq -4.60$, so that is easily (Bonferroni-) significant at $\alpha = 0.05$. (In fact, this difference is significant if we choose any α greater than about 0.0011.)

Similarly, the 110 interval overlaps those for 310, 320, and 330, but just misses the 340 interval, so these means are different (for some choice of α greater than the first, since these two intervals are closer together). The t statistic for this comparison is $t \doteq -3.08$; this is not (Bonferroni-) significant unless we choose α to be about 0.30 or higher.

To put this another way, two means are (Bonferroni-) significantly different if they differ by $0.1080t^{**}$. For $\alpha = 0.05$, this means they must differ by about 0.39; thus the 110 mean differs from the 140, 520, 710, and 720 means at the 5% level.

Output from Minitab:
```
One-Way Analysis of Variance
```

```
Analysis of Variance on ExpPrice
Source       DF        SS        MS        F        p
PromDisc     15   16.8980    1.1265    19.29    0.000
Error       144    8.4087    0.0584
Total       159   25.3067
                                      Individual 95% CIs For Mean
                                      Based on Pooled StDev
Level     N      Mean     StDev   ----------+---------+---------+------
 110     10    4.4230    0.1848                      (---*--)
 120     10    4.2250    0.3856               (---*--)
 130     10    4.6890    0.2331                          (---*---)
 140     10    4.9200    0.1520                             (---*---)
 310     10    4.2840    0.2040                  (---*---)
 320     10    4.0970    0.2346             (--*---)
 330     10    4.5240    0.2707                       (---*---)
 340     10    4.7560    0.2429                          (---*---)
 510     10    4.0580    0.1760               (--*---)
 520     10    3.8900    0.1629          (---*---)
 530     10    4.2510    0.2648                 (---*---)
 540     10    4.3930    0.2685                  (---*---)
 710     10    3.7800    0.2144      (---*--)
 720     10    3.7600    0.2618      (---*---)
 730     10    4.0940    0.2407           (--*---)
 740     10    4.2690    0.2699               (---*---)
                                      ----------+---------+---------+------
Pooled StDev =    0.2416                  4.00      4.40      4.80
```

13.17 **(a)** At right. **(b)** For testing interaction, $F_{AB} = 5.7159$. If there is no interaction, this comes from an $F(1, 36)$ distribution; 5.7159 gives $0.010 < P < 0.025$ (or $P = 0.0222$). **(c)** For testing the main effect of Chromium, $F_A =$

Source	df	SS	MS	F
A(Chromium)	1	0.00121	0.00121	0.04
B(Eat)	1	5.79121	5.79121	192.89
AB	1	0.17161	0.17161	5.72
Error	36	1.08084	0.03002	
Total	39	7.04487		

0.04030. If there is no effect, this comes from an $F(1, 36)$ distribution; 0.04030 gives $P > 0.1$ (or $P = 0.8420$). For testing the main effect of Eat, $F_B = 192.89$. If there is no effect, this comes from an $F(1, 36)$ distribution; 192.89 gives $P < 0.001$. **(d)** $s_p^2 = \text{MSE} = 0.03002$, so $s_p = 0.1733$. **(e)** The observations made in 13.7 are supported by the analysis: The amount the rats were allowed to eat made a difference in mean GITH levels, but chromium levels had no (significant) effect by themselves, although there was a Chromium/Eat interaction.

13.18 **(a)** At right. Note that $N = 4 \times 150 = 600$. **(b)** For testing interaction, $F_{AB} = 7.16$. If there is no interaction, this comes from an $F(1, 596)$ distribution; 7.16 gives $0.001 < P < 0.010$ (or $P = 0.0077$). **(c)** For testing

Source	df	SS	MS	F
A(Gender)	1	62.40	62.40	2.73
B(Group)	1	1599.03	1599.03	69.92
AB	1	163.80	163.80	7.16
Error	596	13633.29	22.87	
Total	599	15458.52		

the main effect of Gender, $F_A = 2.73$. If there is no effect, this comes from an $F(1, 596)$ distribution; 2.73 gives $P \doteq 0.1$ (or $P = 0.099$). For testing the main effect of Group, $F_B = 69.92$. If there is no effect, this comes from an $F(1, 596)$ distribution; 69.92 gives $P < 0.001$. **(d)** $s_p^2 = \text{MSE} = 22.87$, so $s_p = 4.7823$. **(e)** PG students scored (significantly) higher than LU students. Although the means differ by gender, the difference is not overwhelming. There is an interaction: PG females outscored PG males, while LU males had a higher mean than LU females.

13.19 **(a)** All three F values have df 1 and 945, the P values are < 0.001, < 0.001, and 0.1477. Gender and handedness both have significant effects on mean lifetime, but there is no significant interaction. **(b)** Women live about 6 years longer than men (on the average), while right-handed people average 9 more years of life than left-handed people. "There is no interaction" means that handedness affects both genders in the same way, and vice versa.

13.20 **(a)** With A = Series and B = Holder, $F_A = 7.02$ with df 3 and 61; this has $P = 0.0004$. $F_B = 1.96$ with df 1 and 61; this has $P = 0.1665$. $F_{AB} = 1.24$ with df 3 and 61; this has $P = 0.3026$. Only the series had a significant effect; the presence or absence of a holder and series/holder interaction did not significantly affect the mean radon reading. **(b)** Since the ANOVA indicates that these means are significantly different, we conclude that detectors produced in different production runs give different readings for the same radon level—this inconsistency may indicate poor quality control in production.

13.21 The table and plot of the means (at the right) suggest that students who stay in the sciences have higher mean SATV scores than those who end up in the "Other" group. Female CS and EO students have higher scores than males in those majors, but males have the higher mean in the Other group.

Gender	Major		
	CS	EO	Other
Male	$n =$ 39	39	39
	$\bar{x} =$ 526.949	507.846	487.564
	$s =$ 100.937	57.213	108.779
Female	$n =$ 39	39	39
	$\bar{x} =$ 543.385	538.205	465.026
	$s =$ 77.654	102.209	82.184

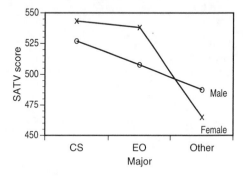

Normal quantile plots (below) suggest some right-skewness in the "Women in CS" group, and also some nonnormality in the tails of the "Women in EO" group. Other groups look reasonably normal.

In the ANOVA, only the effect of major is significant ($F = 9.32$, df 2 and 228, $P < 0.0005$).

Men in CS.

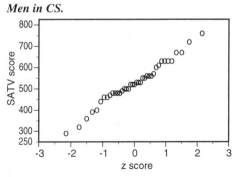

Women in CS.

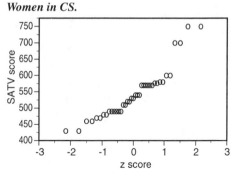

Men in EO.

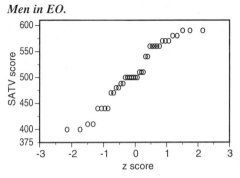

Women in EO.

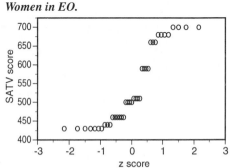

Men in Other.

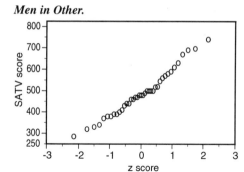

Women in Other.

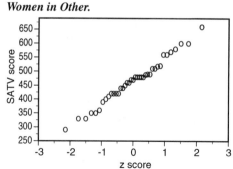

Output from Minitab:

Analysis of Variance for SATV

Source	DF	SS	MS	F	P
Maj	2	150723	75362	9.32	0.000
Sex	1	3824	3824	0.47	0.492
Maj*Sex	2	29321	14661	1.81	0.166
Error	228	1843979	8088		
Total	233	2027848			

13.22 The table and plot of the means (at the right) suggest that, within a given gender, students who stay in the sciences have higher HSS grades than those who end up in the "Other" group. Males have a slightly higher mean in the CS group, but females have the edge in the other two.

Normal quantile plots (below) show no great deviations from normality, apart from the granularity of the grades (most evident among Women in EO).

In the ANOVA, sex, major, and interaction are all significant: For the main effect of gender, $F = 5.06$, df 1 and 228, $P = 0.025$; for major, $F = 8.69$, df 2 and 228, $P < 0.0005$; for interaction, $F = 4.86$, df 2 and 228, $P = 0.009$.

		Major		
Gender		CS	EO	Other
Male	$n = 39$		39	39
	$\bar{x} = 8.66667$		7.92308	7.43590
	$s = 1.28418$		2.05688	1.71364
Female	$n = 39$		39	39
	$\bar{x} = 8.38461$		9.23077	7.82051
	$s = 1.66410$		0.70567	1.80455

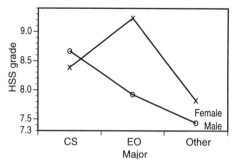

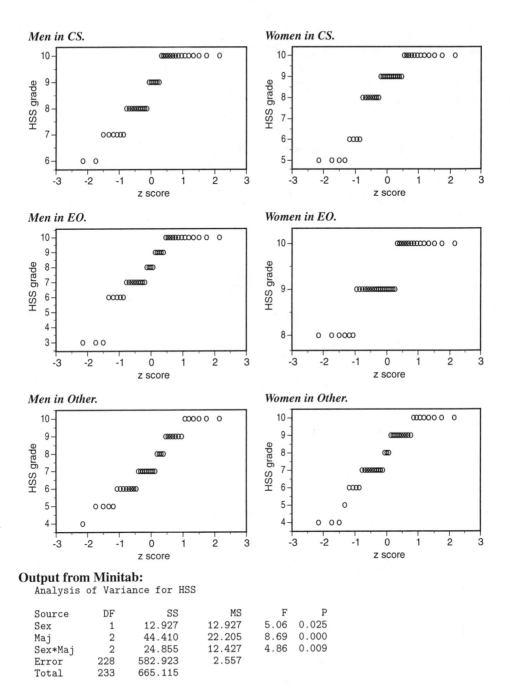

Output from Minitab:

```
Analysis of Variance for HSS

Source      DF        SS        MS       F      P
Sex          1    12.927    12.927    5.06  0.025
Maj          2    44.410    22.205    8.69  0.000
Sex*Maj      2    24.855    12.427    4.86  0.009
Error      228   582.923     2.557
Total      233   665.115
```

13.23 The table and plot of the means (at the right) suggest that females have higher HSE grades than males. For a given gender, there is not too much difference among majors.

Normal quantile plots (below) show no great deviations from normality, apart from the granularity of the grades (most evident among Women in EO).

In the ANOVA, only the effect of gender is significant ($F = 50.32$, df 1 and 228, $P < 0.0005$).

Gender	Major CS	EO	Other
Male	$n = 39$	39	39
	$\bar{x} = 7.79487$	7.48718	7.41026
	$s = 1.50752$	2.15054	1.56807
Female	$n = 39$	39	39
	$\bar{x} = 8.84615$	9.25641	8.61539
	$s = 1.13644$	0.75107	1.16111

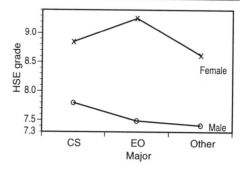

Men in CS.

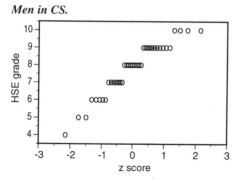

Women in CS.

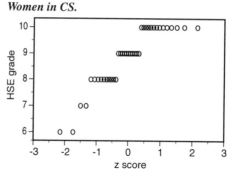

Men in EO.

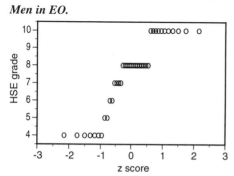

Women in EO.

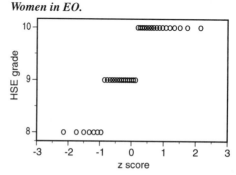

Men in Other.

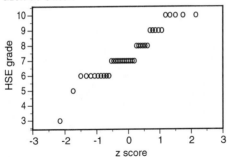

Women in Other.

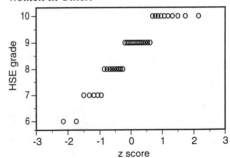

Output from Minitab:

```
Analysis of Variance for HSE
```

Source	DF	SS	MS	F	P
Sex	1	105.338	105.338	50.32	0.000
Maj	2	5.880	2.940	1.40	0.248
Sex*Maj	2	5.573	2.786	1.33	0.266
Error	228	477.282	2.093		
Total	233	594.073			

13.24 The table and plot of the means (at the right) suggest that students who stay in the sciences have higher mean GPAs than those who end up in the "Other" group. Both genders have similar mean GPAs in the EO group, but in the other two groups, females come out on top.

		Major		
Gender		CS	EO	Other
Male	$n = 39$	39	39	
	$\bar{x} = 2.74744$	3.09641	2.04769	
	$s = 0.68399$	0.51297	0.73041	
Female	$n = 39$	39	39	
	$\bar{x} = 2.97923$	3.08077	2.52359	
	$s = 0.53347$	0.64813	0.76556	

Normal quantile plots (below) show no great deviations from normality, apart from a few low outliers in the two EO groups.

In the ANOVA, sex and major are significant, while there is some (not quite significant) evidence for the interaction. For the main effect of gender, $F = 7.31$, df 1 and 228, $P = 0.007$; for major, $F = 31.42$, df 2 and 228, $P < 0.0005$; for interaction, $F = 2.77$, df 2 and 228, $P = 0.065$.

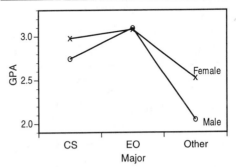

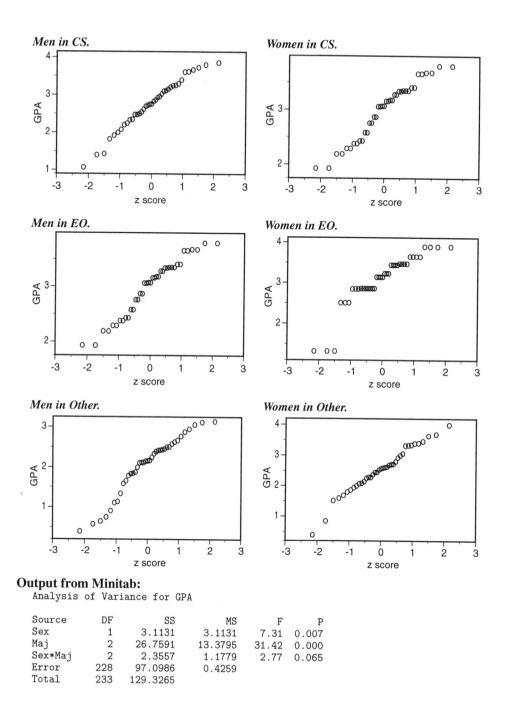

Output from Minitab:
Analysis of Variance for GPA

Source	DF	SS	MS	F	P
Sex	1	3.1131	3.1131	7.31	0.007
Maj	2	26.7591	13.3795	31.42	0.000
Sex*Maj	2	2.3557	1.1779	2.77	0.065
Error	228	97.0986	0.4259		
Total	233	129.3265			

Chapter 14 Solutions

Section 1: The Wilcoxon Rank Sum Test

14.1 (a) Normal quantile plots are not shown. The score 0.00 for child 8 seems to be a low outlier (although with only 5 observations, such judgments are questionable). **(b)** H_0: $\mu_1 = \mu_2$ vs. H_a: $\mu_1 > \mu_2$. $\bar{x}_1 = 0.676$, $\bar{x}_2 = 0.406$, $t = 2.059$, which gives $P = 0.0446$ (df = 5.5). We have fairly strong evidence that high-progress readers have higher mean scores. **(c)** We test

H_0: Scores for both groups are identically distributed   vs.
H_a: High-progress children systematically score higher

$W = 36$, $P \doteq 0.0463$; we have strong evidence against the hypothesis of identical distributions. This is equivalent to the conclusion reached in (b).

Output from Minitab:
```
Mann-Whitney Confidence Interval and Test

HiProg1   N =   5     Median =      0.7000
LoProg1   N =   5     Median =      0.4000
Point estimate for ETA1-ETA2 is      0.2100
96.3 Percent C.I. for ETA1-ETA2 is (-0.0199,0.7001)
W = 36.0
Test of ETA1 = ETA2  vs.  ETA1 > ETA2 is significant at 0.0473
The test is significant at 0.0463 (adjusted for ties)
```

14.2 (a) Normal quantile plots are not shown. The score 0.54 for child 3 seems to be a low outlier. **(b)** H_0: $\mu_1 = \mu_2$ vs. H_a: $\mu_1 > \mu_2$. $\bar{x}_1 = 0.768$, $\bar{x}_2 = 0.516$, $t = 2.346$, which gives $P = 0.0258$ (df = 6.9). We have fairly strong evidence that high-progress readers have higher mean scores. **(c)** We test

H_0: Scores for both groups are identically distributed   vs.
H_a: High-progress children systematically score higher

$W = 38$, $P \doteq 0.0184$; we have strong evidence against the hypothesis of identical distributions. This is equivalent to the conclusion reached in (b).

Output from Minitab:
```
Mann-Whitney Confidence Interval and Test

HiProg2   N =   5     Median =      0.8000
LoProg2   N =   5     Median =      0.4900
Point estimate for ETA1-ETA2 is      0.2600
96.3 Percent C.I. for ETA1-ETA2 is (0.0200,0.5199)
W = 38.0
Test of ETA1 = ETA2  vs.  ETA1 > ETA2 is significant at 0.0184
```

14.3 (a) See table. **(b)** For Story 2, $W = 8 + 9 + 4 + 7 + 10 = 38$. Under H_0,

$$\mu_W = \frac{(5)(11)}{2} = 27.5$$

$$\sigma_W = \sqrt{\frac{(5)(5)(11)}{12}} \doteq 4.787$$

(c) $z = \frac{38-27.5}{4.787} \doteq 2.19$; with the continuity correction, we compute $\frac{37.5-27.5}{4.787} \doteq 2.09$, which gives $P = P(Z > 2.09) = 0.0183$. **(d)** See the table.

Child	Progress	Story 1 Score	Rank	Story 2 score	Rank
1	high	0.55	4.5	0.80	8
2	high	0.57	6	0.82	9
3	high	0.72	8.5	0.54	4
4	high	0.70	7	0.79	7
5	high	0.84	10	0.89	10
6	low	0.40	3	0.77	6
7	low	0.72	8.5	0.49	3
8	low	0.00	1	0.66	5
9	low	0.36	2	0.28	1
10	low	0.55	4.5	0.38	2

14.4 (a) Testing

H_0: Yields are identically distributed   vs.
H_a: Yields are systematically higher with no weeds

we find $W = 26$ and $P \doteq 0.0152$. We have strong evidence against the hypothesis of identical distributions. **(b)** We test H_0: $\mu_0 = \mu_9$ vs. H_a: $\mu_0 > \mu_9$. $\bar{x}_0 = 170.2$, $s_0 = 5.42$, $\bar{x}_9 = 157.6$, $s_9 = 10.1$, $t = 2.20$, which gives $P = 0.042$ (df = 4.6). We have fairly strong evidence that the mean yield is higher with no weeds—but the evidence is not quite as strong as in (a). **(c)** Both tests still reach the same conclusion, so there is no "practically important impact" on our conclusions. The Wilcoxon evidence is slightly weaker: $W = 22$, $P \doteq 0.0259$. The t-test evidence is slightly stronger: $t = 2.79$, df = 3, $P = 0.034$. (The new statistics for the 9-weeds-per-meter group are $\bar{x}_9 = 162.633$ and $s_9 = 0.208$; these are substantial changes for each value.)

14.5 (a) H_0: Nerve response is unaffected by DDT; H_a: Nerve response is systematically different with DDT. **(b)** We find $W = 53$ and $P \doteq 0.0306$. We have strong evidence that DDT affects nerve response. **(c)** The conclusions are essentially the same.

14.6 (a) $W = 579$, which has $P = 0.0064$; the evidence is slightly stronger with the Wilcoxon test. **(b)** For the t test, H_0: $\mu_1 = \mu_2$ vs. H_a: $\mu_1 > \mu_2$. For the Wilcoxon test,

H_0: DRP scores are identically distributed for both groups   vs.
H_a: DRP score are systematically higher for those who had directed reading activities

14.7 (a) $W = 106.5$, which has $P \doteq 0.16$. In Example 7.20, $P = 0.059$, while in Exercise 7.69, $P = 0.06$ or 0.07 (depending on df used). In none of these tests did we conclude that the difference is significant, but the evidence was stronger using the t tests. **(b)** For the two t tests, we use H_0: $\mu_1 = \mu_2$ vs. H_a: $\mu_1 > \mu_2$. For the Wilcoxon test,

H_0: Both BP distributions are identical   vs.
H_a: BP is systematically lower in the calcium group.

(c) For the t tests, we assume we have SRSs from two normal populations (and equal variances, for the first t test). For the Wilcoxon test, we assume only that we have SRSs from continuously distributed populations.

14.8 Testing H_0: Both score distributions are identical vs. H_a: Piano students have systematically higher scores, we obtain $W = 1787$, which has $P < 0.0001$, so we reject H_0.

14.9 For H_0: Responses are identically distributed for both genders vs. H_a: Women's responses are systematically higher, Minitab reports $W = 32,267.5$ and a P-value of 0.0003. Women are also more concerned about food safety in restaurants.

14.10 We do not have independent samples from two populations; rather, we have dependent samples (each person answered both questions).

14.11 (a) $X^2 = 3.955$ with df $= 4$, giving $P = 0.413$. There is little evidence to make us believe that there is a relationship between city and income. (b) Minitab reports $W = 56,370$, with $P \doteq 0.5$; again, there is no evidence that incomes are systematically higher in one city.

Section 2: The Wilcoxon Signed Rank Test

14.12 The hypotheses are

H_0: Pre- and posttest scores are identically distributed vs.

H_a: Posttest scores are systematically higher

(One might also state a two-sided alternative, since the exercise suggests no direction for the difference, but an improvement in scores is a reasonable expectation.) The statistic is $W^+ = 138.5$, and the reported P-value is 0.002—strong evidence that posttest scores are higher.

Output from Minitab:
```
TEST OF MEDIAN = 0.000000 VERSUS MEDIAN G.T. 0.000000

              N FOR   WILCOXON              ESTIMATED
         N    TEST    STATISTIC  P-VALUE     MEDIAN
Diffs    20    17       138.5     0.002       3.000
```

14.13 (a) The hypotheses are

H_0: Pre- and posttest scores are identically distributed vs.

H_a: Posttest scores are systematically higher

(b) The Wilcoxon rank sum test requires two independent samples; we have dependent data. (c) $\bar{x}_{pre} = 27.3$ and $\bar{x}_{post} = 28.75$ (an increase of 1.45), while the median changes from 29 to 30. The signed rank statistic is $W^+ = 154.5$, and the reported P-value is 0.034—strong evidence that posttest scores are higher.

Output from Minitab:
```
TEST OF MEDIAN = 0.000000 VERSUS MEDIAN G.T. 0.000000

              N FOR   WILCOXON              ESTIMATED
         N    TEST    STATISTIC  P-VALUE     MEDIAN
Diff     20    20       154.5     0.034       1.500
```

14.14 There are 17 nonzero differences; only one is negative (the boldface 6 in the list below).

Diff:	1	1	2	2	2	3	3	3	3	3	3	**6**	6	6	6	6	6
Rank:	1	2	3	4	5	6	7	8	9	10	11	12	13	14	15	16	17
Value:	1.5		4					8.5						14.5			

This gives $W^+ = 138.5$. (Note that the only tie we really need to worry about is the last group; all other ties involve only positive differences.)

14.15 For the differences sfair − srest, $\bar{x} = 0.5149$ (other measures may also be used). Applying the Wilcoxon signed rank test to these differences, with the one-sided alternative—"food at fairs is systematically rated higher (less safe) than restaurant food"—we obtain $W^+ = 10,850.5$ ($P < 0.0005$), so we conclude that restaurant food is viewed as being safer.

Output from Minitab:
```
TEST OF MEDIAN = 0.000000 VERSUS MEDIAN G.T. 0.000000

              N FOR   WILCOXON            ESTIMATED
        N     TEST    STATISTIC  P-VALUE   MEDIAN
Diffs   303   157     10850.5    0.000     0.5000
```

14.16 For the differences sfair − sfast, $\bar{x} = 0.0693$ (other measures may also be used). Applying the Wilcoxon signed rank test to these differences, with the one-sided alternative—"food at fairs is systematically rated higher (less safe) than fast food"—we obtain $W^+ = 4,730.5$ ($P = 0.103$), so we conclude that the difference in safety ratings is not significant.

Output from Minitab:
```
TEST OF MEDIAN = 0.000000 VERSUS MEDIAN G.T. 0.000000

              N FOR   WILCOXON            ESTIMATED
        N     TEST    STATISTIC  P-VALUE   MEDIAN
Diffs   303   129     4730.5     0.103     0.000E+00
```

14.17 A stemplot of the differences is left-skewed, which suggests that a nonparametric test is appropriate. The mean difference is −5.71, and the median difference is −3. The Wilcoxon statistic is $W^+ = 22.5$, with P-value 0.032—fairly strong evidence that the wounds healed faster with the natural electric field.

```
-3 | 1
-2 |
-2 | 2
-1 |
-1 | 20
-0 | 7
-0 | 433311
 0 | 34
 0 |
 1 | 0
```

Output from Minitab:
```
TEST OF MEDIAN = 0.000000 VERSUS MEDIAN L.T. 0.000000

              N FOR   WILCOXON            ESTIMATED
        N     TEST    STATISTIC  P-VALUE   MEDIAN
Diffs   14    14      22.5       0.032     -4.000
```

14.18 For Before − After differences, we find $W^+ = 15$ (all five differences are positive), and $P = 0.03$; we conclude that vitamin C is lost in cooking.

Output from Minitab:
```
TEST OF MEDIAN = 0.000000 VERSUS MEDIAN G.T. 0.000000

              N FOR   WILCOXON           ESTIMATED
         N    TEST   STATISTIC  P-VALUE   MEDIAN
Diffs    5     5       15.0      0.030     54.50
```

14.19 The mean change is −5.33; the median is −6. The stemplot is somewhat left-skewed. The Wilcoxon statistic is $W^+ = 37$ ($P < 0.0005$); the differences (drops in vitamin C content) are systematically positive, so vitamin C content is lower in Haiti.

```
-1 | 4
-1 | 3322
-1 |
-0 | 9988
-0 | 7776666
-0 | 5444
-0 | 2
-0 | 1
 0 | 1
 0 | 33
 0 | 4
 0 |
 0 | 8
```

Output from Minitab:
```
TEST OF MEDIAN = 0.000000 VERSUS MEDIAN L.T. 0.000000

               N FOR   WILCOXON           ESTIMATED
          N    TEST   STATISTIC  P-VALUE   MEDIAN
Change   27     27      37.0      0.000     -5.500
```

14.20 The mean and median (right-threaded − left-threaded) differences are −13.32 and −12; the stemplot shows many negative differences, but it looks reasonably normal. Our hypotheses are "Times have the same distribution for both directions" and "Clockwise times are systematically lower." The test statistic is $W^+ = 56.5$, which has $P = 0.004$, so we conclude that clockwise times are lower.

```
-5 | 2
-4 | 853
-3 | 511
-2 | 94
-1 | 66621
-0 | 74331
 0 | 02
 1 | 1
 2 | 03
 3 | 8
```

Output from Minitab:
```
TEST OF MEDIAN = 0.000000 VERSUS MEDIAN L.T. 0.000000

              N FOR   WILCOXON           ESTIMATED
         N    TEST   STATISTIC  P-VALUE   MEDIAN
RH-LH   25     24      56.5      0.004     -14.00
```

Section 3: The Kruskal-Wallis Test

14.21 (a) For ANOVA, H_0: $\mu_0 = \mu_{1000} = \mu_{5000} = \mu_{10000}$ vs. H_a: Not all μ_i are equal. For Kruskal-Wallis,

H_0: The distribution of growth is the same for all nematode counts   vs.
H_a: Growth is systematically larger for some counts

(b) The medians are 10, 11.1, 5.2, and 5.55 cm—noticeably lower for the latter two, suggesting that nematodes retard growth (after a point). The Kruskal-Wallis test statistic is $H = 11.34$, with df = 3; the P-value is 0.01, so we have strong evidence that growth is not the same for all nematode counts (that is, the difference we observed is statistically significant).

Output from Minitab:
```
Kruskal-Wallis Test

LEVEL     NOBS    MEDIAN   AVE. RANK    Z VALUE
  0        4      10.000     12.3        1.82
1000       4      11.100     12.8        2.06
5000       4       5.200      4.2       -2.06
10000      4       5.550      4.7       -1.82
OVERALL   16                  8.5

H = 11.34  d.f. = 3   p = 0.010
H = 11.35  d.f. = 3   p = 0.010 (adjusted for ties)
```

14.22 (a) Normal quantile plots (not shown) suggest that there may be outliers in the lemon yellow counts (38 is low, 59 is high). No other striking violations are evident (given the small sample sizes). (b) For ANOVA, H_0: $\mu_1 = \mu_2 = \mu_3 = \mu_4$ vs. H_a: Not all μ_i are equal. For Kruskal-Wallis,

  H_0: The distribution of the trapped insect count is the same for all board colors   vs.
  H_a: Insects trapped is systematically higher for some colors

(c) In the order given, the medians are 46.5, 15.5, 34.5, and 15 insects; it appears that yellow is most effective, green is in the middle, and white and blue are least effective. The Kruskal-Wallis test statistic is $H = 16.95$, with df $= 3$; the P-value is 0.001, so we have strong evidence that color affects the insect count (that is, the difference we observed is statistically significant).

Output from Minitab:
```
LEVEL     NOBS    MEDIAN   AVE. RANK    Z VALUE
  1        6      46.50      21.2        3.47
  2        6      15.50       7.3       -2.07
  3        6      34.50      14.8        0.93
  4        6      15.00       6.7       -2.33
OVERALL   24                 12.5

H = 16.95  d.f. = 3   p = 0.001
H = 16.98  d.f. = 3   p = 0.001 (adjusted for ties)
```

14.23 We test H_0: All hot dogs have the same calorie distribution vs. H_a: Some type is systematically different (lower/higher) than some other. With

	Min	Q_1	M	Q_3	Max
Beef	111	140.0	152.5	178.5	190
Meat	107	138.5	153.0	180.5	195
Poultry	86	100.5	129.0	143.5	170

$H = 15.89$, df $= 2$, and $P < 0.0005$, we conclude that there is a difference; specifically, poultry hot dogs are lower than the other two types (which differ very little).

Output from Minitab:
```
LEVEL     NOBS    MEDIAN   AVE. RANK    Z VALUE
  1        20     152.5      33.1        2.02
  2        17     153.0      33.5        1.89
  3        17     129.0      14.9       -3.99
OVERALL   54                 27.5

H = 15.89  d.f. = 2   p = 0.000
H = 15.90  d.f. = 2   p = 0.000 (adjusted for ties)
```

14.24 (a) $I = 4$, $n_i = 6$, $N = 24$. (b) The columns in the table at the right are rank, number of insects, and color. The R_i (rank sums) are

1	7	B	12.5	21	B
2	11	B	14	25	G
3	12	W	15	32	G
4	13	W	16	37	G
5.5	14	W	17	38	Y
5.5	14	B	18	39	G
7	15	G	19	41	G
8	16	B	20	45	Y
9.5	17	W	21	46	Y
9.5	17	W	22	47	Y
11	20	B	23	48	Y
12.5	21	W	24	59	Y

Yellow	$17 + 20 + 21 + 22 + 23 + 24 = 127$
White	$3 + 4 + 5.5 + 9.5 + 9.5 + 12.5 = 44$
Green	$7 + 14 + 15 + 16 + 18 + 19 = 89$
Blue	$1 + 2 + 5.5 + 8 + 11 + 12.5 = 40$

(c) $H = \dfrac{12}{24(25)} \left(\dfrac{127^2 + 44^2 + 89^2 + 40^2}{6} \right) - 3(25)$

$= 91.95\overline{3} - 75 = 16.95\overline{3}$.

Under H_0, this has approximately the chi-squared distribution with df $= I - 1 = 3$; comparing to this distribution tells us that $0.0005 < P < 0.001$.

14.25 We test H_0: All hot dogs have the same sodium distribution vs. H_a: Some type is systematically different (lower/higher) than some other. With

	Min	Q_1	M	Q_3	Max
Beef	253	320.5	380.5	478	645
Meat	144	379.0	405.0	501	545
Poultry	357	379.0	430.0	535	588

$H = 4.71$, df $= 2$, and $P = 0.095$, we have some evidence of difference, but not enough to reject H_0.

Output from Minitab:

```
LEVEL     NOBS    MEDIAN   AVE. RANK    Z VALUE
  1         20     380.5      22.0       -1.95
  2         17     405.0      28.1        0.20
  3         17     430.0      33.3        1.83
OVERALL     54                27.5

H = 4.71   d.f. = 2   p = 0.095
H = 4.71   d.f. = 2   p = 0.095 (adjusted for ties)
```

14.26 (a) The five-number summaries (right) suggest that the scores of piano students are higher; there is little difference among the other three (except in the extremes).

Lessons	Min	Q_1	M	Q_3	Max
Piano	-3	2	4	6	9
Singing	-4	-1	0	1	1
Computer	-3	-1	0.5	2	4
None	-6	-1	0	2	7

(b) The normal quantile plots (not shown) show a low outlier (-4) for singing, and another (-6) for the no-lessons group. The others are reasonably normal (aside from granularity). (c) The test statistic is $H = 21$ (df $= 3$), which has $P < 0.0005$—strong evidence against the null hypothesis ("scores are identically distributed for all four groups"). Some treatment (presumably piano lessons) is systematically different (higher) than other treatments.

Output from Minitab:
```
LEVEL     NOBS     MEDIAN  AVE. RANK    Z VALUE
    1       34   4.00E+00      52.6       4.47
    2       10   0.00E+00      23.6      -2.38
    3       20   5.00E-01      29.9      -2.19
    4       14   0.00E+00      32.8      -1.22
OVERALL     78                39.5

H = 21.00  d.f. = 3  p = 0.000
H = 21.25  d.f. = 3  p = 0.000 (adjusted for ties)
```

14.27 For the Kruskal-Wallis test, we need two or more independent samples. Since these data come from different questions being asked of the same people, the responses are not independent.

14.28 (a) Yes, the data support this statement: $\frac{68}{211} \doteq 32.2\%$ of high-SES subjects have never smoked, compared to 17.3% and 23.7% of middle- and low-SES subjects (respectively). Also, only $\frac{51}{211} \doteq 24.2\%$ of high-SES subjects are current smokers, versus 42.3% and 46.2% of those in the middle- and low-SES groups. (b) $X^2 = 18.510$ with df $= 4$; this has $P = 0.001$. There is a significant relationship. (c) $H = 12.72$ with df $= 2$, so $P = 0.002$—or, after adjusting for ties, $H = 14.43$ and $P = 0.001$. The observed differences are significant; some SES groups smoke systematically more.

Output from Minitab:
```
LEVEL     NOBS    MEDIAN  AVE. RANK    Z VALUE
    1      211     2.000      162.4      -3.56
    2       52     2.000      203.6       1.90
    3       93     2.000      201.0       2.46
OVERALL    356                178.5

H = 12.72  d.f. = 2  p = 0.002
H = 14.43  d.f. = 2  p = 0.001 (adjusted for ties)
```

14.29 (a) We compare beef and meat, beef and poultry, and meat and poultry. (b) Minitab output (portions appear below) gives $P = 0.9393$, $P = 0.0005$, and $P = 0.0007$, respectively. (c) The latter two P-values are (quite a bit) less than 0.0167. Beef and meat are not significantly different; poultry is significantly lower in calories than both beef and meat hot dogs.

Output from Minitab:
```
- - - - - - - - - - - - - - - - - -  Beef – Meat  - - - - - - - - - - - - - - - - - -
95.1 Percent C.I. for ETA1-ETA2 is (-19.99,13.00)
W = 377.0
Test of ETA1 = ETA2  vs.  ETA1 ~= ETA2 is significant at 0.9393
The test is significant at 0.9392 (adjusted for ties)

- - - - - - - - - - - - - - - -  Beef – Poultry  - - - - - - - - - - - - - - - - -
95.1 Percent C.I. for ETA1-ETA2 is (15.01,49.99)
W = 495.5
Test of ETA1 = ETA2  vs.  ETA1 ~= ETA2 is significant at 0.0005
The test is significant at 0.0005 (adjusted for ties)
```

(Output continues)
```
----------------- Meat – Poultry -----------------
95.0 Percent C.I. for ETA1-ETA2 is (17.00,52.01)
W = 396.0
Test of ETA1 = ETA2  vs.  ETA1 ~= ETA2 is significant at 0.0007
The test is significant at 0.0007 (adjusted for ties)
```

14.30 The *P*-values (from Minitab; output below) are summarized in the table at the right. To be Bonferroni-significant, we must have $P \leq \alpha/6 = 0.008\overline{3}$, so only the yellow/white and yellow/blue differences are significant. Green is (barely) not significantly different from the other colors.

Yellow – White	0.0051*
Yellow – Green	0.0131
Yellow – Blue	0.0051*
White – Green	0.0202
White – Blue	0.8102
Green – Blue	0.0202

Output from Minitab:
```
----------------- Yellow – White -----------------
95.5 Percent C.I. for ETA1-ETA2 is (25.00,38.00)
W = 57.0
Test of ETA1 = ETA2  vs.  ETA1 ~= ETA2 is significant at 0.0051
The test is significant at 0.0050 (adjusted for ties)

----------------- Yellow – Green -----------------
95.5 Percent C.I. for ETA1-ETA2 is (6.00,30.00)
W = 55.0
Test of ETA1 = ETA2  vs.  ETA1 ~= ETA2 is significant at 0.0131

----------------- Yellow – Blue -----------------
95.5 Percent C.I. for ETA1-ETA2 is (25.00,40.00)
W = 57.0
Test of ETA1 = ETA2  vs.  ETA1 ~= ETA2 is significant at 0.0051

----------------- White – Green -----------------
95.5 Percent C.I. for ETA1-ETA2 is (-25.00,-3.00)
W = 24.0
Test of ETA1 = ETA2  vs.  ETA1 ~= ETA2 is significant at 0.0202
The test is significant at 0.0200 (adjusted for ties)

----------------- White – Blue -----------------
95.5 Percent C.I. for ETA1-ETA2 is (-6.003,6.996)
W = 41.0
Test of ETA1 = ETA2  vs.  ETA1 ~= ETA2 is significant at 0.8102
The test is significant at 0.8092 (adjusted for ties)

----------------- Green – Blue -----------------
95.5 Percent C.I. for ETA1-ETA2 is (4.00,27.00)
W = 54.0
Test of ETA1 = ETA2  vs.  ETA1 ~= ETA2 is significant at 0.0202
```

Chapter 15 Solutions

15.1 (a) For the high blood pressure group, $\hat{p} = \frac{55}{3338} \doteq 0.01648$, giving odds $\frac{\hat{p}}{1-\hat{p}} = \frac{55}{3283} \doteq$ 0.01675, or about 1 to 60. (If students give odds in the form "a to b," their choices of a and b might be different.) (b) For the low blood pressure group, $\hat{p} = \frac{21}{2676} \doteq 0.00785$, giving odds $\frac{\hat{p}}{1-\hat{p}} = \frac{21}{2655} \doteq 0.00791$, or about 1 to 126 (or 125). (c) The odds ratio is about 2.118. Odds of death from cardiovascular disease are about 2.1 times greater in the high blood pressure group.

15.2 (a) For female references, $\hat{p} = \frac{48}{60} = 0.8$, giving odds $\frac{\hat{p}}{1-\hat{p}} = \frac{48}{12} = 4$ ("4 to 1"). (b) For male references, $\hat{p} = \frac{52}{132} = 0.\overline{39}$, giving odds $\frac{\hat{p}}{1-\hat{p}} = \frac{52}{80} = 0.65$ ("13 to 20"). (c) The odds ratio is about 6.154. (The odds of a juvenile reference are more than six times greater for females.)

15.3 (a) Find $b_1 \pm z^* SE_{b_1}$, using either $z^* = 2$ or $z^* = 1.96$. These give 0.2349 to 1.2661, or 0.2452 to 1.2558, respectively. (b) $X^2 = \left(\frac{0.7505}{0.2578}\right)^2 \doteq 8.47$. This gives a P-value between 0.0025 and 0.005. (c) We have strong evidence that there is a real (significant) difference in risk between the two groups.

15.4 (a) Find $b_1 \pm z^* SE_{b_1}$, using either $z^* = 2$ or $z^* = 1.96$. These give 1.0799 to 2.5543, or 1.0946 to 2.5396, respectively. (b) $X^2 = \left(\frac{1.8171}{0.3686}\right)^2 \doteq 24.3023$. This gives $P < 0.0005$. (c) We have strong evidence that there is a real (significant) difference in juvenile references between male and female references.

15.5 (a) The estimated odds ratio is $e^{b_1} \doteq 2.118$ (as we found in Exercise 15.1). Exponentiating the intervals for β_1 in Exercise 15.3(a) gives odds-ratio intervals from about 1.26 to 3.55 ($z^* = 2$), or 1.28 to 3.51 ($z^* = 1.96$). (b) We are 95% confident that the odds of death from cardiovascular disease are about 1.3 to 3.5 times greater in the high blood pressure group.

15.6 (c) The estimated odds ratio is $e^{b_1} \doteq 6.154$ (as we found in Exercise 15.2). Exponentiating the intervals for β_1 in Exercise 15.4(a) gives odds-ratio intervals from about 2.94 to 12.86 ($z^* = 2$), or 2.99 to 12.67 ($z^* = 1.96$). (b) We are 95% confident that the odds of a juvenile reference are about 3 to 13 times greater among females.

15.7 (a) The model is $\log\left(\frac{p_i}{1-p_i}\right) = \beta_0 + \beta_1 x_i$, where $x_i = 1$ if the ith person is over 40, and 0 if he/she is under 40. (b) p_i is the probability that the ith person is terminated; this model assumes that the probability of termination depends on age (over/under 40). In this case, that seems to have been the case, but we might expect that other factors were taken into consideration. (c) The estimated odds ratio is $e^{b_1} \doteq 3.859$. (Of course, we can also get this from $\frac{41/765}{7/504}$.) We can also find, e.g., a 95% confidence interval for b_1: $b_1 \pm 1.96 SE_{b_1} = 0.5409$ to 2.1599. Exponentiating this translates to a 95%

confidence interval for the odds: 1.7176 to 8.6701. The odds of being terminated are 1.7 to 8.7 times greater for those over 40. **(d)** Use a multiple logistic regression model, e.g., $\log\left(\frac{p_i}{1-p_i}\right) = \beta_0 + \beta_1 x_i + \beta_2 y_i$.

15.8 We show the steps for doing this by hand; if software is available, the results should be the same. The model is $\log\left(\frac{p}{1-p}\right) = \beta_0 + \beta_1 x$. We make the arbitrary choice to take x to be the indicator variable for "male"—i.e., $x = 1$ for men, 0 for women. (We could also choose to have $x = 1$ for women, and 0 for men.) Then

$$\log\left(\frac{p_m}{1-p_m}\right) = \beta_0 + \beta_1, \quad \text{and} \quad \log\left(\frac{p_f}{1-p_f}\right) = \beta_0$$

With the given data, we estimate

$$\log\left(\frac{\hat{p}_m}{1-\hat{p}_m}\right) = \log\left(\frac{515}{1005}\right) \doteq -0.6686 = b_0 + b_1 \quad \text{and}$$

$$\log\left(\frac{\hat{p}_f}{1-\hat{p}_f}\right) = \log\left(\frac{27}{164}\right) \doteq -1.8040 = b_0$$

so we find that $b_0 = -1.8040$ and $b_1 = 1.1354$. This gives an odds ratio of about $e^{b_1} \doteq 3.11$; we estimate that the odds for a male testing positive are about three times those for a female.

With software, we find $SE_{b_1} \doteq 0.2146$ and $X^2 = 27.98$ ($P < 0.0001$). The logistic regression is significant (i.e., we conclude that $\beta_1 \neq 0$). A 95% confidence interval for β_1 is $b_1 \pm 1.96 SE_{b_1} = 0.7148$ to 1.5561, so we are 95% confident that the odds ratio is between about 2.04 and 4.74.

15.9 For the model $\log\left(\frac{p}{1-p}\right) = \beta_0 + \beta_1 x$, we obtain the fitted model $\log(\text{ODDS}) = b_0 + b_1 x = -7.2789 + 0.9399 x$. (Here p is the probability that the cheese is acceptable, and x is the value of H2S.) We have $b_1 = 0.9399$ and $SE_{b_1} = 0.3443$, so we estimate that the odds ratio increases by a factor of $e^{b_1} \doteq 2.56$ for every unit increase in H2S. For testing $\beta_1 = 0$, we find $X^2 = 7.45$ ($P = 0.0063$), so we conclude that $\beta_1 \neq 0$. We are 95% confident that β_1 is in the interval $b_1 \pm 1.96 SE_{b_1} = 0.2651$ to 1.6147; exponentiating this tells us that the odds ratio increases by a factor between 1.3035 and 5.0265 (with 95% confidence) for each unit increase in H2S.

15.10 For the model $\log\left(\frac{p}{1-p}\right) = \beta_0 + \beta_1 x$, we obtain the fitted model $\log(\text{ODDS}) = b_0 + b_1 x = -10.7799 + 6.3319 x$. (Here p is the probability that the cheese is acceptable, and x is the value of Lactic.) We have $b_1 = 6.3319$ and $SE_{b_1} = 2.4532$, so we estimate that the odds ratio increases by a factor of $e^{b_1} \doteq 562.22$ for every unit increase in Lactic. For testing $\beta_1 = 0$, we find $X^2 = 6.66$ ($P = 0.0098$), so we conclude that $\beta_1 \neq 0$. We are 95% confident that β_1 is in the interval $b_1 \pm 1.96 SE_{b_1} = 1.5236$ to 11.1402; exponentiating this tells us that the odds ratio increases by a factor between 4.5889 and about 68,884 (with 95% confidence) for each unit increase in Lactic.

15.11 The seven models are summarized below. The P-value in the right column is for the null hypothesis that all slopes equal 0 (i.e., the significance of the regression); all are significant.

For the three new models (those with two predictors), all have only one coefficient significantly different from 0 (in the last case, arguably neither coefficient is nonzero). The standard errors are given in parentheses below each coefficient; the six respective P-values are 0.4276, 0.0238; 0.3094, 0.0355; 0.0567, 0.1449.

In summary, we might conclude that that H2S has the greatest effect: It had the smallest P-value among the three single-predictor models, and in the three multiple logistic regression models in which it was used, it had the minimum P-value. (It was the closest to being significant in the last two models in the table below.)

Fitted Model	P
$\log(\text{ODDS}) = -13.71 + 2.249$ Acetic	0.0285
$\log(\text{ODDS}) = -7.279 \qquad\qquad\qquad + 0.9399$ H2S	0.0063
$\log(\text{ODDS}) = -10.78 \qquad\qquad\qquad\qquad\qquad\qquad + 6.332$ Lactic	0.0098
$\log(\text{ODDS}) = -12.85 + 1.096$ Acetic $+ 0.8303$ H2S $\qquad\qquad\qquad\qquad (1.382) \qquad\quad (0.3673)$	0.0008
$\log(\text{ODDS}) = -16.56 + 1.309$ Acetic $\qquad\qquad + 5.257$ Lactic $\qquad\qquad\qquad\qquad (1.288) \qquad\qquad\qquad\qquad (2.500)$	0.0016
$\log(\text{ODDS}) = -11.72 \qquad\qquad\qquad + 0.7346$ H2S $+ 3.777$ Lactic $\qquad\qquad\qquad\qquad\qquad\qquad\qquad (0.3866) \qquad\quad (2.596)$	0.0003
$\log(\text{ODDS}) = -14.26 + 0.584$ Acetic $+ 0.6849$ H2S $+ 3.468$ Lactic	0.0010

15.12 Portions of SAS and GLMStat output are given below. **(a)** The X^2 statistic for testing this hypothesis is 33.65 (df $= 3$), which has $P = 0.0001$. We conclude that at least one coefficient is not 0. **(b)** The model is $\log(\text{ODDS}) = -6.053 + 0.3710\text{HSM} + 0.2489\text{HSS} + 0.03605\text{HSE}$. The standard errors of the three coefficients are 0.1302, 0.1275, and 0.1253, giving respective 95% confidence intervals 0.1158 to 0.6262, -0.0010 to 0.4988, and -0.2095 to 0.2816. **(c)** Only the coefficient of HSM is significantly different from 0, though HSS may also be useful. (Only HSM was useful in the multiple linear regression model of GPA on high school grades.)

Output from SAS:

```
                           Intercept
                 Intercept     and
Criterion          Only     Covariates    Chi-Square for Covariates

AIC              297.340     269.691          .
SC               300.751     283.338          .
-2 LOG L         295.340     261.691       33.648 with 3 DF  (p=0.0001)
Score               .           .          29.672 with 3 DF  (p=0.0001)
```

(Output continues)
```
                    Analysis of Maximum Likelihood Estimates

              Parameter  Standard    Wald        Pr >     Standardized
   Variable  DF  Estimate   Error   Chi-Square  Chi-Square   Estimate

   INTERCPT  1   -6.0528   1.1562    27.4050     0.0001          .
   HSM       1    0.3710   0.1302     8.1155     0.0044      0.335169
   HSS       1    0.2489   0.1275     3.8100     0.0509      0.233265
   HSE       1    0.0361   0.1253     0.0828     0.7736      0.029971
```

Output from GLMStat:
```
              estimate   se(est)   z ratio   Prob>|z|
   1 Constant -6.053     1.156     -5.236    <0.0001
   2 HSM       0.3710    0.1302     2.849     0.0044
   3 HSS       0.2489    0.1275     1.952     0.0509
   4 HSE       3.605e-2  0.1253     0.2877    0.7736
```

15.13 Portions of SAS and GLMStat output are given below. **(a)** The X^2 statistic for testing this hypothesis is 14.2 (df = 2), which has $P = 0.0008$. We conclude that at least one coefficient is not 0. **(b)** The model is $\log(\text{ODDS}) = -4.543 + 0.003690$ SATM $+ 0.003527$ SATV. The standard errors of the two coefficients are 0.001913 and 0.001751, giving respective 95% confidence intervals -0.000059 to 0.007439, and 0.000095 to 0.006959. (The first coefficient has a P-value of 0.0537, and the second has $P = 0.0440$.) **(c)** We (barely) cannot reject $\beta_{\text{SATM}} = 0$—though since 0 is just in the confidence interval, we are reluctant to discard SATM. Meanwhile, we conclude that $\beta_{\text{SATV}} \neq 0$. (By contrast, with multiple linear regression of GPA on SAT scores, we found SATM useful but not SATV.)

Output from SAS:
```
                             Intercept
                Intercept      and
   Criterion     Only      Covariates   Chi-Square for Covariates

   AIC          297.340     287.119            .
   SC           300.751     297.354            .
   -2 LOG L     295.340     281.119      14.220 with 2 DF (p=0.0008)
   Score           .           .        13.710 with 2 DF (p=0.0011)


                    Analysis of Maximum Likelihood Estimates

              Parameter  Standard    Wald        Pr >     Standardized
   Variable  DF  Estimate   Error   Chi-Square  Chi-Square   Estimate

   INTERCPT  1   -4.5429   1.1618    15.2909     0.0001          .
   SATM      1    0.00369  0.00191    3.7183     0.0538      0.175778
   SATV      1    0.00353  0.00175    4.0535     0.0441      0.180087
```

Output from GLMStat:
```
              estimate   se(est)   z ratio   Prob>|z|
   1 Constant -4.543     1.161     -3.915    <0.0001
   2 SATM      3.690e-3  1.913e-3   1.929     0.0537
   3 SATV      3.527e-3  1.751e-3   2.014     0.0440
```

15.14 The coefficients and standard errors for the fitted model are below. **(a)** The X^2 statistic for testing this hypothesis is 23.0 (df $= 3$); since $P < 0.0001$, we reject H_0 and conclude that high school grades add a significant amount to the model with SAT scores. **(b)** The X^2 statistic for testing this hypothesis is 3.6 (df $= 2$); since $P = 0.1653$, we cannot reject H_0; SAT scores do not add significantly to the model with high school grades. **(c)** For modeling the odds of HIGPA, high school grades (specifically HSM, and to a lesser extent HSS) are useful, while SAT scores are not.

Output from SAS:

Analysis of Maximum Likelihood Estimates

Variable	DF	Parameter Estimate	Standard Error	Wald Chi-Square	Pr > Chi-Square	Standardized Estimate
INTERCPT	1	-7.3732	1.4768	24.9257	0.0001	
HSM	1	0.3427	0.1419	5.8344	0.0157	0.309668
HSS	1	0.2249	0.1286	3.0548	0.0805	0.210704
HSE	1	0.0190	0.1289	0.0217	0.8829	0.015784
SATM	1	0.000717	0.00220	0.1059	0.7448	0.034134
SATV	1	0.00289	0.00191	2.2796	0.1311	0.147566

Output from GLMStat:

	estimate	se(est)	z ratio	Prob>|z|
1 Constant	-7.373	1.477	-4.994	<0.0001
2 SATM	7.166e-4	2.201e-3	0.3255	0.7448
3 SATV	2.890e-3	1.914e-3	1.510	0.1311
4 HSM	0.3427	0.1419	2.416	0.0157
5 HSS	0.2249	0.1286	1.748	0.0805
6 HSE	1.899e-2	0.1289	0.1473	0.8829

15.15 **(a)** The fitted model is log(ODDS) $= -0.6124 + 0.0609$ Gender; the coefficient of gender is not significantly different from 0 ($SE_{b_{Gender}} = 0.2889$, $P = 0.8331$). **(b)** Now log(ODDS) $= -5.214 + 0.3028$ Gender $+ 0.004191$ SATM $+ 0.003447$ SATV. In this model, gender is still not significant ($P = 0.3296$). **(c)** Gender is not useful for modeling the odds of HIGPA.

Output from GLMStat:

	estimate	se(est)	z ratio	Prob>|z|
1 Constant	-5.214	1.362	-3.828	0.0001
2 Gender	0.3028	0.3105	0.9750	0.3296
3 SATM	4.191e-3	1.987e-3	2.109	0.0349
4 SATV	3.447e-3	1.760e-3	1.958	0.0502

15.16 (a) The fitted model is $\log(\text{ODDS}) = 3.4761 + 0.4157x$, $x = 0$ for Hospital A and 1 for Hospital B. With $b_1 \doteq 0.4157$ and $\text{SE}_{b_1} \doteq 0.2831$, we find that $X^2 = 2.16$ ($P = 0.1420$), so we do not have evidence to suggest that β_1 is not 0. A 95% confidence interval for β_1 is -0.1392 to 0.9706 (this interval includes 0). We estimate the odds ratio to be $e^{b_1} \doteq 1.52$, with confidence interval 0.87 to 2.64 (this includes 1, since β_1 might be 0). **(a)** The fitted model is $\log(\text{ODDS}) = -6.930 + 1.009 \text{ Hospital} - 0.09132 \text{ Condition}$; as before, use 0 for Hospital A and 1 for Hospital B, and 1 for good condition, and 0 for poor. Now we estimate the odds ratio to be $e^{b_1} \doteq 2.74$, with confidence interval 0.30 to 25.12. **(c)** In neither case is the effect significant; Simpson's paradox is seen in the increased width of the interval from part(a) to part (b).

Output from GLMStat:

	estimate	se(est)	z ratio	Prob>|z|
1 Constant	-6.930	0.7693	-9.009	<0.0001
2 Hosp	1.009	1.130	0.8928	0.3720
3 Cond	-9.132e-2	1.130	8.080e-2	0.9356

Intervals and Test Statistics for Means

Normal (z) intervals/statistics require large sample size(s), or population(s) almost normal.
Results using the t distributions require that population(s) must be "exactly" normal; samples size(s) large or small.
(But the t procedures are robust—they usually work well even if the requirements are not met.)

One or two populations?

One

  σ^2 known or unknown?

    Known

      CI for μ: $\bar{x} \pm z^* \dfrac{\sigma}{\sqrt{n}}$ TS: $z = \dfrac{\bar{x} - \mu_0}{\sigma/\sqrt{n}}$

    Unknown

      CI for μ: $\bar{x} \pm t^* \dfrac{s}{\sqrt{n}}$ TS: $t = \dfrac{\bar{x} - \mu_0}{s/\sqrt{n}}$

      with df $= n - 1$

Two

  σ_1^2 and σ_2^2 known or unknown?

    Known

      CI for $\mu_1 - \mu_2$: $\bar{x}_1 - \bar{x}_2 \pm z^* \sqrt{\dfrac{\sigma_1^2}{n_1} + \dfrac{\sigma_2^2}{n_2}}$

      TS (for $\mu_1 = \mu_2$): $z = \dfrac{\bar{x}_1 - \bar{x}_2}{\sqrt{\dfrac{\sigma_1^2}{n_1} + \dfrac{\sigma_2^2}{n_2}}}$

    Unknown

      $\sigma_1^2 = \sigma_2^2$ or $\sigma_1^2 \neq \sigma_2^2$?

      $=$

        CI for $\mu_1 - \mu_2$: $\bar{x}_1 - \bar{x}_2 \pm t^* s_p \sqrt{\dfrac{1}{n_1} + \dfrac{1}{n_2}}$

        TS (for $\mu_1 = \mu_2$): $t = \dfrac{\bar{x}_1 - \bar{x}_2}{s_p \sqrt{\dfrac{1}{n_1} + \dfrac{1}{n_2}}}$

        where $s_p^2 = \dfrac{(n_1 - 1)s_1^2 + (n_2 - 1)s_2^2}{n_1 + n_2 - 2}$

        and df $= n_1 + n_2 - 2$.

      $\neq$

        CI for $\mu_1 - \mu_2$: $\bar{x}_1 - \bar{x}_2 \pm t^* \sqrt{\dfrac{s_1^2}{n_1} + \dfrac{s_2^2}{n_2}}$

        TS (for $\mu_1 = \mu_2$): $t = \dfrac{\bar{x}_1 - \bar{x}_2}{\sqrt{\dfrac{s_1^2}{n_1} + \dfrac{s_2^2}{n_2}}}$

        where df $= \dfrac{(s_1^2/n_1 + s_2^2/n_2)^2}{\dfrac{(s_1^2/n_1)^2}{n_1 - 1} + \dfrac{(s_2^2/n_2)^2}{n_2 - 1}}$

        (often df $= \min(n_1, n_2) - 1$ is used).

Intervals and Test Statistics for Proportions

These methods use the normal approximation to the binomial distribution.
Sample size(s) should be large, and the proportion(s) should not be
too close to 0 or 1 (np and nq should both be at least 10).

One or two populations?

One

CI for p: $\hat{p} \pm z^* \sqrt{\dfrac{\hat{p}(1 - \hat{p})}{n}}$

TS: $z = \dfrac{\hat{p} - p_0}{\sqrt{\dfrac{p_0(1 - p_0)}{n}}}$

Two

CI for $p_1 - p_2$: $\hat{p}_1 - \hat{p}_2 \pm z^* \sqrt{\dfrac{\hat{p}_1(1 - \hat{p}_1)}{n_1} + \dfrac{\hat{p}_2(1 - \hat{p}_2)}{n_2}}$

TS (for $p_1 = p_2$): $z = \dfrac{\hat{p}_1 - \hat{p}_2}{\sqrt{\hat{p}(1 - \hat{p}) \left(\dfrac{1}{n_1} + \dfrac{1}{n_2} \right)}}$ where $\hat{p} = \dfrac{n_1 \hat{p}_1 + n_2 \hat{p}_2}{n_1 + n_2}$

Test Statistic for Ratios of Sample Variances

$* * *$ Not robust (requires the populations to be "exactly" normal) $* * *$

Take $F = \dfrac{s_1^2}{s_2^2}$, where s_1 is the larger standard deviation.

Then compare to an F distribution with $n_1 - 1$ and $n_2 - 1$ degrees of freedom
(large values of F are evidence against the null hypothesis of equality).